P9-DXN-466

MANUAL FOR THE CLASSIFICATION

AND DETERMINATION

OF THE ANAEROBIC BACTERIA

MONOGRAPH OF THE PASTEUR INSTITUTE

ANDRE R. PREVOT

Honorary Department Head of the Pasteur Institute
Former Member of the International Committee on Bacterial Nomenclature
Member of the Academy of Sciences (Paris)

MANUAL FOR THE CLASSIFICATION

AND DETERMINATION

OF THE ANAEROBIC BACTERIA

1st American edition

Translated by V. Fredette
MONTREAL
1965

LEA & FEBIGER   Philadelphia
1966

LIBRARY

OCT 04 1983

UNIVERSITY OF THE PACIFIC

411036

All rights reserved for all countries:
translation, adaptation and reproduction
by all methods, even photographic.

—————————
—————————

Copyright 1957 by Masson and Co.,
(Printed in France)

Library of Congress Catalog Card Number 66:16624
Printed in the United States of America

TRANSLATOR'S NOTE

This first American edition is based upon the third French edition which appeared in 1957.

However, to this third edition have been added 56 new species, and 162 corrections (additions and suppressions) have been made—all kindly supplied by the author. This brings the total of well-known anaerobic bacteria to well over 500.

V.F.

PREFACE TO THE FIRST AMERICAN EDITION

The third French edition of this Manual was published in 1957. Since that period, numerous publications have appeared concerning the anaerobic bacteria, with the result that numerous changes had to be made. Some concern the determinative characters of these germs. Others relate to their systematic relationships. Finally, the last improvements involve new species which have been described or recently completed so that their incorporation becomes warranted.

The most important modifications of this present edition concern taxonomy. The published works of Miss Sébald throw new light on the classification of the non-sporeforming Gram-negative anaerobes. The family of *Sphaerophoraceae* was shown to possess a type of deoxyribonucleic acid (DNA) which relates them to the *Ristella*. The genus *Fusiformis* cannot be considered as autonomous any longer, but rather as a sub-genus of *Sphaerophorus* which brings together all the species with pointed ends. This capital change has made possible the introduction of 56 new species or varieties or newly completed species. Many English-speaking bacteriologists are not yet completely familiar with our method of classification and do not accept it in its entirety. Nonetheless, the number of those who accept and use it regularly increases from year to year. When in 1933 I first proposed the new units: *Neisseriaceae, Veillonella, Ramibacterium, Eubacterium, Catenabacterium, Cillobacterium, Sphaerophoraceae, Sphaerophorus,* etc., there was a general outcry of indignation. Little by little these units were integrated in the successive editions of Bergey's Manual and are now used by a continuously greater number of workers.

It is with the hope that this number will increase still more that I have entertained the idea of an American edition. An immunologist friend of mine usually refers to my classification as: "the ambitious system of Prévot." This cliché has always provided me with the greatest satisfaction since in Science ambition is one of highest qualities which I know; my system has indeed the ambition of attempting to reconcile itself with the natural relationships of the bacterial species.

It equally attempts to derive benefit from all discoveries and particularly those in bacterial genetics. I will even go as far as saying that eventually bacterial classification will have an entirely genetic basis. This

7

is the reason why I cannot accept certain units proposed by bacteriologists who do not profess to relate these units to a genetic basis. A typical example is the proposition to define the term *Eggerthella* as bile-requiring non-sporeforming Gram-negative anaerobes not producing butyric acid. Since 1922, several bile-requiring strains of anaerobes have been isolated in my laboratory where they have been studied at length. They gradually lose this requirement and become what they always were genetically speaking, that is *Ristella, Pasteurella, Dialister, Capsularis, Sphaerophorus, Vibrio* or *Leptotrichia*. This simple characteristic is not sufficient to define a genus. The DNA of the bile-requiring strains is identical with that of the non-bile requiring cultures of the same species. On the other hand, the bile-requiring species which constitute the genus *Eggerthella* possess a quite different DNA and their Chargaff coefficient is that of the authentic genera to which they belong. As far as the non-production of butyric acid is concerned, such a negative character cannot be used to define a genus; at the most, the fermentation type can define a phenotypic species.

I do not believe that it is necessary to multiply such examples. As far as I am concerned, *Butyribacterium, Succinovibrio* and all the groups characterized by a single metabolic product are physiological groups only, and should appear as sub-genera.

I fervently hope that the publication of this first American edition will serve to bring closer together the taxonomic concepts of American and French bacteriologists.

André R. Prévot

PREFACE TO THE THIRD FRENCH EDITION

The ever-increasing interest of clinicians the world-over for anaerobic infections, their call for more and more precise biological diagnoses not only of the species but also of types and varieties, and the disruption which antibiotherapy has brought in infectious pathology by causing the practical disappearance of certain groups of diseases while multiplying hitherto rare diseases, have stimulated the bacteriologist to an unremitting effort in the search for and the identification of the anaerobic bacteria. The systematic practice of anaerobic hemoculture, the addition of a series of deep agar tubes to the aerobic methods as well as Hall tubes and reductose broth, have shown that these bacteria play a more important role in pathology than our forerunners had foreseen. Diagnostic bacteriological laboratories are now compelled to the daily practice of the anaerobic technique popularized by Lebert and Tardieux's booklet; when one succeeds in isolating a pure culture of an anaerobe from an infectious process, an attempt is made at identification; this has resulted in the exhaustion of the second edition of this Manual.

Moverover, the non-pathogenic anaerobes, whether of industrial or natural interest, are more and more the order of the day; their identification is still more difficult than in the case of the pathogenic species, but it has been considered with the same care.

This third edition carries the mention that it has been "entirely revised and considerably enlarged." Indeed, the numerous publications which have appeared since 1948 have impelled us to modify several introductions and to make many additions and modifications. There is no single page of the second edition which has not undergone thorough adaptation brought about by more precise knowledge of the habitat, morphology, physiology, cultural characters, biochemical properties and pathogenicity of each species. A very large number of new species have been described and are incorporated into this third edition. Older not so well-known species have been studied anew and described sufficiently to be classified and identified: thus, 93 new species or varieties figure in this third edition, bringing the total number of well-known anaerobic species to 470. On the other hand, several species have been removed: either because their supposedly anaerobic character has been shown to be rather of the facultative type, or because they were identified with previously described species which have priority.

9

In the preface to the second edition, we had hinted at the irritating question of the apparently irreducible opposition between several tenets of classification. We have cautiously but knowingly written "apparently irreducible." Since then, several divergences of opinion have been resolved experimentally. We should mention in particular: 1) the duality of *Cl. sordelli* and *Cl. bifermentans,* asserted by us but denied by Bergey *el al.,* which has been settled by Huet—*Cl. sordelli* being actively urolytic while *Cl. bifermentans* is not (an additional differential characteristic); 2) the duality of *Sph. funduliformis* and *Sph. necrophorus,* asserted by us, denied by Bergey *et al.,* has been worked out by Beerens and Tardieux —*Sph. funduliformis* has no hemagglutinin while *Sph. necrophorus* has one (to be added to the other differential characteristics). Similar examples could be pointed out among the *Ramibacterium, Corynebacterium, Actinobacterium,* the multiplicity of which, after having been demonstrated experimentally, entailed the recognition of the multiplicity of the corresponding infections and reshaped the therapy of each individual disease. Thus are recognized nowadays two types of diseases caused by *Sphaerophorus:* acute infections (*funduliformis, pseudonecrophorus* type) responding rapidly to penicillin, and chronic or subacute infections (*pyogenes, freundi, gulosus* type) resistant to penicillin and for which the exact determination of the sensitivity to antibiotics is a must, otherwise the disease may be fatal.

To be sure, several exceedingly weighty problems still await an answer, such as those which divide Bergey *et al.* and ourselves concerning *Actinomyces bovis* and *Actinobacterium israeli, Lactobacillus acidophilus* and *Bifidobacterium bifidum,* the taxonomical position of the genus *Corynebacterium.* But we believe that these problems are far from insurmountable. To resolve the first of these problems, one has only to look up the original descriptions to discover that *Actinomyces bovis* is aerobic and thus corresponds very well to the definition of the genus *Actinomyces,* while *Actinobacterium israeli* is anaerobic and therefore cannot be an *Actinomyces,* and for this reason, is justly incorporated in the genus *Actinobacterium* by Sampietro. A similar solution is at hand for the second problem: *Lactobacillus acidophilus* is an aerobic *Eubacteriales,* impossible to confuse with *Bidifobacterium bifidum,* an anaerobic *Actinomycetales.* Initial errors in translation and interpretation have given rise to this state of confusion carried over from one book to another, but to which the French school of thought has never subscribed.

Concerning the taxonomical position of the genus *Corynebacterium,* which presently appears to be a question of doctrine, we believe it could be resolved in the near future if bacteriologists would consider it not as a matter of doctrine but solely as an experimental problem. Let us state it explicitly because it is quite simple: there is no doubt whatsoever that the *Actinomyces* form part of the *Actinomycetales.* Now, the *Actinobacterium* are so closely related to the *Actinomyces* (from which they differ only in being strict anaerobes) that they are easily confused (example: *A. bovis* and *A israeli* which Bergey *et al.* place side by side in the same family of *Actinomycetaceae*). As for the *Corynebacterium,* they are morphologically undiscernible from the *Actinobacterium,* and their differentiation lies only in a question of biometrics. The *Corynebacterium* are generally shorter than 3.5μ, while the *Actinobacterium* are longer than 3.5μ. Consequently, we do not understand why Bergey *et al.* class the *Corynebacterium* with the *Eubacteriales* and the *Actinobacterium* (not recognized as such but implicated by the erroneous designation of *Actinomyces israeli*) among the *Actinomycetaceae*. As far as we are concerned, this problem has been resolved after 16 years of current practice with the two groups, having determined several hundred species: before classifying a given strain in one or the other group, we sometimes find it necessary to examine it daily for 2 weeks with serial measurements, and calculating the average. These two genera are highly related, the main difference lying in their pathogenic power: the corynebacterioses being quite different from the actino-bacterioses. This explains a certain hesitancy when confronted by a non-pathogenic strain.

A final word, to dispel the distress of some bacteriologists when they must determine an anaerobe which they have succeeded in isolating. Since the method of the Pasteur Institute has been published, we have had the occasion of identifying more than 1500 strains of anaerobic bacteria; though some cases have proven quite difficult, the method has never failed. Moreover, during this same time, we have received from abroad several hundred strains of anaerobes which could not be determined with the other methods; they were easily identified with the help of the Pasteur Institute method. It is therefore with great confidence that we present this third edition.

We would like to reiterate our most sincere thanks to all those who since 1940 have taken an active part in perfecting this method, and wish to assure professor Jacques Tréfouel, director of the Pasteur Institute and Member of the Institute as well as of the National Academy of Medicine, of our gratefulness for having maintained this Manual in the Collection of Monographs of the Pasteur Institute.

André R. Prévot

CONTENTS

16

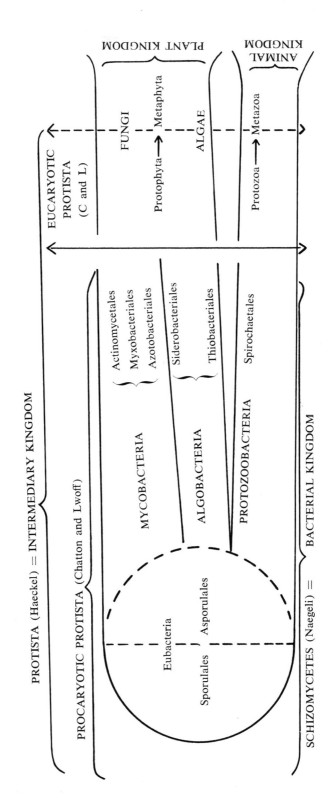

INTRODUCTION

The number of anaerobic species which have been described sufficiently well to be classified increases constantly, and each new species must automatically find its place in a logical scheme of classification. On the other hand, a classification of the anaerobic bacteria must integrate itself without ambiguity in the general scheme of classification of the bacteria. Lastly, the position of the bacteria among other living beings should be stated precisely. The following scheme represents the concept which forms the basis of the classification detailed in this book:

The unquestionably strict anaerobes are up to the present all grouped in the *Eubacteriales,* the *Actinomycetales,* the *Spirochaetales* and the *Thiobacteriales.*

Details concerning their position among the genera, families, orders and classes are supplied by the main lines of the general scheme of classification of the bacteria.

CHAPTER 1

MAIN LINES OF THE GENERAL
CLASSIFICATION OF BACTERIA

———————

Bacteriology has not escaped one of the most imperative needs of the human mind: that of classifying everything. As soon as man learned about microbes, his first impulse was to compare them in order to group or separate them.

It is impossible to survey here the history of the classifications of bacteria, but it may be good to note that they are quite ancient. The first, in fact, that of Müller, dates from 1773; the next, that of Bory Saint-Vincent, appeared in 1826; Ehrenberg's followed in 1838, Davaine's in 1868; then Mangin's in 1878. These were but precursors. The classical systems began with the period of rigourously pure cultures which dates itself from the generalized use of solid media (1881). Among these, two have been used for quite some time: that of Lehmann and Neumann in 1896, and that of Migula in 1902.

Among the modern systems, quite numerous, that of Buchanan, which took form from 1917 to 1925, was quite remarkable and has given birth to Bergey's system (1923 to 1957) which is actually known and used universally. This does not necessarily mean that these two systems are perfect: far from it. They are less imperfect than the others, and more so are they susceptible of perfection. The classification which follows is in some sort derived from the preceding ones of which it tries to correct the contradictions, errors and omissions.

First: the fundamental unity in a system of classification is the *bacterial species*. Nothing is more difficult to define than a bacterial species; no other biological notion has varied as much as it has and will vary as much in the near future.

The study of its nuclear apparatus and the first knowledge afforded by bacterial genetics have entirely renovated the older definitions without permitting the determination of its final limits.

While waiting for the definition which geneticists and cytologists are preparing, we can still consider it provisionally as a mosaic of antigens and enzymes different from the protozoa and the protophyta. The species comprises varieties, sub-varieties, types, races, which are defined by one or several peculiar morphological, physiological, biochemical or antigenic characters.

Bacteriologists usually group in *genera* the species which are morphologically identical or similar and physiologically related. The name of the genus and the name of the species must, in published work, be written in latin, the first name beginning with a capital letter, the second name beginning with a small letter and agreeing with the first name. These are the essentials of the binominal nomenclature which is itself ruled by an international convention[1]. By conforming to it, one simply adheres to the principles of order and scientific discipline which have perfectly succeeded in the other natural sciences. To refuse such a system would only lead to fantasy or chaos.

The genera presenting a cytochemical relationship and morpho-physiological similarities are grouped into *families*. The latin name of the family has *aceae* as suffix. Certain families having several genera are subdivided into *tribes,* a facultative step, the suffix of which is *eae.* Families showing the same general structure are grouped into *orders,* the suffix of which is *ales.* Orders of the same general morphology are grouped into *classes.* The classes form the branch of bacteria.

This is the essence of the constructive or experimental classification, which starts from the bottom, and groups together related living beings which constitute units of higher rank. It must cöincide exactly with the analytical classification which considers the whole ensemble of the bacterial kingdom and subdivides it into smaller and smaller groups. Taxonomists are unanimous in thinking that the bacterial kingdom, which Nageli has called *Schizomycetes,* and which Chatton and Lwoff call *Procaryotic Protista,* is a singular autonomous group which no valuable reason authorizes anybody to attach to either the plant or to the animal kingdom.

Indeed, the bacterial cell differs from that of other living beings by structures which are proper; these have been described recently by R. Y. Stanier:

(1) The bacterial cell has no intra-cytoplasmic mitochondria (its membrane contains the enzymatic equivalent of its mitochondrial system). (2) The mucopolysaccharides of its cell-wall are different from those of other unicellular organisms, plants or animals. (3) Finally, bacterial cytoplasm contains an amino acid, diaminopimelic acid, which is found nowhere else and which induces the synthesis of lysine, a fundamental property characteristic of the bacterial world. This amino acid is moreover in some cases an indispensable part of the cell-wall.

---

[1] At the Copenhagen meeting in July 1947, it was a great pleasure to see completion of the Code of Bacterial Nomenclature to which I had been collaborating since 1930. This Code has been translated in several languages. The French edition has been published in the "Annales de l'Institut Pasteur", 1948, v. 74, p. 271. The 28-page document comprises General Considerations, General Principles, Rules and recommendations, exceptions and modifications, finally provisions.

Let us consider the bacterial kingdom, contrariwise to classic opinion, as an autonomous branch and not as a botanical class, the main divisions of which are schematized in the following table:

Branch	Sub-branches	Classes	Orders
Schizomycetes	Eubacteria	Non-sporeforming Eubacteriales	Micrococcales Bacteriales Spirillales
		Sporeforming Eubacteriales	Bacillales Clostridiales Plectridiales Sporovibrionales
	Mycobacteria	Actinomycetales	Actinobacteriales Mycobacteriales
		Myxobacteriales	Myxococcales Angiobacteriales Asporangiales
		Azotobacteriales........................	
	Algobacteria	Siderobacteriales	Chlamydobacteriales Caulobacteriales
		Thiobacteriales	Rhodobacteriales Chlorobacteriales
	Protozoobacteria	Spirochetales..........................	

SUB-BRANCH: EUBACTERIA

Definition.—Simple and undifferentiated forms, without true branching; spherical, cylindrical (or flat) or spirally-curved. Motile or non-motile; sporeforming or non-sporeforming; pigmented or not; some species may show reserve substances such as volutin, glycogen, or fat; no deposit of iron or sulphur.

We divide the *Eubacteria* into two classes: non-sporeforming
                                                        sporeforming

CLASS I: *NON-SPOREFORMING EUBACTERIA or ASPORULALES*
Prévot 1948.

Subdivision into three orders
- spherical forms: *Micrococcales,*
- cylindrical rods: *Bacteriales,*
- slightly-curved or spiral forms: *Spirillales.*

ORDER I: *Micrococcales* Prévot.

Spherical non-sporeforming *Eubacteriales.*

Subdivision into two families { Gram-negative: *Neisseriaceae,*
Gram-positive: *Micrococcaceae.*

FAMILY I: *Neisseriaceae* Prévot.

Gram-negative *Micrococcales:* two genera { in pairs: *Neisseria,*
in masses: *Veillonella.*

Genus I: *Neisseria Trevisan.*

Gram-negative cocci occurring in pairs.

Type species: *N. gonorrhoeae.* Other species: *N. intracellularis, catar-rhalis, sicca, perflava, flava, subflava, flavescens.*

Strictly anaerobic species: *N. discoides, reniformis, orbiculata, vulvova-ginitis.*

Genus II: *Veillonella* Prévot.

Cocci of very small size, 0.2 to 0.3 micron, Gram-negative, occurring in irregular masses.

Type species: *V. parvula.* Other species: *V. gazogenes.*

Species *incertae sedis: Peptococcus elsdeni.*

FAMILY II: *Micrococcaceae* Pribram 1929.

Gram-positive *micrococcales;* three tribes:
in pairs or in chains: *Streptococceae,*
in masses occurring in one plane: *Staphylococceae,*
in masses occurring in more than one plane: *Micrococceae.*

Tribe I: *Streptococceae* Trevisan.

Micrococcaceae occurring in pairs or in short chains. Three genera:
in pairs: *Diplococcus,*
in chains: *Streptococcus,*
in encapsulated chains: *Leuconoctoc.*

Genus I: *Diplococcus* Weichselbaum.

Gram-positive cocci occurring in pairs, sometimes in very short chains, often encapsulated.

Type species: *D. pneumoniae.*

Anaerobic species: *magnus, constellatus, plagarum-belli,* etc.

Genus II: *Streptococcus* Billroth (Rosenbach).

Gram-positive cocci occurring in chains.

Type species: *Str. pyogenes.* Other species: *equi, agalactiae, salivarius, bovis, equinus, faecalis, thermophilus, lactis, cremoris,* etc.

Anaerobic species: *anaerobius, foetidus, putridus, micros, intermedius, parvulus,* etc.

Sub-genus incertae sedis: *Ruminococcus.* Type species: *R. flavefaciens,* and its variety: *albus.*

Genus III: *Leuconostoc* van Tieghem.

Gram-positive cocci occurring in encapsulated chains.

Type species: *L. mesenteroides.* Other species: *dextranicum, citrovorum.*

Tribe II: *Staphylococceae* Prévot.

Gram-positive cocci occurring in masses of one plane.

Two genera $\begin{cases} \text{in tetrads: } Gaffkya \\ \text{in irregular masses of one plane: } Staphylococcus. \end{cases}$

Genus I: *Gaffkya* Trevisan.

Gram-positive cocci occurring in tetrads.
Type species:*Gaffkya tetragena.* Other species: *tardissima, anaerobia.*

Genus II: *Staphylococcus* Rosenbach.

Gram-positive cocci occurring in irregular masses of one single plane; pigment present or not.

Type species: *St. aureus.* Other species: *citreus, epidermitis, albus,* etc.

Anaerobic species: *anaerobius, aerogenes, asaccharolyticus, activus.*

Tribe III: *Micrococceae* Prévot.

Gram-positive cocci occurring in masses of more than one plane.

Two genera $\begin{cases} \text{cubic masses of 8: } \quad Sarcina, \\ \text{irregular clustera: } \quad Micrococcus. \end{cases}$

Genus I: *Sarcina* Goodsir.

Gram-positive cocci occurring in cubical packets of 8.

Types species: *Sarcina ventriculi.* Anaerobic species: *S. beijerincki, maxima, methanica, barkeri.* Aerobic species: *conjonctivae, flava, lutea, aurantiaca, urea.*

Genus II: *Micrococcus* Cohn.

Gram-positive cocci occurring in irregular masses of more than one plane. Pigment often present.

Type species: *M. luteus.* Other species: *aurantiacus, varius,* etc. (46 species).

Anaerobic species: *M. grigoroffi, M. niger.*

Sub-genus *Incertae sedis: Methanococcus. M. mazei, M. vannieli.*

ORDER II: **Bacteriales** Prévot.

Elongated, straight, cylindrical or flat, non-sporeforming *Eubacteria.* Six families:

Family   I: *Parvobacteriaceae* ⎫
Family   II: *Ristellaceae*   ⎪
Family III: *Sphaerophoraceae*   ⎬ Gram-negative
Family IV: *Enterobacteriaceae*   ⎪
Family   V: *Pseudomonadaceae*   ⎪
Family VI: *Protobacteriaceae*   ⎭
Family VII: *Bacteriaceae*   ⎰ Gram-positive

FAMILY I: **Parvobacteriacceae** Rahn 1937.

Small rods, Gram-negative, growing well on ordinary media; do not liquefy gelatin; carbohydrates weakly fermented. Parasites of warm-blooded animals which they infect by penetrating through skin and mucous membranes. Three tribes:

Tribe I: *Pasteurelleae* Castellani and Chalmers.

Ovoid or elongated rods of small size, showing bipolar staining, motile or non-motile, Gram-negative. Four genera.

Genus I: *Pasteurella* Trevisan.

Small rods, Gram-negative, ovoid or elongated, showing bipolar staining; non-motile. Aerobic, anaerobic and facultative forms requiring low initial rH; weakly fermentative, the aerobic species do not attack lactose, while the anaerobic species may do so; produce no gas. Parasites of man, animals and birds.

Type species: *P. avicida.* Other species; *muricida, cuniculicida; suilla, pestis, tularensis.*

Anaerobic species: *vulgata, ovata, convexa, coagulans, serophila.*

Genus II: *Cillopasteurella* Prévot.

Similar to *Pasteurella* but motile and flagellated.

Types species: *C. pseudotuberculosis-rodentium.*

Genus III: *Malleomyces* Pribram.

Shorts rods with rounded ends, sometimes filamentous; with tendancy to pseudo-branching; non-motile: Gram-negative. Bipolar staining. Parasites.

Type species: *M. mallei*[1]

Temporary listing:

Genus IV: *Actinobacilus* Brumpt 1910.

Gram-negative non-sporeforming rods of average size, slightly pleomorphic; frequent coccoid forms. Tendency to show bipolar staining. Acid but no gas from carbohydrates. Grow well in the presence of CO_2, especially upon primary isolation. Pathogenic for animals, sometimes for man; produce clumps similar to those found in actinomycosis.

Type species: *A. lignieresi* Brumpt (aerobic, causes actinomycosis of cat and hog).

Other species: *A. actinomycetem-comitans,* aerobic or facultative. *A. actinoides,* microaerophilic.

Tribe II: *Brucelleae* Breed, Murray and Smith.

Small, non-motile, Gram-negative rods. Grow on ordinary media.

Single genus: *Brucella* Meyer and Shaw.

Short rods with coccoid forms; non-motile. Gram-negative. Parasitic. Infections of genital tract, mammary and lymphatic tissue, respiratory and intestinal tracts.

Type species: *Br. melitensis.* Other species: *abortus, suis.*

Tribe III: *Hemophileae* Winslow.

Rods of small size. Gram-negative; motile or non-motile; parasitic, requiring hemoglobin for primary isolation. Three genera:

Genus I: *Hemophilus* Winslow.

Short rods or filaments, pleomorphic; non-motile; Gram-negative, hemoglobinophilic or serophile.

Type species: *H. influenzae.* Other species: *parainfluenzae, suis, hemolyticus, pertussis, ducreyi, hemoglobinophilus.*

---

[1] The species *pseudomallei* being motile (cephalotrichous), it should be excluded from the genus *Malleomyces.* With Whitmore and Gochenhour, we relate it to the *Pseudomonadaceae* (see further on).

Genus II: (temporary listing): *Noguchia* Olitsky, Syverton and Tyler.

Small slender rods, Gram-negative, motile, encapsulated, aerobic or facultative. Optimum temperature 28° to 30°. Mucoid growth. Conjonctiva of man and animals (follicles).

Type species: *N. granulosis*. Other species: *simiae, cuniculi*.

Genus III. *Dialister* Bergey et al.

Rods of very small size, filter through candles; occurring singly, in pairs or in short chains. Non-motile. Parasites. Strict anaerobes; require fresh albumin.

Type species: *D. pneumosintes* varieties *septicemiae* and *septicus*. Other species: *granuliformans*. In temporary position, two genera, obligate parasites of red blood cells, not too well-defined, to be related probably to the *Rickettsiales:*

Grahamella Brumpt. Type species: *Grahamella talpae*.

Bartonella Strong et al. Type species: *Bartonella bacilliformis*.

FAMILY II: *Ristellaceae* Prévot.

Anaerobic, Gram-negative rods, motile or non-motile, encapsulated or not. Parasitic or saprophytic. Three genera.

Genus I: *Ristella* Prévot.

Gram-negative rods, non-motile, unencapsulated. Parasitic or saprophytic. Strict anaerobes.

Type species: *R. fragilis* (and 31 others).

Species *incertae sedis: R. vesca, R. corrodens, R. soehngeni*.

Genus *incertae sedis: Ruminobacter. R. parvum, R. amylogenes, R. amylophilum, R. ruminicola, R. succinogenes; Desulforistella hydrocarbonoclastica.*

Genus II: *Zuberella* Prévot.

Gram-negative rods, motile, unencapsulated. Parasitic. Strict anaerobes.

Type species: *Z serpens* (and 10 others).

Genus III: *Capsularis* Prévot.

Gram-negative rods, non-motile, encapsulated. Parasitic. Strict anaerobes.

Type species: *C. zoogleiformans* (and 3 others)

FAMILY III: *Sphaerophoraceae* Prévot.

Pleomorphic, non-sporeforming, Gram-negative rods showing swollen forms, numerous spheroids and sometimes pointed ends.

Type genus: *Sphaerophorus* Prévot.

Highly pleomorphic rods, straight or slightly-curved; ovoid forms with bipolar staining; branching, very long filamentous forms; sausage-shaped forms; swellings; chromaffinic, sessile or free spheroids; metachromasia in the elongated forms. Non-motile. No spores. Gram-negative. Generally strict anaerobes.

Type species: *S. necrophorus* (and 16 others).

Sub-genus: *Fusiformis* Hoelling.

Sphaerophoraceae with pointed ends, showing a fusiform shape.

Type species: *F. fusiformis* (and 4 others).

Genus *incertae sedis*: *Leptotrichia* Trevisan.

Long, filamentous, straight rods with rounded or pointed ends; non-motile; finely vacuolized cytoplasm; no spores; no branching; ovoid, fusiform or spherical swellings giving a violet color with iodine; metachromatic granules. Generally Gram-negative with irregularly Gram-positive segments; aerobic and anaerobic species. Type species: *L. buccalis*. Anaerobic species: *L. innominata* (and 3 others).

FAMILY IV: *Enterobacteriaceae* Rahn.

Gram-negative rods, motile with peritrichous flagella or non-motile; grow well on ordinary media. Acid and sometimes gas (H_2) from carbohydrates. Nitrites produced from nitrates. Widely distributed in nature. Parasites of man and animals, especially intestinal tract of mammals. Three tribes:

Tribe I: *Eschericheae* Bergey, Breed and Murray.

Acid and gas from glucose and lactose. Gelatin not liquefied, except slowly by *Aerobacter*. Three genera:

Genus I: *Escherichia* Castellani and Chalmers.

Gram-negative rods, non-sporeforming, motile. Acid and gas ($CO_2 = H_2$) from glucose and lactose. Facultative aerobes. Quite frequent in intestinal tract of man and animals. Methyl-red test positive. Voges-Proskauer test negative.

Type species: *E. coli*. Other species: *freundi*.

Genus II: *Aerobacter* Beijerinck.

Gram-negative rods, non-sporeforming, encapsulated. Acid and gas ($CO_2/H_2 = 2$) from glucose and lactose. Facultative aerobes. Frequent. Methyl-red test negative. Voges Proskauer test positive.

Type species: *A. aerogenes*. Other species: *A. cloacae*.

Genus III: *Klebsiella* Trevisan.

Short, plump, Gram-negative rods with rounded ends, encapsulated, non-motile. Acid and gas from several carbohydrates. Nitrites produced from nitrates. Respiratory tract of man. Aerobic.

Type species: *Kl. pneumoniae* (Friedlander). Other species: *ozaenae, granulomatis, capsulata, paralytica, rhinoscleromatis*.

Tribe II: *Proteae* Castellani and Chalmers.

Gram-negative rods, motile. Acid and gas from glucose but not lactose. Gelatin liquefied.

Single genus: *Proteus* Hauser.

Pleomorphic rods, filamentous, slightly-curved, Gram-negative, motile with peritrichous flagella; climbing growth on agar slant. Voges-Proskauer test negative. Urea decomposed.

Type species: *Pr. vulgaris*. Other species: *mirabilis* and 6 others.

Temporary Listing: *Providencia*.

Proteae which ferment glucose with the production of gas; ferment occasionally without gas production: mannitol, adonitol, inositol, salicin, sucrose; indole produced; utilize ammonium citrate; Voges-Proskauer test negative; methyl-red test positive, urea not hydrolyzed; nitrites produced from nitrates.

Type species: *Providencia providenciae*.

Tribe III: *Salmonelleae* Bergey, Breed and Murray.

Gram-negative rods, motile with peritrichous flagella, or non-motile; non-sporeforming; acid and gas from several carbohydrates; Voges-Proskauer test negative. Gelatin not liquefied. Urea not hydrolized. Milk not peptonized.

Two main genera; one sub-genus; one genus in temporary position.

Genus I: *Salmonella* Lignières.

Gram-negative rods, motile; acid and gas from glucose and numerous other carbohydrates. Lactose, sucrose and salicin not attacked. Indole not formed.

Type species: *S. paratyphi*. Other species: *S. cholerae suis, typhi-suis, schottmülleri, typhi-murium, morbificans, enteritidis, breslaviensis, pullorum,* and several others (more than 180).

Sub-genus: *Eberthella* Buchanan.

Motile Gram-negative rods; acid but no gas from several carbohydrates. Acetylmethylcarbinol not formed.

Type species: *E. typhosa* (and 13 other species.)

Genus III. *Shigella* Castellani and Chalmers.

Non-motile, Gram-negative rods; acid but no gas from carbohydrates. Acetylmethylcarbinol not formed.

Type species: *Shigella dysenteriae* (14 others among which *paradysenteriae, gallinarum,* etc.)

In temporary position:

Genus IV: *Moraxella* Lwoff 1939.

Non-motile rods of average size, often in pairs and short chains, with long involution forms, no capsules, no spores. Gram-negative. Carbohydrates not fermented. Parasites of conjunctiva.

Type species: *Moraxella lacunata.* Other species: *duplex, lwoffi,* etc.

FAMILY V: *Pseudomonadaceae* Winslow.

Elongated cells; straight or slightly-curved rods, non-sporeforming Gram-negative, motile with polar flagella or non-motile. Either soil or water forms. Some species parasitic for plants and animals. Three tribes:

Tribe I: *Pseudomonadeae* Kluyver and van Niel.

Straight, Gram-negative rods, motile with polar flagella or non-motile. Found in soil or water. Parasitic for plants; saprophytic or free. Seven genera:

Genus I: *Pseudomonas* Migula.

Motile, Gram-negative rods producing blue-green or greenish-yellow, or brown pigment, water-soluble, usually fluorescent and diffusible. Found in soil and water.

Types species: *Ps. aeruginosa* (Schroeter) Migula (=*Ps. pyocyaneus* Gessard) (and 103 others).

Genus II: *Phytobacterium* Magrou and Prévot 1948.

Non-sporeforming, Gram-negative rods, motile with monotrichous or lophotrichous flagella. White colonies. Plant pathogens.

Type species: *Phytobacterium fabae* (and 21 other species named according to the plant parasitized).

Genus III: *Agrobacterium* Conn 1942 emend. M. and P. 1948.

Short Gram-negative rods, motile by means of peritrichous or polar flagella; no detectable gas or acidity on ordinary media but CO_2 produced in synthetic media. Gelatin not liquefied or slowly liquefied. Utilizes inorganic nitrogen (NO_3 or NH_3). Opt. T. = 25 to 30°. Found in soil, roots and stem of plants where they produce hypertrophies.

Type species: *Agrobacterium tumefaciens* (and 2 other species).

Genus IV: *Xanthomonas* Dowson 1939.

Gram-negative rods; motile, usually with monotrichous flagella; yellow pigment insoluble in water. Proteins usually digested. Milk made alkaline. H_2S formed. Require sources of carbon and nitrogen other than asparagin. Mono- and di-saccharides are fermented. Plant pathogens (necrosis).

Type species: *X. hyacinthi* (and 52 other species).

The following sub-genus may be located here:
Sub-genus: *Cellulomonas* Bergey.

Small, Gram-negative, non-sporeforming rods with rounded ends; motile with peritrichous flagella. Cellulose digested. Poor growth on ordinary media. Found in soil.
Type species: *C. biazotea* (and 25 others).
With Brygoo, we place here the new genus:

Genus V: *Whitmorella* Brygoo 1957.

Gram-negative rods, motile with peritrichous flagella; non-diffusible yellow pigment; isolated from lesions of pseudo-glanders and in nature.

Type species: *Whitmorella pseudo-mallei*.

Genus VI: *Erwinia Winslow*.

Gram-negative rods, motile with peritrichous flagella. Acid and gas from glucose and lactose. Pectin usually attacked. Plant pathogens, invading the tissues with production of lesions which may destroy them.

Type species: *E. amylovora* (and 29 others).

Genus VII: *Aplanobacter* E. F. Smith 1905 emend.

Non-motile, Gram-negative rods. Plant pathogens.

Type species: *A. stewartii* (and 5 other species).

Tribe II: *Achromobactereae* Magrou and Prévot 1948.

Non-pigmentforming *Pseudomonadaceae*. Non-pathogenic for plants.

Genus I: *Achromobacter* (Bergey *et al.*) Brisou and Prévot emend.

Definition—Gram-negative rods, motile by means of polar or peritrichous flagella; non-pigmentforming. Litmus milk slightly acid, unchanged or alkaline. Found in soil, water, man, terrestrial or marine animals.

Type species: *A. liquefaciens* (Eisenberg) Bergey *et al.*

Genus II: *Acinetobacter* Brisou and Prévot 1954.

Definition: Colorless *pseudomonadaceae,* non-motile, sometimes encapsulated. Very short, coccoid forms are frequent. Good growth on ordinary media. Some species are often found in clinical cases of purulent urethritis, sinusitis and in urine. Other characteristics identical with those of *Achromobacter.*

Type species: *Acinetobacter stationis.*

Genus III: *Mycoplana* Gray and Thornton 1928.

Gram-negative rods, motile; pseudo-branching in some forms. Capable of utilizing phenol or similar aromatic compounds as source of energy. Found in soil.

Type species: *M. dimorpha.* Other species: *bullata.*

Tribe III. *Chromobactereae* Prévot 1948.

Gram-negative rods, pigmented. Five genera:

Genus I: *Chromobacterium* Bergonzini.

Gram-negative rods, motile with polar or peritrichous flagella. Aerobic. Produce violet pigment, soluble in alcohol but insoluble in chloroform. Soil and water forms.

Type species: *Chr. violaceum* (Schroeter) Bergonzini (and 2 others).

Genus II: *Flavobacterium* Bergey *et al.* 1923.

Gram-negative rods of average size, motile with peritrichous flagella; yellowish or orange-coloured pigment. Carbohydrates feebly fermented. Acid but no gas from hexoses. Found in soil and water.

Type species: *Fl. aquatile* (and 57 others).

Genus III. *Empedobacter* Brisou 1957.

Same definition as *Flavobacterium* but comprising only non-motile species producing yellow or orange pigment.

Type species: *Emp. lutescens.*

Genus IV: *Serratia Bizio.*

Gram-negative rods of small size, motile with peritrichous flagella; produce red or pink pigment on agar or gelatin. Gelatin rapidly liquefied. Nitrites produced from nitrates. Milk coagulated, then digested. Serum liquefied. Produce CO_2, H_2, acetic, formic, lactic and succinic acids, acetylmethylcarbinol and 2, 3-butylene-glycol.

Type species: *S. marcescens* (= *prodigiosus*) and 5 others.

Genus V: *Protaminobacter* (den Dooren de oJng 1926).

Gram-negative rods, motile; growing feebly on ordinary media and on peptone agar; capable of dissimilating one or several lower alkylamines and specialized in attacking substances which contain $HN < {C \atop C}$. Pigment-forming.

Type species: *Protaminobacter rubrum.*

FAMILY VI: **Protobacteriaceae** Pribam emend.

Gram-negative rods or spheres, motile with polar or peritrichous flagella, or non-motile; non-sporeforming; branching involution forms in certain cases. Autotrophic (do not need organic C and N). Find energy in oxidation of H, CH_4, CO, N, NH_3, S and thiosulfates. Free forms, not parasitic; found in water and soil. Five tribes:

Tribe I: *Protobacterieae* Rahn.

Rods, oxidize H_2 and C or their simple mineral combinations. Three genera:

Genus I: *Hydrogenomonas* Orla-Jensen.

Short rods, growing in the absence of organic matter, oxidizing H_2 to H_2O.

Type species: *H. pantotropha* (and 2 others).

Genus II: *Methanomonas* Orla-Jensen.

Short rods, motile with monotrichous flagella, growing in the absence of organic matter; oxidize CH_4 to CO_2 and H_2O.

Type species: *M. methanica.*

Genus III: *Carboxydomonas* Orla-Jensen.

Autotrophic rods, oxidizing CO to CO_2.

Type species: *C. oligocarbophila.*

Tribe II: *Nitrobacterieae* Winslow.

Rods or spherical forms. Oxidize NH_3 to NO_2. Three genera:

Genus I: *Nitrobacter* Winogradsky.

Gram-negative rods, non-motile; growing slowly on organic matter. Oxidize nitrite to nitrate.

Type species: *N. winogradskyi* (and several others).

Genus II: *Nitrosomonas* Winogradsky.

Gram-positive motile rods (polar flagellum); oxidize NH_3 to NO_2. Grow on artificial media containing little or no organic matter.

Type species: *N. europaea* (and a few others).

Genus III: *Nitrosococcus* Winogradsky.

Spheres of large size; cannot grow on ordinary media; oxidize NH_3 to NO_2 in soil and in appropriate media.

Type species: *N. nitrosus*.

Tribe III: *Rhizobieae* Prévot 1948.

Non-sporeforming rods motile or non-motile (1 to 4 flagella), with tendency to be Gram-negative. Capable of utilizing mineral nitrogen. Heterotrophic.

single genus: *Rhizobium* Frank.

Strictly aerobic Gram-negative rods; motile when young; heterotrophic; give bacteroidal forms on artificial media containing alkaloids and glucosides. Produce nodules on *Leguminosae* and fix atmospheric N during this symbiosis. Addition of yeast, malt, or plant extract necessary for rapid growth on artificial media. Slight reduction of nitrates to nitrites. Nitrites are not utilized. Gelatin not liquefied.

Type species: *R. leguminosarum*. Other species: *phaseoli, trifolii, lupini, meliloti, japonicum*.

Tribe IV: *Thiobacilleae* Bergey, Breed, and Murray.

Rods oxidizing sulfur or its compounds.

Single genus: *Thiobacillus* Beijerinck.

Small motile rods, oxidizing sulfur and thiosulfate to sulfide, sulfate or persulfate in acid or alkaline media and deriving their carbon from CO_2, carbonates and bicarbonates. Obligate or facultative autotrophic. Aerobic or anaerobic.

Type species: *Th. thioparus* (and 6 other aerobic species) and one facultative anaerobic species: *Th. denitrificans*.

Tribe V: *Acetobacterieae* Prévot 1948.

(Old family *Acetobacteriaceae*).

Gram-negative rods, showing elongated, pseudo-branching, and swollen forms. Oxidize alcohol to acetic acid.

Single genus: *Acetobacter* Beijerinck.

Gram-negative rods in short chains, non-motile. Grow on the surface of alcoholic solutions under strictly aerobic conditions. Oxidize alcohol to acetic acid. Utilize other carbon compounds, such as sugar and acetic acid. Involution forms elongated, filamentous, swollen and pseudo-branched.

Type species: *A. aceti* (*Kützing*) and 20 others, among which *A. xylinum*.

FAMILY VII: *Bacteriaceae* Cohn 1872 emend.

Gram-negative rods, motile or non-motile, non-sporeforming. Aerobic and anaerobic. Complex metabolism. Utilize amino acids and carbohydrates. Eight genera:

Genus I: *Bacterium* Ehrenberg emend.

Gram-positive rods, motile, non-sporeforming aerobic.
Type species: *B. incertum*.

Genus II: *Eubacterium* Janke 1930 emend.

Gram-positive rods, non-motile, non-sporeforming, anaerobic.

Type species: *Eub. foedans* (and 22 others).
Sub-genus: *Zymobacterium*. Type species: *Z. oroticum*.
Sub-genus: *Butyribacterium*. Type species: *B. rettgeri*.

Genus III: *Catenabacterium* Prévot

Gram-positive rods, non-motile, non-sporeforming, occurring in long chains: anaerobic.

Type species: *C. helminthoides* (and 10 others).

Genus IV: *Ramibacterium* Prévot.

Gram-positive rods, non-motile, non-sporeforming, showing pseudo-branching; anaerobic.

Type species: *R. ramosum* (and 5 others).

Genus V: *Cillobacterium* Prévot.

Gram-positive rods, motile, non-sporeforming; anaerobic.
Type species: *C. moniliforme* (and 9 others).

Genus VI: *Microbacterium* Orla-Jensen.

Small, Gram-positive rods, non-motile, non-sporeforming; ferment carbohydrates (with production of lactic acid); nitrites produced from nitrates; catalase-positive.
Type species: *M. lacticum* (and 2 others).

Genus VII: *Kurthia* Trevisan.

Long, Gram-positive rods, occurring in curved chains, motile with peritrichous flagella; growth as in *Proteus;* carbohydrates and gelatin not attacked; H_2S not formed.
Type species: *K. zopfi* (and 1 other).

Genus VIII: *Lactobacillus* Beijerinck 1882.

(Could be replaced advantageously by *Lactobacter* Beijerinck 1900).

Gram-positive rods, long and slender, non-motile, non-sporeforming; produce lactic acid from carbohydrates (CO_2 without H_2 when gas formed); several species are thermophilic.
Type species: *L. caucasicus* (and 13 others).

ORDER III: *Spirillales* Prévot.

Gram-negative, non-sporeforming *Eubacteriales,* curved into a comma or a spiral; motile; facultatively aerobic or anaerobic. Free forms (soil and water) and saprophytes. Heterotrophic parasitic forms. Two families:

FAMILY I: *Vibrionaceae* Prévot.

Gram-negative *Spirillales* curved into a comma; motile; aerobic and anaerobic. Four genera:

Genus I: *Vibrio* Müller 1773.

Short, Gram-negative cells, curved into a comma, occurring singly or united in short spiral-like chains. Motile with a single polar or 2-3 short flagella. Non-sporeforming. Water forms and parasites.
Type species: *V. comma* (Schroeter)—*V. cholerae* (Pfeiffer) (and 20 other aerobic species). 11 anaerobic species: type—*V. stomatitis.*
Sub-genus: *Butyrivibrio.* Type species: *B. fibrisolvens.*
Sub-genus: *Succinovibrio.* Type species: *S. dextrinosolvens.*

Sub-genus *incertae sedis: Campylobacter.* Type-species: *C. bubulus.*
Selenomonas. Type-species: *S. palpitans* and 1 other.

Genus II: *Cellvibrio* Winogradsky.

Long, slender, Gram-negative rods, slightly-curved, with rounded ends;
motile with a single polar flagellum; strongly chromaffinic granule. Oxidize cellulose to oxycellulose. Feeble growth on ordinary media.

Type species: *C. ochraceus* (and 4 other species).

Genus III: *Cellfalcicula* Winogradsky.

Gram-negative rods, short, spindle-shaped, with metachromatic granules; coccoid forms in old cultures; motile with peritrichous flagella. Oxidize cellulose to oxycellulose. Feeble growth on ordinary media.

Type species: *C. viridans* Winogradsky (and 2 others).

Genus IV: *Desulfovibrio* Kluyver and van Niel.

Type species: *D. desulfuricans* and 1 other.

FAMILY II: **Spirillaceae** Prévot.

Gram-negative *Spirillales* presenting an elongated body, spirally-curved,
motile with peritrichous flagella in variable number. Found in water and
putrid infusions.
Single genus: *Spirillum* Ehrenberg.

Same definition as the family.

Type species: *Sp. undula* (and 4 others of which *morsus muris*).

CLASS II:

SPOREFORMING *EUBACTERIA* OR *SPORULALES* Prévot

Sporeforming *Eubacteriales*, i.e. capable of producing a thermoressitant
spore (reserve cytoplasm and DNA which are not coagulated after heating
from 70° to 110°C for a few minutes to several hours, ensheathed in a
complex system of spore envelopes). Three orders:

ORDER I: **Bacillales** Prévot.

Sporulated *Eubacteriales* with endospore. Aerobic or facultatively
anaerobic. Motile or non-motile. Heterotrophic. Parasites, saprophytes or
free forms. Two families:

FAMILY I: *Innominaceae* Prévot.

Gram-negative *Bacillales.*

Single genus: *Innominatus* Prévot.

Type species: *I. danicus.* Other species: *albus, morulans.*

FAMILY II: *Bacillaceae* Fischer.

Gram-positive rods with endospore, motile with peritrichous flagella, or non-motile. Two genera:

Genus I: *Bacillus* Cohn.

Gram-positive, aerobic rods, occurring singly or in chains. Sporangia not bulged by spore. Motile with peritrichous flagella.

Type species: *B. subtilis* (more than 100 species, grouped in four sub-genera: *subtilis-mesentericus-vulgatus* group; *megatherium-cereus* group; *polymyxa* group; indefinite group.

Genus II: *Bacteridium* Davaine 1868.

Gram-positive, aerobic rods, occurring singly or in chains; sporangia not bulged by spore. Non-motile.

Type species: *Bacteridium anthracis* (and 12 other species: *funicularis, panis, fulminans, adhaerens, viridi, glaucescens, aurantium, viridulum, thermocellulolyticum, pepo, peptogenes*).

ORDER II: *Clostridiales* Prévot.

Gram-positive and Gram-negative rods with central or subterminal spore: sporangia bulged by spore. Motile and non-motile. Usually anaerobic, some forms are facultative. Pigment may or may not be present. Two families:

FAMILY I: *Endosporaceae* Prévot.

Gram-negative *Clostridiales.* Two genera:

Genus I: *Endosporus* Prévot.

Motile *Endosporaceae.*
Type species: *End. utriculus* (and 5 others).

Genus II: *Paraplectrum* Fischer.

Non-motile *Endosporaceae.*
Type species: *P. malenominatum* (and 2 others).

FAMILY II: Clostridiaceae (Fischer) emend.

Gram-positive *Clostridiales*. Three genera:

Genus I: *Inflabilis* Prévot.

Non-motile *Clostridiaceae*, unencapsulated.
Type species: *I. satellitis* (and 16 other species).

Genus II: *Welchia* Pribram.

Non-motile, encapsulated *Clostridiaceae*.
Type species: *W. perfringens* (and *W. agni*).

Genus III. *Clostridium* Prazmowski.

Motile *Clostridiaceae;* 94 species grouped in 9 sub-genera.

Sub-genus   I (Butyric fermentation). Type species: *Cl. butyricum.*
        II (Cellulose fermentation). Type species: *Cl. naviculum.*
       III (Pectin fermentation). Type species:
                                  Cl. aurantibutyricum.
       IV (Red malignant oedema). Type species: *Cl. septicum.*
       V (Gelatinous malignant oedema). Type species:
                                  Cl. oedematiens.
      VI (Botulism).   Type species: *Cl. botulinum.*
     VII (Peptolytic).   Type species: *Cl. sporogenes.*
    VIII (Peptolytic).   Type species: *Cl. fallax.*
       X (Residual group).   Type species: *Cl. rubellum.*

ORDER III: Plectridiales Prévot.

Sporeforming *Eubacteriales* with terminal spore. Two families:

FAMILY I: Terminosporaceae Prévot.

Gram-negative *Plectridiales*. Two genera:

Genus I: *Terminosporus* Prévot.

Motile *Terminosporaceae*.
Type species: *T. thermosaccharolyticus,* and 12 others among which *thermocellus, cellulosam fermentans.*

Genus II: *Caduceus* Prévot.

Non-motile *Terminosporaceae*.
Type species: *C. thermoaerogenes* and 3 others: *C. cellulosae disolvens.*

FAMILY II: *Plectridiaceae* Fischer emend.

Gram-positive *Plectridiales*. Two genera:

Genus I: *Plectridium* Fischer.

Motile *Plectridiaceae*.
Type species: *Pl. tetani* (and 25 others among which *tertium, calori-tolerans, putrificum, cellulolyticum, virens*).

Genus II: *Acuformis* Prévot.

Non-motile *Plectridiaceae*.
Type species: *A. spermoides* (and 11 others).

ORDER *incertae sedis: Sporovibrionales* Prévot.

Cells crescent-shaped, motile, sporeforming, Gram-positive.

FAMILY *incertae sedis: Sporovibrionaceae.*

Genus *incertae sedis: Sporovibrio* Starkey 1938.
Type-species: *Sp. orientis* and 1 other.

SUB-BRANCH: MYCOBACTERIA

(Bacteria related to the lower fungi).

CLASS I: *ACTINOMYCETALES* Buchanan emend.

Short and elongated rods, filamentous, with a tendency to form branches and sometimes even a rudimentary mycelium. Numerous swollen and spheroid forms, free or sessile. No endospores but possibility of segmentation into specialized cells (conidia) made up of a mass of nuclear substance. Pigmented or not. Affinity with the lower fungi. Two orders:

ORDER I: *Actinobacteriales* Prévot.

Non-acid-fast *Acinomycetales,* generally non-motile, Gram-positive. One single family: *Actinomycetaceae.*

FAMILY I: *Actinomycetaceae* Buchanan emend.

Gram-positive *Actinobacteriales.* Eight genera: two sub-genera[1].

Genus I: *Actinomyces* Harz.

Branched mycelium, breaking up into elements which function as conidia; non-motile; aerobic and microaerophilic. Parasitic forms presenting swollen ends and radiate arrangement in the lesions; saprophytic forms. Gram-positive.

Type species: *Actinomyces bovis.*

Genus II: *Nocardia* Trevisan 1889.

Non-sporeforming Gram-positive rods, producing swollen filamentous forms, occasionally branched, forming a discrete mycelium; coccoid forms in old cultures; no conidia; non-motile. Some species may show a slight degree of acid-fastness. Colonies similar to those of the *Eubacteria* or of the *Mycobacteria.* Aerobic. Several pathogenic species.

Type species: *Nocardia farcinica* (and some 30 others).

---

[1] The classification of the *Actinomycetaceae* is rapidly developing. No single author has yet seen his principles adopted by others. Concerning the genera which comprise numerous anaerobic species: *Corynebacterium, Actinobacterium* and *Bifidobacterium,* one may have to consider the last two as sub-genera of the first, much in the same manner that *Propionibacterium* is considered a sub-genus of *Corynebacterium.*

Genus III: *Streptomyces* Waksman and Henrici 1943.

Cells producing a highly branched mycelium with aerial hyphae. Chain-like conidiospores. Aerobic. Soil forms, plant and animal parasites. Numerous species are pigmented.

Type species: *Streptomyces albus* (and more than 70 others).

Genus IV: *Micromonospora* Orskov 1925.

Fine, non-septate mycelium, no aerial hyphae. Reproduction by means of small-sized conidia occurring singly at the tip of a very short conidiophore. Proteolytic. Several thermophilic species (65°). Usually saprophytic (manure, soil, dust, lake deposits). Sometimes pigmented.

Type species: *Micromonospora chalcea,* and 2 other anaerobic species.

Genus V: *Corynebacterium* Lehmann and Neumann.

Slender Gram-positive rods, straight or slightly-curved, with swellings and curved, branching forms in old cultures. Irregular staining. Non-acid-fast. Non-motile. Aerobic and anaerobic species.

Type species:*C. diphtheriae* (11 anaerobic species).

Sub-genus: *Propionibacterium* Orla Jensen.

Gram-positive rods; non-sporeforming; under anaerobic conditions give rise to diphteroids or streptococci, and irregular swollen, branching filaments in the presence of oxygen. Metachromatic granules. Production of propionic acid. Anaerobic by predilection.

Type species: *Prop. freudenreichi,* and 5 other species: *P. pentosaceum.*

Genus VI: *Actinobacterium* Hass (Syn. *Cohnistreptothrix*).

Gram-positive rods; non-motile; non-sporeforming; filamentous forms showing club-shaped swellings and branching in artificial culture, but radiate masses of branched forms in pathological products; anaerobic.

Type species: *Act. israeli.* Other species: *meyeri, abscessus, cellulitis.*

Sub-genus: *Bifidobacterium* Orla Jensen.

Gram-positive rods; non-sporeforming; non-motile; club-shaped swellings and bifid or doubly-bifid ends; microaerophilic and anaerobic.

Type species: *Bif. bifidum.*

Genus VII: *Erysipelothrix* Rosenbach.

Gram-positive rods; filamentous, branching; non-motile; granules. Microaerophilic. Pathogenic.

Type species; *E. rhusiopathiae* (swine erysipelas).

Genus VIII: *Listeria* Pirie [1].

Small Gram-positive rods; motile (1 single polar flagellum); micro-aerophilic to aerobic. Good growth on ordinary media. Carbohydrates attacked. Pathogenic (listerioses).

Type species; *L. monocytogenes.*

ORDER II: *Mycobacteriales* Prévot.

Acid-fact *Actinomycetales.*
Single Family: *Mycobacteriaceae* Chester.

Slender rods, sometimes filamentous, straight or slight-curved, frequently irregular with occasional and small branching forms. Acid-fast. No conidia. Non-motile. Aerobic.

Single genus: *Mycobacterium* Lehman and Neumann.

Acid-fast rods; swollen, cuneiform and branching cells. Slow growth on ordinary media. Aerobic; nearly all pathogenic.

Type species: *M. tuberculosis* (and *M. leprae*).

---

[1] The genus *Listeria* has long been considered as an *Eubacteriales,* family *Bacteriaceae.* The work of Sedaillan *et al,* a thesis by Coulombier have shown it to be related to *Erysipelothrix* by its morphological and physiological characteristics. We concur in this idea and place the genus *Listeria* right next to *Erysipelothrix* in the family *Actinomycetaceae.*

CLASS II: *MYXOBACTERIALES* Jahn.

(Slime bacteria = synbacteria)

Colonies of slender rods, relatively flexible (pseudo-plasmodium). The cells move as a unit advancing in masses by excretion of slime. No flagella. The fruiting bodies are made up of numerous spores which are formed either by shortened rods or in cysts containing more or less large numbers of short rods. These corpuscles are sometimes sessile, frequently pediculated, usually pigmented (yellow or red). Grow on dung media. Habitat: dung and soil; aquatic and parasitic forms. Three orders:

ORDER I: *Myxococcales* Tchan, Pochon and Prévot.

Spherical myxobacteriales. One single family:

Single Family: *Myxococcaceae* Jahn.

Rods becoming short when cysts are formed and developing into spherical microcysts or dormant cells. Elongation into rods without rupture of the membrane. Three genera:

Genus I: *Myxococcus* Thaxter.

Spherical microcysts or conical, spherical or ovoid fruiting bodies united by more or less motile slime.

Type species: *M. fulvus.*

Genus II: *Chondrococcus* Jahn.

Microcysts imbricated in a viscous slime which hardens. Fruiting bodies divided by constrictions, often branched, relatively small.

Type species: *Ch. coralloides.*

Genus III: *Angiococcus* Jahn.

Fruiting bodies in the shape of round cysts with thin membrane and microcysts within.

Type species: *A. disciformis.*

ORDER II: *Angiobacteriales* Tchan, Pochon and Prévot 1948.

Elongated *Myxobacteriales*. Three families:

FAMILY I: *Archangiaceae* Jahn 1924.

The pseudoplasmodium produces irregular swellings, either twisted fruiting bodies, or columnar or finger-like forms. No differentiated membrane. Two genera:

Genus I: *Archangium* Jahn.

Depressed, irregular fruiting bodies, swollen masses, resembling coiled intestines; constrictions; the fruiting body has no membrane.

Type species: *A. gephyra.*

Genus II: *Stelangium* Jahn.

Fruiting bodies are columnar or finger-like without a definite stalk.

Type species: *Stelangium muscorum.*

FAMILY II: *Sorangiaceae* Jahn.

The short rods of the fruiting bodies are enclosed within angular and polygonal cysts. Several of these cysts are surrounded by a common membrane.

Single genus: *Sorangium* Jahn.

Same definition as for the family.

Type species: *S. schroeteri.*

FAMILY III: *Polyangiaceae* Jahn.

In the fruiting bodies, the more or less short rods are contained in a round cyst of definite form. The wall is composed of hardened mucus, yellow, red or brown slime; the cyst may be surrounded by a visible slime membrane. Five genera:

Genus I: *Polyangium* Link.

Cysts round or coiled, surrounded by a well-developed membrane either free or contained in a second slime layer.

Type species: *P. vitellinum.*

Genus II: *Synangium* Jahn.

Cysts presenting a smooth point, which is more or less completely united to either hemispherical or spherical fruiting bodies in the shape of a rosette.

Type species: *S. sessile.*

Genus III: *Podangium* Jahn.

Cyst acorn-like, brownish or reddish-brown, occurring singly or on a more or less white stalk.

Type species: *P. erectum.*

Genus IV: *Chrondromyces* Berkeley and Curtis.

Cysts in a compact group on the end of pigmented stalk. Cystophore simple or branched.

Type species: *Ch. crocatus.*

ORDER III: *Asporangiales* Tchan, Pochon and Prévot 1948.

Definition: Imperfect forms producing no sporangium, only star-shaped bodies.

Single family: *Cytophagaceae* Stanier 1942.

Definition: Cells elongated, sometimes bacillary, slender; Gram-negative. Motility by reptation and gliding movements. Microcysts present or absent. Certain species may attack cellulose; others are polyphagic. Pigmented or not. Three genera:

Genus I: *Sporocytophaga* Stanier 1942.

Definition: Long, flexible, vegetative cells forming microcysts capable of sporulation.

Type species: *Sporocytophaga myxococcoides* Stanier 1942.

Genus II: *Cytophaga Winogradsky.*

Definition: Vegetative cells presenting at least a stage of elongated forms forming no microcysts.

Type species: *Cytophaga hutchinsoni W.*

Genus III: *Flexibacter (Soriano)* emend.

Definition: bacillary forms, never elongated, but flexible.

Type species: *Flexibacter flexilis.*

CLASS III: *AZOTOBACTERIALES* Prévot.

Cells of large size, rod-shaped or ellipsoidal, utilizing free nitrogen. Vacuome present. Yeast-like in appearance.

Single family: *Azotobacteriaceae* Bergey, Breed and Murray.

Rods of large size, coccoid or yeast-like cells, motile or non-motile. A single polar flagellum or a tuft of polar flagella. Outline of a vacuome. Obligate aerobes, growing in a film on the surface of the culture medium. Oxidize carbohydrates. Fix free nitrogen in carbohydrate solutions deficient in combined nitrogen.

Single Genus: *Azotobacter* Beijerinck.

Characteristics of the family. Several species.

Type species: *A. chroococcum.* Other species: *agile, achroococcum, vinelandi, beijerincki, vitreum, woodstowni.*

Sub-genus: *Beijerinckia. Nov.* species: *B. indicum.*

SUB-BRANCH: *ALGOBACTERIA*

Bacteria with general morphology recalling that of unicellular algae. Two classes:

CLASS I: *SIDEROBACTERIALES* Prévot.
(Ferruginous or iron bacteria).

Algobacteria showing iron inclusions (granules or impregnation of ferric hydroxyde); in some forms the iron may be replaced by Mn. Two orders:

ORDER I: *Chlamydobacteriales* Buchanan.
(Sheathed bacteria).

Filamentous bacteria, aquatic, sheathed, no branching or false branching. The sheaths may be encrusted with iron hydroxyde or with organic matter impregnated with iron; it may even be entirely organic. Conidia or swarm cells. Motile. No endospores.

Single family: *Chlamydobacteriaceae* Migula.

Characters of the order. Four genera.

Genus I: *Sphaerotilus* Kutzing.

Filaments bound together; colorless, false branching, ovoid, sheathed rods; non-motile conidia; swarm cells. Motile with lophotrichous flagella.

Type species: *Sph. natans.*

Genus II: *Clonothrix* Roze.

Filaments bound together; false branching; organic sheath, encrusted with iron or manganese, has broad base and a tapering apex. Colorless, cylindrical conidia.

Type species: *Clonothrix fusca.*

Genus III: *Leptothrix* Kutzing.

Cylindrical cells, filamentous, colorless, with sheaths, colored yellow or brown, encrusted with iron oxide; branching.

Type species: *Leptothrix ochracea.*

Genus IV: *Crenothrix* Cohn.

Unbranched filaments, attached to a firm substrate. Differentiation of base and apex: visible sheath, thin and colorless at the apex, thick and encrusted with iron at the base. Cells are cylindrical or spherical, divided into three planes. Non-motile conidia.

Type species: *C. polyspora.*

ORDER II: *Caulobacteriales* Henrici and Johnson 1935.
(stalked bacteria).

Filamentous, stalked bacteria. Asymmetrical cells surrounded by ferric hydroxide gum; multiplication by transverse fission. Cells occur singly or in pairs. Unsheathed. Aquatic. Four families.

FAMILY I: *Nevskiaceae* Henrici and Johnson.

Stalked bacteria, with the long axis at right angles to the stalk. Stalks branched, composed of gum. Multiplication by transverse fission. Unsheathed. Grow as viscous masses in water and sirups.

Single genus: *Nevskia* Famintzin.

Same characters as those family.

Type species: *N. ramosa.*

FAMILY II: *Gallionellaceae* Henrici and Johnson.

Stalked bacteria; long axis of the bacteria at right angles to that of the stalk. Stalk is straight or dichotomously branched, and encrusted with iron oxide. Multiplication by binary division.

Single genus: *Gallionella* Ehrenberg.

Characters of the family.

Type species: *G. ferruginea.*

FAMILY III: *Caulobacteriaceae* Henrici and Johnson.

Stalked bacteria, long axis of the cell coinciding with the stalk. Stalk is straight, attached to the substrate by a holdfast. No branching; multiplication by binary division. Epiphytic, growing upon submerged surfaces.

Single genus: *Caulobacter* Henrici and Johnson.

Characters of the family.

Type species: *C. vibrioides.*

FAMILY IV: *Pasteuriaceae* Laurent, emend. Henrici and Johnson.

Stalked bacteria with spherical or pyriform cells, the long axis of which coincides with that of the stalk. Stalk is short, or absent or very thin. Multiplication by longitudinal division. Epiphytic. Two genera:

Genus I: *Pasteuria* Metchnikoff.

Pyriform cells. Stalk very short or absent. Sessile cells.
Single species: *P. ramosa.*

Genus II: *Blastocaulis* Henrici and Johnson.

Pyriform cells. Stalk slender and long.
Single species: *B. sphaerica.*

CLASS II: *THIOBACTERIALES* Buchanan emend [1].
(Sulfobacteria or sulfur bacteria).

Cells of various shapes, containing either a granule of free sulfur, or bacterio-purpurin along with carotenoid pigments, or both; grow best in the presence of H_2S and light. Cells with plant characteristics, producing no pseudoplasmodium, with highly developed resting stage. No spores. Three orders:

---

[1] This chapter has been entirely revised according to Bourelly 1954.

ORDER I: *Rhodobacteriales* Pringsheim emend.

Bacteria normally growing in H_2S rich media; a red pigment usually accompanies the bacteriochlorophyll. Unicellular and flagellated, colorless forms. Three families:

FAMILY I: *Thiorhodaceae* (Molisch) van Niel 1944.

Purple bacteria with intracellular reserve sulfur. Five sub-families:
SUB-FAMILY I: *Thiocapsoideae* Migula emend.
Cells dividing along three planes to form full colonies which are globular, cubical or shapeless. Three genera:

Genus I: *Thiocystis* Winogradsky 1888.

Compact colonies containing from 4 to 30 cells with gelatinous sheath; multiplication by swarms of flagellated swimming cells. Cells may be purple or red, or colorless. Two species.
Type species: *Th. violacea.*

Genus II: *Thiocapsa* Winogradsky 1888.

Shapeless cells producing no swarmers. Two species (pink, red).
Type species: *Th. roseopersicina.*

Genus III: *Thiosarcina* Winogradsky 1888.

Pink cells forming cubical colonies which do not give rise to swarmers. Single species: *Th. rosea.*

SUB-FAMILY II: *Lamprocystoideae* Migula emend.

Hollow spherical cells, often perforated. Division of cells occurs first in three planes, then in two.
A single genus: *Lamprocystis* Schroeter 1889.
Ellipsoidal, purple cells. Multiplication by swarms of flagellated swimming cells. Five species grouping the former synonymous genera: *Thiosphaera, Thioderma* and *Thiosphaerion.*
Type species: *L. roseopersicina.*

SUB-FAMILY III: *Thiopedioideae* Migula emend.

Sheet-like colonies, multiplying by swimming cells with a single polar flagellum.
Single genus: *Thiopedia* Winogradsky 1888.
Single-plane colonies capable of swarming. Cells colored pink.
Type species: *Th. rosea.*

SUB-FAMILY IV: *Amoebobacteroideae* Migula emend.

Cells dividing in one single plane to form shapeless colonies. Four genera:

Genus I: *Amoebobacter* Winogradsky 1888.

Spherical or cylindical cells united into gelatinous colonies with ameboid movement.
Type species: *A. roseus.*

Genus II: *Thiothece* Winogradsky 1888

Non-motile gelatinous colonies, giving rise to swarmers.
Type species: *Th. gelatinosa.*

Genus III: *Thiopolycoccus* Winogradsky 1888.

Non-motile colonies, consisting of closely packed cells; colonies multiply by simply breaking up.
Single species: *Th. ruber.*

Genus IV: *Thiodyction* Winogradsky 1888.

Fusiform cells arranged end to end in a net-like structure. Reproduction by fragmentation of the colony.
Single species: *Th. elegans.*

SUB-FAMILY V: *Chromatioideae* Migula emend.

Free isolated cells. Two tribes.

Tribe I: *Chromatieae* Buchanan.

Motile cells with polar flagella. Four genera.

Genus I: *Chromatium* Perty 1852.

Red, ovoid or kidney-shaped cells with a single lateral flagellum. Dark sulfur granules.
Type species: *Chr. okeni.*

Genus II: *Chromatiopsis* Skuja 1948.

Globular or ovoid cells with a single polar flagellum.
Type species: *Chr. elektron.*

Genus III: *Rhabdochromatium* Winogradsky 1888.

Red, fusiform cells with either a single polar flagellum or a tuft of flagella.

Type species: *Th. roseum.*

Genus IV: *Thiospirillum* Winogradsky 1888

Spirally-curved cells, motile by means of a tuft of polar flagella.
Type species: *Th. sanguineum.*

Tribe II: *Rhodocapsieae* Migula emend.

Non-motile, isolated cells with a gelatinous sheath and gazeous
pseudovacuoles (aerosomes). Two genera:

Genus I: *Rhodocapsa* Molisch 1906.

Elongated, red cells, encapsulated, giving rise to motile forms without
capsules.
Type species: *Rh. suspensa.*

Benus II: *Rhodothece* Molisch 1906.

Spherical cells occurring in pairs, surrounded by a spherical capsule not
producing motile forms.
Type species: *Rh. pendens.*

FAMILY II: **Thiobacteriaceae** Janke 1924.

Colorless, motile, unicellular organisms, without pigment or bacteriochlorophyll. Four genera:

Genus I: *Macromonas* Utermohl and Koppe 1932.

Kidney-shaped, ellipsoidal, globular or fusiform cells with a single
polar flagellum.
Type species: *M. mobile.*

Genus II: *Thiospira* Wislouch 1914.

Spirally-curved cells, with a tuft of polar flagella.
Type species: *Th. winogradskyi.*

Genus III: *Taphrospira* Skuja 1948.

Spirally-curved cells with a longitudinal carinate groove recalling the
crista of spirochetes. One or two polar flagella.
Type species: *Taph. elongata.*

Genus IV: *Thiovulum* Hinze 1935.

Motile, ovoid cells with peritrichous flagella.
Type species: *Th. majus.*

FAMILY III: *Athiorhodaceae* (Molisch) van Niel 1944.

Red cells containing no intracellular reserve granules of sulfur; require growth factors. Three genera:

Genus I: *Rhodopseudomonas* Kluyver and van Niel.

Globular cells, rod- or comma-shaped, occurring singly, free an motile, or in gelatinous masses.
Type species: *Rh. palustris.*

Genus II: *Rhodospirillum* Molisch 1907.

Spirally-curved cells with polar flagella.
Type species: *Rh. rubrum.*

Genus III: *Pelochromatium* Lauterborn 1915.

Brownish or reddish cells growing inside a gelatinous sheath of the colorless host-cell which possesses a single polar flagellum (*Endosoma palleum*).
Type species: *P. roseum.*

Bourelly places in the neighborhood of the *Athiorhodaceae* the genus: *Rhodomicrobium* Duchow and Douglas 1949: Pigmented photosynthetic cells dividing by budding; formation of dendroid branching colonies. Cannot utilize sulfur or sulfides; hydrogen donators are organic compounds.
Type species: *Rh. vannieli.*

ORDER II: *Chlorobacteriales* Skuja 1948.

Green photosynthetic sulfur bacteria growing in media which contain high amount of H_2S. Two families:

FAMILY I: *Chlorobacteriaceae* (Lauterborn) Bergey *et al.* emend.
Free *chlorobacteriales.* Five genera:

Genus I: *Chlorobium* Nadson 1912.

Globular cells, occurring singly or in short filaments imbedded in slime, or in more or less regular masses.
Type species: *Ch. limicola.*

Genus II: *Tetrachloris* Pascher 1935.

Globular cells occurring in groups of 2 or 4 in a shapeless gelatinous thallum.
Type species: *T. inconstans.*

Genus III: *Clathrochloris* Geitler 1925.

Spherical cells arranged in chains forming an irregularly perforated colony.

Type species: *Cl. sulfurica.*

Genus IV: *Pelodictyon* Lauterborn 1913.

Fusiform cells dividing along three planes, the ends adhering together to make up an irregular network.

Type species: *P. clathratiforme.*

Genus V: *Microchloris* Pringsheim 1953.

Non-motile cells occurring singly as elongated cylindrical rods (2.5— 6.0 by 0.4μ) which may unite into fluid gelatinous masses. Multiplication by transverse division.

Type species: *M. nadsoni.*

FAMILY II: ***Chlorochromatiaceae*** Skuja 1948.

Small green bacteria adhering to another organism (bacterium or flagellate). Three genera:

Genus I: *Chlorobacterium* Lauterborn 1915.

Green rod-shaped bacteria stuck perpendicularly on the surface of the host (amoeba or flagellate).

Type species: *Ch. symbioticum.*

Genus II: *Chlorochromatium* Lauterborn 1906.

Small green bacteria similar to Chlorobium but growing symbiotically with a colorless bacterium possessing a single polar flagellum.

Type species: *Ch. aggregatum.*

Genus III: *Cylindrogloea* Perfiliev 1914.

Small, green bacteria occurring as a continuous coating over a filamentous bacterium exhibiting a mucous sheath.

Type species: *C. bactifera.*

In the neighborhood of this family, Bourrelly locates the genus: *Pelosphaera* Lauterborn.

Small, green bacteria with a single polar flagellum, forming hollow colonies.

Type species: *P. rotans.*

ORDER III: *Beggiatoales* Buchanan 1955.

Single family: *Beggiatoaceae* Migula.

Colorless, filamentous bacteria containing a granule of sulfur; oscillating movement. Seven genera:

Genus I: *Beggiatoa* Trevisan 1842.

Free, unbranched filaments made up of septate cells. Creeping movement with oscillation of the apex as in *Oscillatoria*. Multiplication by fragmentation.

Type species: *B. alba*.

Genus II: *Thiothrix* Winogradsky 1888

Filaments attached by their base which is surrounded by a delicate sheath. Multiplication by non-motile hormogonia.

Type species: *Th. nivea*.

Genus III: *Thiospirillopsis* Uphoff 1927

Motile, spirally-curved filaments recalling the *Spirulina*.

Type species: *Th. floridana*.

Genus IV: *Thioploca* Lauterborn 1907.

Beggiatoa-like motile filaments occurring in bundles enclosed by a common sheath.

Type species: *Th. schmiedlei*.

Genus V: *Thiosiphon* Klas 1936.

Non-motile non-septate filaments attached by their base. The apical portion tapers off and gives rise to conidia.

Type species: *Th. adriaticum*.

Genus VI: *Thiogloea* Devidé 1952.

Non-motile cells grouped into gelatinous colonies.

Type species: *Th. ruttneri*.

Genus VII: *Achromatium* Schewiakoff 1893.

Ellipsoidal or spherical cells occurring singly; motile without flagella. Granule of CO_3 Ca.

Type species: *E. oxaliferum*.

SUB-BRANCH: PROTOZOOBACTERIA

Elongated, flexuous, spirally-curved cells. Multiplication by transverse division. Motility is serpent-like, helicoidal or whirling.

SINGLE CLASS: *SPIROCHAETALES* Buchanan 1917.

Slender, flexuous bodies, spirally-curved, measuring from 6 to 500 microns. Some forms possess an axial filament, a lateral crista, or transverse striations. The short forms have a lower refraction index than the bacteria and cannot be seen otherwise than with dark-field illumination. Some forms do not stain well with aniline dyes but take Giemsa very well. Reproduction by transverse division. No known sexual cycle. Granules are present in some species. All are motile. No flagella, but sometimes a single polar flagellum. Serpent-like or whirling movements. Free, saprophytic or parasitic. Two families:

FAMILY I: *Spirochaetaceae* Swellengrebel 1907.

Spiral organisms, 30 to 500 μ long, with a definite protoplasmic structure. Found in stagnant, fresh or salt water and in the intestinal tract of *Labellibranchiata*. Three genera:

Genus I: *Spirochaeta* Ehrenberg 1833.

Flexuous, undulating bodies of great length, with ends terminating into a flagelliform filament. Well-defined axial filament around which the protoplasm is spirally wound. No periplastic membrane and no cross striation. Motility by creeping movement. Free forms living in stagnant, fresh or salt water, especially where H_2S is present. Mud and slime.

Type species: *Spirochaeta plicatilis.*

Genus II: *Saprospira* Gross 1911.

Axial filament not evident. Shallow spirals. Transverse septum visible without staining. Distinct periplastic membrane. Actively motile with rotating movement. Free forms living in marine sediments.

Type species: *Saprospira grandis.*

Genus III:*Cristispira* Gross 1910.

Flexuous bodies with coarse spirals, 28 to 120 μ long. More or less prominent crista. Cross striations. Highly motile. Intestinal tract of molluscs.

Type species: *Cristispira balbioni.*

FAMILY II: *Treponemataceae* Schaudinn 1905.

Coarse or slender spirals, 4 to 16 μ long; longer forms due to delayed division. Protoplasm without definite structure. Some forms show a terminal filament. Spirals are regular or irregular, fiexible or rigid. Most cells are visible only with dark-field illumination. Parasitic in vertebrates. Several are pathogenic. Only a few have been cultivated. Three genera:

Genus I: *Treponema* Schaudinn 1905

Cells, 3 to 18 μ, long forms due to incomplete division. Spirals are slender and regular or irregular. Terminal filament in some forms. Visible only under dark-field. Stain only with Giemsa, or by silver impregnation after mordancing. Cultivated only under anaerobic conditions. Pathogenic for man and certain other animal species.

Type species: *Treponema pallidum.*

Genus II:*Borrelia* Swellengrebel 1907.

Cells, 8 to 16 μ long. Coarse and shallow spirals which are irregular and obtuse-angled. Taper terminally into fine filaments visible without dark-field. Stain easily with aniline dyes. Parasitic for numerous animal species. Some are pathogenic for man, other mammals and birds. May be transmitted by arthropods.

Type species: *Borrelia anserina.*

Genus III:*Leptospira* Noguchi 1917.

Cells 6 to 20 μ long. Spirals measure 0.3 μ in depth and 0.4-0.5 μ in amplitude. Hook on one or both ends. Spinning movements. Visible without dark-field. Stain only with Giemsa. Aerobic.

Type species: *Leptospira icterohemorrhagiae.*

CHAPTER 2

KEY TO THE DETERMINATION
OF THE LARGE GROUPS CONTAINING
STRICTLY ANAEROBIC BACTERIA

Practically all the strictly anaerobic species of bacteria are found in the *Eubacteriales,* the *Actinomycetales,* the *Spirochaetales* and the *Thio-bacteriales.* The key to these large groups is the classic general key modified as follows:

I. Simple and undifferentiated forms, without true branching. Spheres; staight or slightly-curved rods, long or short. Motile or non-motile. Spore-forming or non-sporeforming. Several species produce pigment. Some species may show reserve material such as volutin, glycogen or fat. Never any visible deposit of iron or sulfur.

Sub-branch of *Eubacteria,* page 62

II. Long or short rods, long filaments, sometimes flexuous and undulating; differentiated forms such as spheroids, clubs, free and sessile conidia. Branching. No endospores, but specialized form (conidia), sometimes more resistant to inimical agencies than the vegetative cells. A few species produce pigment.

Class of*Actinomycetales,* page 343

III. Pleomorphic cells containing either one or more sulfur granules, or bacteriochlorophyll along with carotenoid pigments, sometimes both. Photosynthetic in a strictly anaerobic medium. No spores.

Class of *Thiobacteriales,* page 366

IV. Spiral, flexuous cells; multiplication by transverse division; non-polar motility. Single terminal filament. No spores.

Class of *Spirochaetales,* page 374

In each of these groups, only the following subdivisions comprise anaerobes:

A. SUB-DIVISION OF *EUBACTERIA.*

I. NON-SPOREFORMING FORMS:

Class of the *non-sporeforming Eubacteriales* or *ASPORULALES,* page 62

1. Spherical cells:

   Order I: *Micrococcales,* page 62

   a) Gram-negative: family of *NEISSERIACEAE,* page 62
   b) Gram-positive: family of *MICROCOCCACEAE,* page 68

2. Elongated, cylindrical cells:

   a) Simple, straight or slightly-curved:

   Order II: *BACTERIALES,* page 91

   a) Gram-negative cells of small size: family of *PARVOBACTE RIACEAE,* page 91
   b) Gram-negative cells of average or large size, but showing no pleomorphism nor spheroids: family of *RISTELLACEAE,* page 96
   c) Gram-negative cells, pleomorphic, with numerous spheroids: family of *SPHAEROPHORACEAE,* page 133
   d) Gram-positive cells: family of *BACTERIACEAE,* page 152
   e) Spirally-curved or in the shape of a comma:

   Order III: *SPIRILLALES,* page 186

   a) Gram-negative cells: family of *VIBRIONACEAE,* page 186

II. SPOREFORMING FORMS:

Class of sporeforming *Eubacteriales* or *SPORULALES,* page 200

1. Straight forms:

   a) central or subterminal spores swelling the bacillary body to a clostridium:

   Order I: *CLOSTRIDIALES,* page 200

   a) Gram-negative cells: family of *ENDOSPORACEAE,* page 200
   b) Gram-positive cells: family of *CLOSTRIDIACEAE,* page 211
   c) spores strictly terminal:

   Order II: *PLECTRIDIALES,* page 303

   a) Gram-negative cells: family of *TEMINOSPORACEAE,* page 303
   b) Gram-positive cells: family of *PLECTRIDIACEAE,* page 313

2. Comma-shaped forms as in the *Vibrios:*

   Order III: *SPOROVIBRIONALES,* page 343

   a) Gram-negative cells: family of *SPOROVIBRIONACEAE,* page 343

B. SUBDIVISION of the *ACTINOMYCETALES*

1. Non-acid fast: *ACTINOBACTERIALES*, page 344
    a) Gram-positive cells: family of *ACTINOMYCETACEAE*, page 344

C. SUBDIVISION of the *THIOBACTERIALES*

1. Red or colorless forms:
    Order I: *RHODOBACTERIALES*, page 366
    a) red: family of *THIORHODACEAE*, page 366
    b) colorless: family of *THIOBACTERIACEAE*, page 367
    c) purple or brown: family of *ATHIORHODACEAE*, page 368

2. Green or colorless forms:
    Order II: *CHLOROBACTERIALES*, page 371
    a) free: family of *CHLOROBACTERIACEAE*, page 371
    b) adhering to another organism: family of *CHLOROCHROMA-TIACEAE*, page 372

3. Colorless forms:
    Order III: *BEGGIATOALES*, page 372
    Single family: *BEGGIATOACEAE*, page 372

D. SUBDIVISION of the *SPIROCHAETALES*

Single family: *TREPONEMATACEAE*, page 374

The general concept of the situation which the anaerobes occupy in the general classification of the bacteria is outlined in the following table.

SUB-BRANCHES	CLASSES	ORDERS	FAMILIES	TRIBES	GENERA
EUBACTERIA	ASPORULALES	MICROCOCCALES	NEISSERIACEAE	Neisserieae	Neisseria
				Veillonelleae	Veillonella
				Streptococceae	Diplococcus
					Streptococcus
			MICROCOCCACEAE	Staphylococceae	Gaffkya
					Staphylococcus
				Micrococceae	Sarcina
					Micrococcus
		BACTERIALES	PARVOBACTERIACEAE	Pasteurelleae	Pasteurella
				Haemophileae	Dialister
			RISTELLACEAE		Ristella
					Zuberella
					Capsularis
			SPHAEROPHORACEAE		Sphaerophorus
					Fusiformis
					Leptotrichia
			BACTERIACEAE		Eubacterium
					Catenabacterium
					Ramibacterium
					Cillobacterium
		SPIRILLALES	VIBRIONACEAE		Vibrio
					Selenomonas
					Desulfovibrio
	SPORULALES	CLOSTRIDIALES	ENDOSPORACEAE		Endosporus
					Paraplectrum
					Inflabilis
		PLECTRIDIALES	CLOSTRIDIACEAE		Welchia
					Clostridium
			TERMINOSPORACEAE		Terminosporus
					Caduceus

Class	Order	Suborder	Family	Genera
MYCOBACTERIA	SPOROVIBRIONALES		PLECTRIDIACEAE	Plectridium / Acuformis
			SPOROVIBRIONACEAE	Sporovibrio
	ACTINOMYCETALES	ACTINOBACTERIALES	ACTINOMYCETACEAE	Corynebacterium / Propionibacterium / Actinobacterium / Bifidobacterium
			THIORHODACEAE	Thiosarcina / Thiopedia / Chromatium
ALGOBACTERIA	RHODOBACTERIALES		THIOBACTERIACEAE	Macromonas / Thiovulum / Rhodopseudomonas
			ATHIORNODACEAE	Rhodospirillum / Rhodomicrobium
	THIOBACTERIALES	CHLOROBACTERIALES	CHLOROBACTERIACEAE	Chlorobium
			CHLOROCHROMATIACEAE	Chlorochromatium
		BEGGIATOALES	BEGGIATOACEAE	Achromatium
PROTOZOOA	SPIROCHAETALES		TREPONEMATACEAE	Treponema / Borrelia

Note — This table does not take into account the physiological sub-genera nor the *incertae sedis* genera.

CHAPTER 3

SUB-BRANCH I: EUBACTERIA

CLASS A: ASPORULALES

ORDER I: MICROCOCCALES

We have seen in the preceding chapter that the cocci forming the Order: *Micrococcales* are subdivided into *Neisseriaceae* (Gram-negative) and *Micrococcaceae* (Gram-positive).

FAMILY I: *NEISSERIACEAE* Prévot 1933.

Gram-negative cocci.

The anaerobic species in this group are arranged in two genera:

1. Gram-negative cocci occurring in pairs, with adjacent sides flattened.

Genus I: *Neisseria* Trevisan, page 62

2. Gram-negative cocci of very small size, occurring in irregular masses (seldom in pairs or short chains).

Genus II: *Veillonella* Prévot, page 65

GENUS I: *Neisseria* Trevisan.

Gram-negative cocci occurring in pairs, with adjacent sides flattened.

The anaerobic species of this genus are four in number. They are seldom met. Their isolation is difficult. They keep poorly. For these reasons their very existence is denied by some bacteriologists unfamiliar with the difficulties of studying the anaerobes.

A) Species producing no gas:
  1. Medium size; produces indole; non-proteolytic.
    1. *Neisseria reniformis,* page 63

2. Large size; does not produce indole; non-proteolytic.

2. *Neisseria orbiculata,* page 63

3. Medium size; does not produce indole; liquefies gelatin; digests milk.

3. *Neisseria vulvovaginitis,* page 64

B) Species producing gas:

4. Medium size; lenticular colonies growing as a narrow disk in the critical zone of deep agar.

4. *Neisseria discoides,* page 64

1. **Neisseria reniformis** (Cottet) Prévot 1933.

Synonym: Diplococcus or *Micrococcus reniformis* Cottet.

Habitat: Urogenital system. Quite frequent.

Morphology: Kidney-shaped cocci, with adacent sides flattened; 0.8 to 1.0 micron in diameter. Gram-negative.

Physiology: pH$=$7.0; t$=$37°; killed in half an hour at 60°.

Cultural characteristics: No gas produced.

Deep agar: Lenticular colonies, 0.5 mm.

Glucose broth: Turbid; flakes; rancid odor; indole.

Peptone water: Slightly turbid; traces of indole.

Gelatin: No liquefaction.

Milk: Unchanged.

Coagulated proteins: Not attacked.

Carbohydrates: Glucose only is slightly fermented.

Pathogenicity, natural: Suppurations of the urogenital tract; vulvo-vaginitis, urinary abscess, pyonephritis, cystitis; urogenital gangrenous phlegmon.

Pathogenicity, experimental: Localized abscess in the guinea-pig. Hemolysin: Very weak.

Serology: Antiserum agglutinates homologous strain at 1:500.

2. **Neisseria orbiculata** (Tissier) Prévot 1933.

Synonym: Diplococcus orbiculus Tissier.

Habitat: Intestinal tract of young children, Uncommon.

Morphology: Large cocci, 1.5 to 2.0 μ. Gram-negative.

Physiology: t$=$ 37°. Non-thermoresistant. Does not live more than 8 days.

Cultural characteristics: No gas produced.

Deep agar: Large, lenticular colonies.

Glucose broth: Turbid; clotted sediment; no odor.

Peptone water: Indole not formed.

Gelatin: No growth at 22°.

Milk: Unchanged.

Coagulated proteins: Not attacked.

Proteoses: Digested without formation of indole.

Carbohydrates: Glucose fermented (acid); lactose slightly fermented; sucrose not attacked.

Pathogenicity: Non-pathogenic.

3. *Neisseria vulvovaginitis* Reynes 1947.

Habitat: Female genital tract. Uncommon.

Morphology: Diplococci, similar to the gonococcus; rarely in short chains or irregular masses. 0.8 μ. Gram-negative.

Physiology: Strict anaerobe; optimum pH=7.4; opt. t.=37°; killed in 15 min. at 55°. Longevity: 2 months. Reducing powers weak (phenosafranine not reduced).

Cultural characteristics: No gas produced. Slight odor, rancid and unpleasant.

Deep agar: Punctiform colonies; maximum growth in critical zone.

Peptone water: Meagre, clotty growth; auto-agglutination.

Glucose VF broth: Slightly turbid, clotty, no gas.

Gelatin: Liquefied in 12 days.

Milk: Digested in 8 days without previous coagulation.

Coagulated serum: Slightly altered (becomes transparent in 30 days).

Fibrin: Slightly altered.

Coagulated egg-white: Not attacked.

Brain: Not blackened.

Carbohydrates: Not fermented (verified by quantitative analysis).

Biochemistry: Nitrites not formed from nitrates. Produces NH_3; H_2S; acetic and propionic acids; volatile amines; acetone; aldehydes; indole not formed; urea decomposed.

Pathogenicity, natural: Isolated from a case of vulvovaginitis in a 5-year old girl.

Pathogenicity, experimental: Non- pathogenic for the guinea-pig and mouse. No toxin or hemolysin.

4. *Neisseria discoides* Prévot 1933.

Habitat: Buccal cavity. Teeth. Respiratory tract. Nasopharyngeal cavity. Quite common.

Morphology: Cocci, 0.6-0.7 μ, in pairs. Gram-negative.

Physiology: pH 7-8; t=37°. Non-thermoresistant. Survives for only two days. Some strains may survive for 3 weeks. Neutral red: Not reduced or partially reduced.

Cultural characteristics: Gas produced in solid and liquid media.

Deep agar: Lenticular colonies, 1 mm., growing as a thin disk (2 to 3 mm.) at 1 cm. below the surface of the agar. After several transfers, may grow in the deeper layers of the agar.

Glucose broth: Turbid in 24 to 48 hours. Granular sediment. Rancid odor. Inflammable gas (H_2).

Peptone water: Slightly turbid; slight gas formation; indole not formed.

Gelatin: No liquefaction.

Milk: Unchanged.

Coagulated proteins: Not attacked.

Carbohydrates: Not fermented, except sometimes glucose.

Biochemistry: Nitrites formed from nitrates. Produces a trace of SH_2, NH_3; aldehydes; acetylmethylcarbinol; formic, propionic and lactic acids.

Pathogenicity: Pyogenic; focal infections: buccal, dental, gingival, tonsillar, rhinopharyngeal and bronchial. Non-pathogenic for the guinea-pig. No toxin nor hemolysin.

GENUS II: *Veillonella* Prévot 1933.

Very small cocci, sometimes in pairs or short chains, but mostly in irregular masses; Gram-negative. This genus comprises actually three anaerobic species along with their varieties:

1. Saccharolytic, acidifying, fetid (SH_2), indole-forming, gasogenous, nitrite-forming.

    1. *Veillonella parvula,* page 65

2. Saccharolytic, acidifying, fetid, gasogenous, serophile, variable.

    2. *Veillonella variabilis,* page 66

3. Non-saccharolytic, alkali-forming, not fetid, indole not produced, gasogenous.

    3. *Veillonella alcalescens,* page 67

1. ***Veillonella parvula*** (Veillon and Zuber) Prévot 1933.

Synonym: Staphylococcus or *Micrococcus parvulus* Veillon and Zuber, 1898.

Habitat: Natural cavities of man and animals, especially the digestive tract. Sea water. Very frequent.

Morphology: Very small cocci: 0.3 μ, in irregular masses. Gram-negative.

Physiology: pH 6.5 to 8; t=22° to 37°. Strict anaerobe (some strains microaerophilic). Non-thermoresistant. Longevity rather short. Can filter through L2 candles. Reduces safranine temporarily. Neutral red: Reduced by some strains.

Cultural characteristics: Abundant gas.

Deep agar: Lenticular colonies of 1 to 2 mm.

Blood agar: Hemopeptolysis.

Glucose broth: Turbid or clotty growth. Rancid odor, faintly fetid. $CO_2 + H_2 + H_2S$. Indole.

Peptone water: Turbid. Gas. Indole.

Gelatin: No liquefaction.

Milk: Unchanged.

Coagulated proteins: Not attacked.

Carbohydrates: Glucose and levulose fermented; galactose and sucrose, xylose and inulin feebly fermented. Mannitol, maltose irregularly fermented. Gas. $CO_2 + H_2$.

Biochemistry: Nitrites formed from nitrates. Produces H_2S, NH_3; indole; volatile amines; aldehydes; ketones; acetylmethylcarbinol; acetic, propionic and lactic acids.

Pathogenicity, natural: Pyogenic; alveolar pyorrhea; dental abscess; follicular tonsillitis; pulmonary gangrene and suppuration; cholecystitis; appendicitis; urogenital suppurations; suppurative canaliculitis; purulent pleurisy; cystitis.

Pathogenicity, experimental: Abscess in the guinea-pig. Several strains non-pathogenic. No haemolysin.

Agglutination: Specific and non-specific (normal serum).

Varieties of *V. parvula.*

1. *V.p.* variety *minima* (Gioelli).

Synonym: Staphylococcus minimus (Gioelli).

Very small (0.1 to 0.15μ), grows only at 37°; filters through Berkefeld candles; no growth on gelatin; clotty growth in broth (not turbid).

2. *V.p.* variety *thomsoni* (Thomson) P. 1933.

Requires a growth factor (fresh serum or tissue extracts).

3. *V.p. branhami* (Branham) P. 1933.

Synonym: Micrococcus branhami (Bergey *et al.*).

Liquefies gelatin slowly.

2.   *Veillonella variabilis* Magrassi 1944.

Habitat: Unknown. Probably the human intestine. Very uncommon

Morphology: Very small cocci, in irregular masses; sometimes in pairs and tetrads. Non-motile, no spores. Gram-negative.

Physiology: Strict anaerobe. Opt. t.=37°. Killed in 30 minutes at 58°. Longevity: 1 month.

Cultural characteristics: Gas, fetid odor. After heating at 54-56°, loses its power to ferment even in the presence of fresh tissue. Serophile.

Deep agar: Punctiform colonies. Gas.

Serum agar slope: Punctiform colonies, transparent, bluish.

Peptone water: Meager growth; no gas.

Broth: Slow and meager growth; no gas.

Broth+albumin: (serum or ascitic fluid): Rapid and abundant growth; gas; putrid odor.

Broth+liver or brain or pieces of organs: Turbid throughout, with abundant sediment. Gas; fetid odor.

Gelatin: No liquefaction.

Milk: No growth.

Coagulated proteins: Not attacked.

Carbohydrates: Glucose, levulose and sucrose fermented.

Pathogenicity, natural: Isolated from a case of double relapsing mastitis of 6 years' duration with abscesses alternating from the right to the left.

Pathogenicity, experimental: Guinea pig: localized abscess which heals. Not pathogenic for mice.

3. *Veillonella alcalescens* (Lewkowicz) Prévot 1933.

Synonym: Micrococcus gazogenes alcalescens anaerobius Lewkowicz 1901; *Micrococcus gazogenes* Hall and Howitt 1925; *Veillonella gazogenes* (Hall and Howitt) Bergey *et al.*

Habitat: Natural cavities of man and animals. Extremely frequent.

Morphology: Very small cocci: 0.3 to 0.4 μ, in irregular masses. Gram-negative.

Physiology: Strict anaerobe or microaerophilic. t$=27°$ to $37°$. pH$=6$ to 8. Not thermoresistant. Longevity is average. Filters through L2 candles. Slight reducing powers. Neutral red: Feebly reduced (orange red).

Cultural characteristics: Gas produced in all media.

Deep agar: Lenticular colonies. Gas.

Blood agar: No hemolysis.

Glucose broth: Turbid or clotty. Gas not fetid; no acid produced; indole not formed.

Peptone water: Turbid; gas; indole not formed.

Gelatin: No liquefaction.

Milk: Unchanged.

Coagulated proteins: Not attacked.

Media with Pb: Not blackened. No H2S formed.

Carbohydrates: Not fermented.

Biochemistry: Nitrites formed from nitrates.

Produces volatile amines produced; aldehydes; NH$_3$; acetylmethyl-carbinol; acetic, valerianic and lactic acids.

Pathogenicity, natural: Pyogenic; purulent arthritis; focal infections; purulent pleurisy; abscess of the parotid gland; lung abscess; pulmonary gangrene; dental caries; infected fronhiectasis; gingivitis.

Pathogenicity, experimental: Several strains not pathogenic. No toxin nor haemolysin. Some strains can give in the guinea-pig and the rabbit purulent arthritis, alveolar pyorrhea, abscesses and focal infections.

Agglutination: Specific and non-specific (normal serum).

Varieties of *V. alcalescens.*

1. *V.a.* variety *gingivalis* (Ozaki) Prévot 1933.

Synonym: Micrococcus gingivalis (Bergey *et al.*).

2. *V.a.* Growth enhanced by reducing sugars; non-pathogenic.

3. *V.a.* variety *syzygios* (Herzberg) Prévot.

Synonym: M. syzygios scarlatinae Herzberg.

Microaerophilic; traces of H_2S produced; filters thruough candles; nitrites formed from nitrates.

Species incertae sedis: Peptostreptococcus elsdeni.

Peptostreptococcus elsdeni Gutierrez, Davis, Lindahl and Warmick 1959.

Probable synonym: Veillonella elsdeni (G.D.L. and W.) Prévot.

Habitat: Rumen of cattle and sheep.

Morphology: Large coccus, occurring in pairs or chains containing 16 to 20 cells. They measure 2.0 to 2.4 x 2.6μ in wet preparations and 1.6 to 1.8μ after staining. Adjacent sides are flattened. Nonmotile; unencapsulated. Gram-negative (with sometimes a few Gram-positive cells). Highly pleomorphic in old cultures; chains are longer in the rumen.

Physiology: Strict anaerobe. Catalase-negative. Opt. T.: 39°C.

Cultural characters: Gas produced, but not fetid.

Deep agar + yeast extract + Na lactate: Lenticular colonies 1 to 4 mm.; tan-colored, fatty; surface colonies are regular, smooth, convex, brilliant.

Peptone broth + yeast extract: Slight turbidity, sediment.

Gelatin: Not liquefied.

Milk: Unchanged.

Carbohydrates: Glucose, levulose, and maltose fermented.

Biochemistry: Nitrites not formed from nitrates; indole not formed nor acetoin. H_2S produced. Lactates fermented.

Fermentation products: CO_2, H_2, acetic, propionic, butyric and valeric acids, sometimes caproic.

Pathogenicity, natural: Abdominal flatulence when abundant or associated with *Str. bovis.*

FAMILY II: *MICROCOCCACEAE*

The *Micrococcaceae* or Gram-positive cocci comprise three tribes:

1. Cocci occurring in pairs or short chains: *Streptococceae,* page 68
2. Cocci occurring in single-plane masses: *Staphylococceae,* page 80
3. Cocci occurring in cubical or irregular masses: *Micrococceae,* page 83

Tribe I: **STREPTOCOCCEAE** Trevisan

Cocci occurring in pairs or short chains. Gram-positive.

Of the genera forming this tribe, only two contain anaerobic species:

1. Cocci usually in pairs (seldom in short chains).
   Genus I: *Diplococcus* Weichselbaum, page 69

2. Cocci usually in short chains (seldom in pairs).

Genus II: *Streptococcus* Billroth, page 73

GENUS I: *DIPLOCOCCUS* Weichselbaum.

Gram-positive cocci occurring in pairs.

This genus contains seven anaerobic species:

A) Species producing no gas:
1. Cocci of large size, forming viscous zooglea; no gas, no indole produced; non-saccharolytic; alkali-forming.
    1. *Diplococcus magnus,* page 69
2. Cocci of large size, producing no gas nor indole; black pigment in Vf broth.
    2. *Diplococcus tropicus,* page 70
3. Cocci of medium size; no gas formed; non-saccharolytic.
    3. *Diplococcus paleopneumoniae,* page 70
4. Cocci of medium size; no gas formed; saccharolytic; serophile.
    4. *Diplococcus morbillorum,* page 71
5. Cocci of medium size; no gas formed; milk coagulated; saccharolytic.
    5. *Diplococcus plagarum-belli,* page 71
6. Cocci of small size; no gas formed; constellated colonies.
    6. *Diplococcus constellatus,* page 72

B) Gas-producing species:
7. Cocci of 1.2 μ spherical colonies, ferments glycine.
    7. *Diplococcus glycinophilus,* page 72
    1. **Diplococcus magnus** (Tissier and Martelly) Prévot 1933.

Synonym: Diplococcus magnus anaerobius T. and M.

Habitat: Putrefying butcher's meat. Appendix. Quite frequent.

Morphology: Cocci of 1.5 to 1.8 μ, in pairs. Gram-positive.

Physiology: Strict anaerobe. t $= 18°$ to $37°$. Not thermoresistant. pH $= 5.5$ to 8.5. Average longevity. Reducing powers (neutral red permanently reduced, safranin temporarily).

Cultural characteristics: No gas formed.

Deep agar: Lenticular colonies.

Glucose broth: Turbid; viscous sediment.

Peptone water: Turbid; indole not formed.

Sterile urine: Turbid; splitting of urea.

Gelatin: No liquefaction.

Milk: Unchanged.

Fibrin: Not attacked.

Coagulated proteins: Not attacked.

Proteoses: Digested with formation of NH₃.

Carbohydrates: Not fermented. Glucose weakly fermented.

Biochemistry: Nitrites not formed from nitrates. NH₃ formed; traces of H₂S; volatile amines; traces of aldehyde; pure acetic acid.

Pathogenicity, natural: Pyelonephritis, puerperal infection, pulmonary gangrene, suppurative parotitis, two cases of pulmonary suppuration, as well as from an osteomyelitic fistula.

2. *Diplococcus tropicus* Magara, Go, So, Akima 1948.

Habitat: Rice fields of Japan. Quite uncommon.

Morphology: Mostly diplococcus, seldom isolated, short chains or irregular masses; 1.3 to 1.8 μ in diameter. Non-motile, no endospore nor capsule. Gram-positive.

Physiology: Strict anaerobe; slight reducing power (neutral red not reduced).

Cultural characteristics: No gas nor fetid odor produced.

Deep Agar: Lenticular colonies, becoming granular.

Peptone water: Turbid; indole and H₂S not produced.

Vf broth: Rapid growth; turbid, then flaky precipitate; no gas.

Gelatin: No liquefaction.

Milk: Unchanged.

Vf broth + liver: Very heavy growth. Black pigment slowly appearing at the surface.

Vf broth + eggwhite: Unchanged.

Carbohydrates: Not fermented.

Biochemistry: Nitrites not formed from nitrates; produces NH₃, volatile amines, aldehydes, ethanol, ketones, phenol and acetic acid.

Pathogenicity, natural: Tropical ulcer in Japan (isolated in 10 out of 19 cases) in association with *fusiform-treponema* symbionts.

Pathogenicity, experimental: Intracutaneous injection of Vf broth + liver culture into the guinea pig or rabbit gives rise to ecthyma in which the diplococci may be isolated in pure culture.

Serology: Agglutinated by patient and by normal serum.

Differential diagnosis: Differs from *D. magnus* by its black pigment and pathogenic power.

3. *Diplococcus paleopneumoniae* (Rist) Prévot 1933.

Habitat: Buccal and rhinopharyngeal cavities of man and animals. Quite frequent.

Morphology: Cocci of 0.7 to 1 μ, in pairs. Gram-positive.

Physiology: Strict anaerobe. Some strains may become facultative. t = 37° Killed at 55°.

Cultural characteristics: No gas formed.

Deep agar: Lenticular colonies.

Glucose broth: Turbid.

Gelatin. No liquefaction.

Milk: Partial coagulation.

Beef serum: Abundant growth with partial coagulation.

Carbohydrates: Glucose and lactose fermented, as well as fructose, maltose, sucrose and galactose.

Biochemistry: Nitrites not formed from nitrates; produces NH_3, volatile amines, indole, addehyde, ethanol, ketones, volatile acids (traces) and lactic acid.

Pathogenicity, natural: In man: bronchiectasis, bony abscess. In the rabbit: epizootic pleuropneumonia.

Pathogenicity experimental: Highly pathogenic: fibrinous pleurisy.

Variety: Anaerobic by predilection: Becomes facultative by transfers in artificial media. The strains isolated terminally in epizootic diseases are anaerobic by predilection.

4. *Diplococcus morbillorum* (Tunnicliff) Prévot 1933.

Synonym: Diplococcus rubeolae Tunnicliff 1933.

Habitat: Throat, mucous secretions and blood from cases of measles. Quite frequent.

Morphology: Cocci of 0.6 to 0.8 μ. Sometimes in short chains and small, irregular masses. Gram-positive.

Physiology: Strict anaerobe on isolation, becomes facultative. t $=37°$. Killed at 57°. Withstands freezing and drying. Filters through porcelain candles.

Cultural characteristics: No gas formed. Obligate serophile.

Serum deep agar: Punctiform colonies.

Serum glucose broth: Light flakes in a clear liquid.

Serum gelatin: No liquefaction.

Milk: Unchanged by most strains. Coagulated by some strains.

Carbohydrates: Glucose, sucrose and maltose fermented.

Biochemistry: Produces NH_3 H_2S, volatile amines, aldehydes, ketones, formic, propionic and lactic acids.

Blood agar: Colonies surrounded by a greenish halo.

Pathogenicity: Secondary invader ("germe de sortie") in measles. Isolated also from phrenic abscess and dental infections.

Evolutive variety: Anaerobic by predilection.

5. *Diplococcus plagarum-belli* (Adamson) Prévot 1933.

Habitat: Septic war wounds. Quite common.

Morphology: Cocci of 0.6 to 1 μ. Gram-positive.

Physiology: Strict anaerobe. t $= 37°$. Withstands 80°. Longevity rather marked. Reducing powers: neutral red permanently, safranin temporarily.

Cultural characteristics: Neither gas nor odor produced.

Deep agar: Lenticular colonies of 1 to 2 mm.

Glucose broth: Abundant growth which precipitates.

Gelatin: No liquefaction.

Milk: Coagulated without retraction of the curd.

Coagulated proteins: Not attacked.

Carbohydrates: Glucose, maltose, lactose and sucrose fermented, with the formation of lactic acid but no gas. Levulose, galactose, arabinose, sorbose, sorbitol, and mannitol also fermented.

Biochemistry: Nitrites not formed from nitrates. Produces H_2S; NH_3; volatile amines; acetylmethylcarbinol; acetic acid and traces of lactic acid.

Pathogenicity, experimental: Non-pathogenic (isolated from a phlegmon following lipoma).

6. *Diplococcus constellatus* Prévot 1924.

Habitat: Tonsils. Appendix. Pleura.

Morphology: Cocci of 0.5 to 0.6 μ, in pairs, seldom in tetrads or short chains. Gram-positive.

Physiology: Strict anaerobe. t $= 22°$ to $37°$. Killed at $55°$. Longevity: 12 to 15 days. pH 6 to 8.

Cultural characteristics: No gas produced.

Deep agar: Lenticular colonies, constellated.

Glucose broth: Turbid, sediment.

Peptone water: Meager growth; indole not formed.

Gelatin: No liquefaction.

Milk: Unchanged.

Coagulated proteins: Not attacked.

Neutral red: Not reduced.

Carbohydrates: Glucose, levulose, galactose, maltose, saccharose, and arabinose fermented without gas formation.

Biochemistry: Produces NH_3, volatile amines, aldehydes, acetone, acetylmethylcarbinol, acetic and lactic acids.

Pathogenicity, natural: White-grained tonsillitis. Associated in appendicitis and purulent pleurisy.

Pathogenicity, experimental: Non-pathogenic.

7. *Diplococcus glycinophilus* Cardon and Barker 1946.

Habitat: Black marine sediment of the Pacific (California). Uncommon.

Morphology: Cocci in pairs, short chains and small irregular masses. 0.7 to 2.5 μ in diameter (average $= 1.2$). Some elongated forms. Gram-positive.

Physiology: Strict anaerobe; Opt. t $= 37°$ (grows very well at $30°$); opt. pH $= 7.2$. Moderate amount of catalase.

Cultural characteristics: CO_2 produced. Require glycine.

Deep agar: Spherical colonies with an irregular, rough surface.

Broth: Not turbid; growth precipitates to the bottom. Does not grow on ordinary media free from glycine.

Biochemistry: Glycine is fermented to produce CH_2, H_2 and NH_3. Benzoylglycine and acetylglycine may also be utilized. Nitrites not formed from nitrates; produces NH_3, H_2S, amines, acetoin, aldehydes, ketones, indole, scatole (traces), phenol, cresol, acetic and butyric acids.

GENUS II: *Streptococcus* Billroth 1874.

Gram-positive cocci occurring in short chains.

Here are the nine anaerobic species of the genus *Streptococcus:*

A) Species producing gas and fetid odor:
  1. Chains normal; no turbidity in broth; gas in peptone water; H_2S produced.
     1. *Streptococcus anaerobius,* page 73
  2. Chains normal; turbidity in broth; no gas in peptone water; H_2S produced.
     2. *Streptococcus putridus,* page 74
  3. Chains abnormal (division in second, accessory direction). No turbidity in broth; gas in peptone water; H_2S produced.
     3. *Streptococus foetidus,* page 75
  4. Ovoid or lancet-shaped organisms; no H_2S produced. Starch fermented.
     4. *Streptococcus lanceolatus,* page 75
  5. Spherical and ovoid cells; viscous sediment in glucose broth; milk slowly coagulated; saccharolytic.
     5. *Streptococcus productus,* page 76
  5 bis. Hemolytic.
     5 bis. *S. productus var. hemolyticus* page 77
B) Species producing no gas and no fetid odor:
  6. Very small cocci; milk unchanged.
     6. *Streptococcus micros,* page 77
  7. Small cocci; thin colonies; milk coagulated.
     7. *Streptococcus parvulus,* page 78
  8. Cocci of average size; whitish colonies; milk coagulated.
     8. *Streptococcus intermedius,* page 78
  9. Anaerobic by predilection after evolution. Phenomena of alternating zones in deep agar. Greyish colonies.
     9. *Streptococcus evolutus,* page 78

1. *Streptococcus anaerobius* (Krönig and Menge) emed. Natvig.

Habitat: Natural cavities of man and animals, especially the vagina. Quite frequent.

Morphology: Cocci of 0.8 μ, in long irregular chains. Gram-positive.

Physiology: Strict anaerobe. t $= 26°$ to $38°$; killed at $80°$; pH 6 to 8. Longevity marked. Reducing powers (neutral red and safranin permanently reduced).

Cultural characteristics: Gas and fetid odor in all media.

Deep agar: Lenticular colonies.

Glucose broth: Clotty growth, not turbid. Acid produced.

Peptone water: Clotty growth. Gas; neither indole nor H_2S produced.

Gelatin: No liquefaction.

Milk: Unchanged.

Coagulated proteins: Not attacked.

Unheated proteins: Disintegrated with production of H_2S.

Carbohydrates: Glucose and levulose fermented.

Biochemistry: Nitrites not formed from nitrates. Produces NH_3, H_2S; volatile amines; traces of aldehyde; ethanol; acteylmethylcarbinol; acetic and formic acids.

Pathogenicity, natural: Pulmonary, genital, intestinal suppuration, etc., gangrenous processes. Purulent pleurisy; myositis; puerperal fever; sinusitis. No toxin nor hemolysin.

VARIETIES OF *Streptococcus anaerobius.*

a) Variety described by Silberschmidt: small organisms.

b) Variety described by Sédaillan and Vincent: turbidity in broth.

2. **Streptococcus putridus** Schottmüller 1910.

Synonym: Streptococcus putrificus Schottmüller.

Habitat: Cavities of man and animals, especially the vagina. Sea water. Quite frequent.

Morphology: Long chains. Organisms of 0.8 μ. Gram-positive.

Physiology: Strict anaerobe. t $= 28$ to $37°$. Killed at $80°$. Longevity marked. pH 6.5 to 8.5. Reducing powers: neutral red and safranin are reduced.

Cultural characteristics: No gas formed in heated media. Gas produced in media containing fresh proteins (blood).

Deep agar: Lenticular colonies of 1 to 2 mm. No gas.

Glucose broth: Turbid. No gas. Slightly fetid odor. Black pigment.

Peptone water: Very meager growth.

Gelatin: No liquefaction.

Milk: Unchanged.

Coagulated proteins: Not attacked.

Unheated proteins: Disintegrated with formation of H_2S.

Carbohydrates: Glucose, levulose and maltose fermented.

Biochemistry: Nitrites not produced from nitrates. Produces NH_3; H_2S; volatile amines; ketones; aldehydes; ethanol; acetylmethylcarbinol; acetic, butyric and valerianic acids.

Pathogenicity, natural: Putrid septicemia. Fetid puerperal thrombophlebitis. Focal infections in the bronchi and lungs. Vulvovaginitis. Extensive cutaneous gangrene. Brain abscess.

Pathogenicity, experimental: Edema or rapidly fatal gangrene in the guinea pig. Many strains lose their pathogenicity.

No toxin nor hemolysin.

Agglutination: Specific.

VARIETIES OF *Streptococcus putridus.*

a) Described by Ozaki: gas in glucose broth.
b) De Marwedel and Wehrsig: gas in glucose broth.

3. *Streptococcus foetidus* (Veillon) Prévot 1933.

Synonym: Micrococcus foetidus Veillon 1893.

Habitat: Natural cavities of man and animals. Very frequent.

Morphology: Large cocci, 0.8 to 1 μ, in short chains, double or agglomerated, tetrads (2nd accessory direction of fission). Gram-positive.

Physiology: Strict anaerobe. t $= 26$ to $37°$. pH 6 to 8. Killed at $60°$. Longevity marked. Reduces neutral red.

Cultural characters: Gas in all media.

Deep agar: Lenticular colonies.

Blood deep agar: Brown colonies. No hemolysis.

Glucose broth: No turbidity. Clotty growth. Fetid gas.

Peptone water: No turbidity. Clotty growth. Gas. Indole not formed.

Gelatin: No liquefaction.

Milk: Unchanged.

Coagulated proteins: Not attacked.

Unheated proteins: Attacked; H_2S formed.

Carbohydrates: Volatile acids and gas from glucose, levulose, galactose and sucrose.

Biochemistry: Produces NH_3, H_2S, formic, butyric and acetic acids.

Pathogenicity, natural: Purulent and gangrenous processes of the genital organs, of the lungs and viscera. Septicemia. Pulmonary abscess. Urinary abscess. Suppurative adeniditis.

Pathogenicity, experimental: In the guinea pig, localized edematous lesions with gangrenous suppuration.

No toxin nor hemolysin.

Agglutination: Specific.

Variety of *Streptococcus foetidus*

S. foetidus Variety *buccalis* Ozaki: Very small spheres.

4. *Streptococcus lanceolatus* (Tissier) Prévot 1933.

Synonym: Coccus lanceolatus (Tissier) 1926.

Habitat: Human intestine. Buccal cavity. Quite uncommon.

Morphology: Large ovoid cells with pointed ends: 1.2 to 1.4 μ. Gram-positive.

Physiology: Strict anaerobe. t=37°. pH=6-8. Longevity average. Reduces neutral red.

Cultural characters: Gas and slightly fetid odor.

Deep agar: Large, lenticular colonies.

Glucose broth: Turbid. Viscous sediment.

Peptone water: Turbid. Gas produced.

Gelatin: No liquefaction.

Milk: Unchanged.

Coagulated proteins: Not attacked.

Proteoses: Attacked with formation of $CO_2 + CO_3(NH_4)_2 + NH_3$.

Carbohydrates: Glucose and sucrose fermented with liberation of acetic, butyric and valerianic acids. Starch fermented.

Biochemistry: Produces NH_3; acetic, butyric and valerianic acids.

Pathogenicity, natural: Putrid enteritis with diarrhoea; dental infection; purulent arthritis; pseudo-actinomycosis in animals; vulvovaginitis.

Pathogenicity, experimental: Non-pathogenic.

5. *Streptococcus productus* Prévot 1941.

Habitat: Natural cavities of man, especially respiratory system. Uncommon.

Morphology: Cocci, 0.7 to 1.2 μ, in chains of 6 to 20 cells. In culture the cells become oval. Gram-positive.

Physiology: Strict anaerobe; opt. pH 6.5 to 8.2; opt. t $=$ 30° to 37°. Longevity very marked (more than 6 years); reduces neutral red definitely.

Cultural characters: Fetid gas.

Deep agar: Flat, lenticular colonies; little gas produced.

Glucose broth: Uniform turbidity, viscous growth, coherent and mucoid sediment. Little gas (H_2S) produced.

Peptone water: Uniform turbidity, neither gas nor indole formed.

Gelatin: No liquefaction.

Milk: Coagulated in 8 to 10 days. Clot retracted.

Coagulated proteins: Not attacked.

Carbohydrates: Acid and gas from glucose, levulose, lactose, arabinose, xylose and sorbose.

Biochemistry: Nitrites not formed from nitrates. Produces NH_3; H_2S; 5 parts of propionic to 1 part of acetic acid with traces of lactic acid; acetylmethylcarbinol.

Pathogenicity, natural: Isolated from a human case of subacute pulmonary gangrene; maxillary osteophlegmon; brain abscess; post-abortal septicemia.

Pathogenicity, experimental: Non-pathogenic for guinea pig, rabbit and mouse.

5 bis-*Streptococcus productus,* var *hemolyticus* Beuwkes and
Aladame 1948.

Habitat: Lungs.

Morphology: Cocci in chains, average size: 0.8 to 0.9 μ Gram-positive.

Physiology: Strict anaerobe; opt. t = 37°C. Not thermoresistant.
Survives for several months. Poor reducing power (neutral red and
safranin not reduced).

Cultural characteristics: Gas produced; not fetid.

Blood agar: β hemolysis.

Deep agar: Lenticular colonies.

Peptone water; Turbid; viscous sediment.

Glucose broth: Abundant turbidity, gas, viscous sediment.

Gelatin: No liquefaction.

Milk: Unchanged.

Coagulated proteins: Not attacked.

Carbohydrates: Glucose, levulose, maltose, galactose, sucrose, dextrin,
mannitol and starch fermented.

Biochemistry: Nitrites not formed from nitrates. Indol nor H_2S formed.
Produces NH_3, acetic, propionic and lactic acids, volatile amines.

Pathogenicity, natural: Isolated from a pulmonary infection.

Pathogenicity, experimental: Non-pathogenic for mouse and guinea
pig. No toxin. No soluble hemolysin produced, but a zone of β hemolysis
occurs around the colonies. Sensitive to 0.1 OU of penicillin.

6.   *Streptococcus micros* (Lewkowicz) Prévot 1923.

Synonym: Streptococcus anaerobius micros Lewkowicz 1901.

Habitat: Natural cavities of man and animals. Common.

Morphology: Very small cocci, 0.2 to 0.4 μ, in long chains. Gram-
positive.

Physiology: Strict anaerobe. t = 36 to 38°. Killed at 60°. Longevity
average. pH = 7; filters through L2 candles. Reduces neutral red.

Cultural characters: No gas produced.

Deep agar: Lenticular colonies.

Glucose broth: Powdery growth; no gas produced.

Peptone water: Very meager growth. Indole not formed.

Gelatin: No liquefaction.

Milk: Unchanged.

Coagulated proteins: Not attacked.

Carbohydrates: Glucose, levulose, maltose, galactose, sucrose,
arabinose and starch are fermented.

Biochemistry: Produces NH_3; aldehydes; small quantities of acetone
and acetylmethylcarbinol, propionic, formic and lactic acids.

Pathogenicity, natural: Abscesses; suppuration; leucorrhea; brain
abscess; dental abscess.

Pathogenicity, experimental: Pyogenic. No toxin nor hemolysin.
Agglutination: Specific.

7. Streptococcus parvulus (Repaci) W.N.P. 1937.

Synonym: Streptococcus parvulus non liquefaciens Repaci 1910.
Habitat: Respiratory tract. Buccal cavity. Quite uncommon.
Morphology: Small cocci: 0.3 to 0.4 μ, in short chains. Gram-positive.
Physiology: Strict anaerobe. t = 37 to 41°. Longevity marked.
Reduces neutral red and safranin.
Biochemistry: Nitrites not formed from nitrates. Produces NH_3;
aldehydes; traces of acetone; abundant acetylmethylcarbinol; acetic,
propionic and formed lactic acids.

8. Streptococcus intermedius Prévot 1924.

Habitat: Respiratory tract. Appendix. Genital system of women. Quite
frequent.
Morphology: Cocci in chains, of average size: 0.5 to 0.7 μ. Gram-
positive.
Physiology: Strict anaerobe. t = 36 to 38°. Killed at 70°. Longevity
marked. pH = 6 to 8. Reduces neutral red.
Cultural characters: No gas nor odor produced.
Deep agar: Lenticular colonies.
Glucose broth: Uniform turbidity. Medium strongly acidified.
Peptone water: Weak growth, powdery aspect; indole not formed.
Gelatin: No liquefaction.
Milk: Massive coagulation.
Coagulated proteins: Not attacked.
Carbohydrates: Glucose, levulose, maltose, galactose and lactose
actively fermented with abundant formation of acid. Arabinose, sucrose
and inulin fermented by some strains (lactic acid).
Biochemistry: Nitrites not formed from nitrates. Produces NH_3,
aldehydes, acetone; acetylmethylcarbinol; formic, propionic, and lactic
acids.
Pathogenicity: Pyogenic (no toxin nor hemolysin). Brain abscess.
Pulmonary abscess. Dental caries.
Agglutination: Specific.

9. Streptococcus evolutus (Graf and Wittneben) P. 1924.

Synonym: Streptococcus strain "Schwarzenbeck" G. and W. 1907.
Habitat: Natural cavities of man, especially respiratory and digestive
tracts. Quite frequent.
Morphology: Streptococci of average size, often elongated: 0.7 to
0.8 μ, sometimes 1.0 μ. Gram-positive.
Physiology: Strict anaerobe, becoming facultative. t = 36 to 38°.

Longevity marked. pH = 6 to 8.5.

Cultural characters: No gas produced.

Deep agar: Lenticular or round colonies. When becoming facultative anaerobe, alternate zones of growth and sterility appear in the upper part of the agar. Colonies become black upon aging.

Glucose broth: Growth resembling bread crumbs, sometimes turbid. Medium acidified.

Peptone water: Meager growth.

Gelatin: Liquefied in 2 to 8 days.

Milk: Curdled.

Coagulated proteins: Not attacked.

Carbohydrates: Glucose, levulose, maltose, lactose, galactose and scucrose are fermented.

Biochemistry: Nitrites not formed from nitrates; produces NH_3, volatile amines, aldehydes, ketones, sometimes acetoin, acetic and lactic acids with sometimes a third acid.

Pathogenicity, natural: Abscesses; gangrenous suppuration; bronchiestasis; puerperal fever; appendicitis; cutaneous gangrene; endocarditis, empyema.

Pathogenicity, experimental: Pyogenic. In association with staphylococcus: extensive cutaneous gangrene.

Variety: Described by Lemierre, Reilly and Font-Réault: Pleomorphic.

Other variety: Str. microapoikia (Cooper, Keller and Johnson 1934): highly pleomorphic; viridans type on blood-agar.

APPENDIX

It would appear to be feasible to relate, tentatively at least, the following micro-organism to the genus *Streptococcus:*

Ruminococcus flavefaciens Kaars Sypersteyn 1948.

Habitat: Rumen of cattle and other ruminants. Cecum and colon of herbivorous animals.

Morphology: Spherical cells, 0.8-0.9 μ, generally occurring in chains of 8 to 20 units. Non-motile; non-sporeforming. Gram-positive.

Physiology: Strict anaerobe. Chemoheterotrophic. Yellow pigment. Cellulose fermented, but starch not attacked. Catalase-negative. Mesophilic. Mesophilic.

Location in the scheme: May be identical with or related to *Streptococcus jodophilus* Hennberg 1922-1946, reviewed by Backer and Hungate.

A colorless variety has been described by E. R. Hall in 1952, after its isolation from the cecum of a domestic rabbit. Occurring as a Gram-positive diplococcus or streptococcus, it has no pigment; stains with iodine; strict anaerobe; opt. t = 38-40°C; opt. pH = 6.6-7.1 on a mineral medium added with cellulose which it ferments (gas). Cellulose and cellobiose fermented only. Fermentation products are formic, acetic and succinic acids, ethanol, CO_2 and H_2. This variety may be named: *R. flavefaciens* var. *albus*.

TRIBE II: **STAPHYLOCOCCEAE** Prévot 1933.

Definition: Gram-positive cocci occurring in single-plane masses. This tribe actually comprises two genera:

1. Cocci grouped in tetrads after division.
   Genus I: *Gaffkya Trevisan,* page 80
2. Cocci grouped in single-plane, irregular masses.
   Genus II: *Staphlyococcus Rosenbach,* page 80

GENUS I: *Gaffkya* Trevisan.

Gram-positive cocci grouped in tetrads after division.
This genus contains only one anaerobic species:

Gaffkya anaerobia (Choukevitch) Prévot 1933.

Synonym: Tetracoccus anaerobius Choukevitch 1911; *Micrococcus tetragenes anaerobius* Hamm 1912.

Habitat: Large intestine of the horse. Genital tract of the woman. Quite uncommon.

Morphology: Large cocci in tetrads; 1 to 1.5 μ in diameter. Gram-positive.

Physiology: Strict anaerobe. t $= 37°$. Acidophilic. Longevity short.

Cultural characteristics: Abundant production of gas.

Deep agar: Colonies of 2 to 3 mm., compound lenticular type.

Glucose broth: Meager growth.

Gelatin: No liquefaction.

Milk: Unchanged.

Coagulated proteins: Not attacked.

Pathogenicity: Non-pathogenic.

GENUS II: *Staphylococcus* Rosenbach.

Gram-positive cocci grouped in single-plane, irregular masses. This genus contains four anaerobic species, and one variety.

A) Species producing no gas:
1. Feebly saccharolytic; neutral red partly or not reduced.
   1. *Staphylococcus anaerobius,* page 81
B) Species producing gas:
2. Non-saccharolytic, produces indole:
   2. *Staphylococcus asacharolyticus,* page 81 and *variety indolicus.*
3. Saccharolytic, serophile.

3. *Staphylococcus aerogenes,* page 82
4. Proteolytic, putrid, saccharolytic.
    4. *Staphylococcus activus,* page 82

1. **Staphylococcus anaerobius** (Jungano) Hamm.

Habitat: Urogenital system; intestine; buccal cavity; eye. Common.

Morphology: Cocci, 0.5 to 0.6 micron, in single-plane, irregular masses. Gram-positive.

Physiology: Strict anaerobe. t = 22 to 38°. Killed at 60°.

Longevity: 2 months. pH = 6 to 8. Neutral red partly or not reduced.

Cultural characteristics: No gas produced.

Deep agar: Lenticular colonies.

Glucose broth: Turbid, clotty, clearing later.

Peptone water: Meager growth; turbid; indole not formed.

Gelatin: No liquefaction.

Milk: Unchanged.

Coagulated proteins: Not attacked.

Carbohydrates: Glucose and galactose feebly fermented, sometimes also sucrose, maltose and levulose.

Biochemistry: Nitrites not formed from nitrates. Produces NH_3, SH_2, volatile amines, acetone, acetylmethylcarbinol, acetic, butyric and lactic acids.

Pathogenicity, natural: Visceral suppurations; focal infections; purulent tonsillitis; cystitis, vaginitis; sinusitis; urinary infections.

Pathogenicity, experimental: Pyogenic. No toxin nor hemolysin.

2. **Staphylococcus asaccharolyticus** Distaso 1912.

Habitat: Large intestine of man. Buccal cavity. Pleura. *Utérus.* Uncommon.

Morphology: Large staphylococci of 1 to 1.2 μ. Gram-positive.

Physiology: Strict anaerobe. t = 37°. Neutral red reduced.

Cultural characteristics: Gas and unpleasant odor produced.

Deep agar: Delicate, lenticular colonies.

Glucose broth: Turbid; viscous, zoogleal sediment. Unpleasant odor.

Peptone water: Turbid; indole produced.

Gelatin: No liquefaction.

Milk: Unchanged.

Coagulated proteins: Not attacked.

Carbohydrates: Not fermented.

Biochemistry: Nitrites not formed from nitrates; produces NH_3; H_2S; indole; volatile amines; acetic and propionic acids.

Pathogenicity, natural: Suppurative tonsillitis; purulent pleurisy; maxillary abscess; uterine abscess; suppurative axillary adenopathy; brain abscess.

Pathogenicity, experimental: Most strains lose their pathogenicity upon culture; others are pyogenic. One strain killed guinea pigs in 8 to 15 days without marked lesions. No toxin nor hemolysin.

2 bis. Staph. asaccharolyticus variety indolicus (Christiansen).

Synonym: Micrococcus indolicus Christiansen 1934.
Habitat: Mammary gland of the cow.
Morphology: No large clusters formed.
Cultural characteristics: Abundant gas produced.
Deep agar: Colonies of 1 to 2 mm., with opaque center.
Glucose broth: Abundant gas, viscous zooglea. Indole produced.
Gelatin: No liquefaction.
Pathogenicity: Suppurative galactophoritis of the heifer, contagious and transferable. Mastitis following foot-and-mouth disease.
Agglutination: Specific.

3. Staphylococcus aerogenes Schottmüller 1912.

Habitat: Genital tract of the woman; respiratory tract; digestive tract. Tonsils. Quite common.
Morphology: Staphylococci of average size: 0.6 to 0.8 μ; pleomorphic. Gram-positive in young cultures.
Physiology: Strict anaerobe. t $= 37°$. Killed at $60°$. pH $= 6$ to 8. Longevity: 4 to 5 weeks. Reduces neutral red.
Cultural characteristics: Abundant gas produced. Serophile. May grow without serum after serial transfers.
Deep agar + serum: Lenticular, yellowish colonies. Gas.
Glucose broth + serum: Turbid. Gas produced.
Peptone water + serum: Turbid. Indole formed.
Gelatin: No liquefaction.
Milk: Unchanged.
Coagulated proteins: Not attacked.
Carbohydrates: Glucose and levulose fermented. Galactose, sucrose, maltose, arabinose, mannitol and starch are sometimes fermented.
Biochemistry: Produces NH_3; H_2S; indole; acetylmethylcarbinol; volatile amines; acetone; aldehyde; acetic, butyric and lactic acids. Nitrites not formed from nitrates (Douglas has described strains which reduce both nitrates and nitrites).
Pathogenicity, natural: Puerperal fever; peritonitis; endometritis; salpingitis; focal infection of the tonsils; brain abscess; myositis.
Pathogenicity, experimental: Non-pathogenic or feebly pathogenic (abscess in the mouse). No toxin, nor hemolysin: Blood-broth is hemopeptolyzed with formation of methemoglobin.

4. Staphylococcus activus Prévot and Taffanel 1944.

Habitat: Genital tract of the woman. Uncommon.

Morphology: Cocci of 0.8 to 1 μ, in single-plane, irregular masses. Non-motile. No endospores. Gram-positive.

Physiology: Strict anaerobe. Opt. t $= 37°$. Killed at 70°. Reduces neutral red temporarily. Longevity: more than 3 years.

Cultural characteristics: Rapid, abundant growth; gas and fetid odor produced.

Deep agar: Lenticular colonies; abundant gas produced.

Peptone water: Slightly turbid; gas produced.

Vf glucose broth: Highly turbid, abundant gas and highly fetid odor formed.

Gelatin: Liquefaction in 48 hours.

Milk: Coagulation followed by digestion and hydrolysis of the lipids. Highly fetid odor.

Coagulated serum, coagulated egg-white, fibrin, brain: Partial digestion; blackening; H_2S formed.

Carbohydrates: Glucose, levulose, maltose, galactose, sucrose are actively fermented; lactose, arabinose and xylose weekly fermented.

Biochemistry: Nitrites not formed from nitrates. Produces NH_3; H_2S; propionic, butyric and lactic acids; indole; volatile amines; aldehydes; acetylmethylcarbinol.

Pathogenicity, natural: Isolated by hemoculture from a case of fatal puerperal septicemia with multiple metastases: kidney, liver, lung, etc. Isolated also from a brain abscess and a pleural abscess.

Pathogenicity, experimental: Non-pathogenic for guinea pig, mouse and rabbit. No toxin nor hemolysin.

Agglutination: 1/2.500 by homologous serum.

TRIBE III: **MICROCOCCEAE** Prévot 1933.

Definition: Cocci occurring in regular or irregular masses of more than one plane. This tribe comprises two genera:
1. Cocci occurring in cubical packets of 8.
   1. *Sarcina,* page 83
2. Cocci occurring in irregular masses of more than one plane.
   2. *Micrococcus,* page 86

GENUS I: *Sarcina* Goodsir 1842.

Gram-positive Cocci in cubical packets or 8, 16 and 32 cells.
This genus comprises four anaerobic species:
1. Peptolytic, saccharolytic, acidophilic; acetolactic fermentation.
   1. *Sarcina ventriculi,* page 84
2. Peptolytic, saccharolytic; acetobutyric fermentation.
   2. *Sarcina maxima,* page 84

3. Non-proteolytic, non-saccharolytic; produces methane from CO_2.

   3. *Sarcina methanica,* page 85

4. Non-proteolytic, non-saccharolytic; produces methane from CH_3 (methanol or acetic acid) or CO.

   4. *Sarcina barkeri,* page 85

1. *Sarcina ventriculi* (Goodsir) emend. Beijerinck.

Synonym: Sarcina beijerincki Prévot 1933 and *Zymosarcina ventriculi* Smit 1930. (The modern description of this species is due to Beijerinck. In 1930, Smit identified Beijerinck's *Sarcina* with *Sarcina ventriculi* Goodsir and proposed the name of *Zymosarcina ventriculi*. We do not accept the physiological basis for the subdivision of the *Sarcina* into aerobic and anaerobic species, and therefore retain Goodsir's denomination).

Habitat: Soil; sand, mud, marine sediment; human stomach; frequent.

Morphology: Large cocci, 3 to 4 μ, in cubical packets of 8, 16 and 32 cells. Cellulose membrane. Gram-positive. Nonmotile.

Physiology: Microaerophilic anaerobe; t = 30° (15° to 45°). Killed at 65°. Resistant to drying. pH 1,5 to 5. Longevity: very great in soil; very short in culture. Neutral red reduced.

Cultural characteristics: Acidophilic: isolation possible only in glucose-yeast extract, pH = 3. Produces large quantities of gas. Requires presence of fermentable sugars.

Deep agar: Complex, starred or cloudy, lenticular colonies.

Glucose broth: Abundant flaky growth, gas; marked acidity.

Peptone water: No growth. Does not utilize amino-acids nor free N.

Glucose peptone water: Abundant growth; active fermentation.

Gelatin: No liquefaction.

Milk: Slowly coagulated.

Coagulated proteins: Not attacked.

Carbohydrates: Glucose, levulose, maltose, saccharose, lactose and galactose actively fermented with abundant gas and marked acidity.

Biochemistry: CO_2, H_2, C_2H_5OH, HCO_2H, CH_3CO_2H and lactic acid. Nitrites not formed from nitrates. Glycolysis according to Embden-Meyerhof scheme gives rise to $CO_2 + H_2 + C_2H_5OH + CH_3COOH$.

Pathogenicity, natural: Gaseous gastritis.

Pathogenicity, experimental: Non-pathogenic.

2. *Sercina maxima* Lindner 1888.

Synonym: Zymosarcina maxima Smit.

Habitat: Soil. Acidified flour paste. Quite frequent.

Morphology: Very large cocci, 4 to 4.5 μ, in cubical masses of 8, 16 and 32 cells, quite regular. Gram-positive.

Physiology: Microaerophilic anaerobe. t = 30° (15° to 40°). Killed at 55°. pH 4.5 to 8.5. Longevity: 3 weeks. Neutral red reduced.

Cultural characteristics: Abundant gas formed. Requires the presence of carbohydrates.

Deep agar: Starred colonies.

Glucose broth: Flaky growth; marked acidity.

Gelatin: No liquefaction.

Milk: Unchanged.

Coagulated proteins: Not attacked.

Carbohydrates: Glucose, levulose, maltose, galactose, saccharose and lactose fermented with production of acid and gas.

Products of metabolism: CO_2, H_2, HCO_2H, CH_3COOH, C_3H_7COOH; succinic and lactic acids.

Pathogenicity, experimental: Non-pathogenic.

3.   *Sarcina methanica* (Söhngen) W.N.P. 1937.

Synonym: Zymosarcina methanica (Söhngen) Smit. *Methonosarcina methanica* (S.) Barker *et al.*

Habitat: Methane-producing mud. Quite uncommon.

Morphology: Large cocci, 4 μ, in cubical packets. No cellulose membrane. Gram-positive.

Physiology: Strict anaerobe.

Cultural characteristics: Grows on mineral media.

Carbohydrates: Not fermented.

Metabolism: Nitrogen sources: ammonium salts; carbon sources: salts of the acyclic acids containing even numbers of atoms, as well as formiates. Produces CH_4, CO_2 and acyclic acids with C_{nx2}.

Biochemistry: Can reduce CO_2 to CH_4.

4.   *Sarcina barkeri* (Schnellen) nov. comb.

Synonym: Methanosarcina barkeri Schnellen 1947. Probably identical with *Methanosarcina* Stadtman and Barker.

Habitat: Black mud of methane-producing stagnant waters.

Morphology: Large sized cocci in cubical packets of 8.

Physiology: Strict anaerobe: opt. t $= 30°$. Isolation: Mineral medium (ammonium chloride 0.1%, dipotassium phosphate 0.04, magnesium chloride 0.01, agar 2% $+$ methanol).

Cultural characteristics: Grows in sodium acetate solution or in sodium bicarbonate-buffered methanol.

Biochemistry: Whatever the substrate, CH_4 is reduced according to the equation:

$$4 CH_3OH - 3CH_4 + CO_2 + 2 H_2O$$

but the same anaerobe may equally reduce CO to CH_4 in accordance with the following scheme:

$$4 CO + 2 H_2O - CH_4 + 3 CO_2$$

Pathogenicity: Non-pathogenic.

GENUS II: *Micrococcus* Cohn.

Gram-positive cocci occurring in irregular masses of more than one plane.

This genus comprises 6 anaerobic species:

A) Species producing no gas:
1. Coagulates milk; saccharolytic.
> 1. *M. grigoroffi,* page 86
2. Milk unchanged; gelatin not liquefied; saccharolytic.
> 2. *M. saccharolyticus,* page 86
3. Milk unchanged; getlatin liquefied; non-saccharolytic.
> 3. *M. variabilis,* page 87

B) Species producing gas:
4. Black colonies; milk unchanged.
> 4. *M. niger,* page 87
> White colonies; milk unchanged; gelatin not liquefied; saccharolytic.
> 5. *M. prevoti,* page 88
6. White colonies; milk unchanged; gelatin not liquefied; non-saccharolytic; lactate, pyruvate and maltose fermented.
> 6. *M. lactilyticus,* page 89

1. *Micrococcus grigoroffii* (Grigoroff) Prévot 1933.

Habitat: Human digestive tract, buccal cavity. Uncommon.

Morphology: Cocci of average size, 0.7 μ, in irregular masses. Gram-positive.

Physiology: Strict anaerobe. t $= 37°$. Killed at $60°$. Some strains resist at $70°$ for 15 minutes. Longevity: 1 to 2 months. Reducing powers not marked (neutral red, safranin and phenosafranin not reduced).

Cultural characteristics: No gas or odor produced.

Deep agar: Lenticular colonies, yellowish-white.

Glucose broth: Turbid, sediment, no gas produced; medium is acidified.

Gelatin: No liquefaction.

Milk: Acidified and coagulated.

Carbohydrates: Glucose, levulose, maltose, lactose and sorbitol fermented. Galactose, saccharose, xylose, mannitol, sorbitol fermented. Some strains also attack inulin.

Biochemistry: Nitrites not formed from nitrates. Produces NH_3, H_2S; indole, aldehydes, traces of acetone, formic, buryic and lactic acids.

Pathogenicity, natural: Appendicitis, tonsillitis, sinusitis and salpingitis.

Pathogenicity, experimental: Slightly pathogenic or non-pathogenic.

2. *Micrococcus saccharolyticus* Foubert and Douglas 1948.

Habitat: Human intestinal tract; plasma; skin.

Morphology: Cocci, 0.6 to 0.8, sometimes 0.8 to 1.0, occurring singly in pairs, tetrads or in irregular masses. Gram-positive.

Physiology: Strict anaerobe; opt. T $= 37°$. Slight reducing powers.

Cultural characteristics: No gas or fetid odor produced.

Agar slant: Colonies 0.5 to 1.0 mm, round, convex, glistening, opaque, white, butyrous.

Deep agar: Lenticular colonies.

Glucose VF froth: Diffuse turbidity.

Peptone water: No gas produced.

Gelatin: No liquefaction.

Coagulation proteins: Not attacked.

Litmus milk: Unchanged; slight reduction.

Carbohydrates: Acid but no gas from glucose, fructose, mannose; glycerol and sucrose. Arabinose, galactose, maltose, lactose, raffinose, starch, inulin, salicin and mannitol not fermented.

Biochemistry: Lactate and malate not fermented. Fermentation of glucose leads to CO_2 (not visible), ethanol, acetic, formic and lactic (traces) acids. No H_2S nor indole formed. Nitrites not produced from nitrates.

Pathogenicity, natural: Subphrenic abscess.

Pathogenicity, experimental: Non-pathogenic.

3. *Micrococcus variabilis* Foubert and Douglas 1948.

Habitat: Uterus, tonsils and maxillary sinuses.

Morphology: Cocci, 0.5 to 1.5 (with all possible intermediate sizes in the same culture), occurring singly, in pairs, tetrads or irregular masses in which contiguous pairs of cocci appear to be arranged on several different planes). Gram-positive.

Physiology: Strict anaerobe; opt. t $= 37°$. Reducing powers slight: a few strains reduce neutral red.

Cultural characteristics: No gas nor fetid odor produced.

Agar slant: Colonies 0.5 to 1.0, round, glistening, slightly convex, opaque, greyish white, butyrous.

Deep agar: Red colonies, sometimes lenticular.

Glucose VF broth: Curdled growth; sediment.

Gelatin: Liquefied.

Coagulated proteins and casein: Not attacked.

Litmus milk: Unchanged, slight reduction.

Carbohydrates: Not attacked.

Biochemistry: Nitrites not formed from nitrates. Lactate not fermented. Small quantities of H_2S produced. Indole not formed. Produces acetic and propionic acids.

Pathogenicity, natural: Metritis, tonsillitis, sinusitis, septicemia.

Pathogenicity, experimental: Non-pathogenic.

4. *Micrococcus niger* Hall 1930.

Habitat: Human bladder. Genital organs of the woman. Very frequent.

Morphology: Small cocci 0.6 μ. Gram-positive.

Physiology: Strict anaerobe. t=30° to 37°. Reduces neutral red.

Cultural characteristics: Little gas formed.

Deep agar: Colonies are irregular, globular, becoming black in primary culture.

Glucose broth: Uniformly turbid. Abundant gas formed; H_2S produced; black sediment (iron).

Gelatin: No liquefaction.

Milk: Unchanged.

Coagulated proteins: Not attacked.

Carbohydrates: Not fermented.

Pathogenicity, natural: Urogenital infection, leucorrhea, purulent cystitis, cervicitis, puerperal fever; coccygeal abscess; osteomyelitis; pulmonary abscess.

Pathogenicity, experimental: Non-pathogenic.

Biochemistry: Nitrates not formed from nitrites. Produces NH_3, H_2S; indole, acetone, acetic, butyric and lactic acids. The nature of the black pigment is a melanin. It disappears upon transfer.

5. *Micrococcus prevoti* Foubert and Douglas 1948.

Morphology: Cocci 0.6 to 0.8, sometimes 1.0 to 1.5 or .75 μ, occurring singly, in pairs, tetrads, irregular masses (some in a single plane). Gram-positive.

Physiology: Strict anaerobe; opt. t = 37°. Some strains exhibit slight reducing powers (Janus green reduced).

Cultural characteristics: Slight amount of gas produced, but no fetid odor.

Peptone water: Little gas produced.

Deep agar: Colonies, 0.5 to 1.0 mm, round, glistening, slightly convex, sometimes translucent, sometimes opaque, greyish to greyish-white, butyrous.

Gelatin: No liquefaction.

Coagulated proteins: Not attacked.

Litmus milk: Unchanged; reduced in 3 to 4 days.

Casein: Not attacked.

Carbohydrates: Some strains produce acid but no gas from glucose, fructose, galactose, mannose, maltose, raffinose; lactose, starch, inulin, salicin, glycerol and mannitol not attacked.

Biochemistry: produces little or no H_2S; indole not formed; produces NH_3, volatile amines, ethanol. Fermentation type has more than 2 volatile acids (acetic and butyric), a third being either formic or propionic. Nitrites not formed from nitrates. Lactate and maltate not fermented.

Pathogenicity, natural: Lung abscess, purulent cystitis, suppuration of the lips, recurring subcutaneous abscesses.

Pathogenicity, experimental: Non-pathogenic.

6. *Micrococcus lactilyticus* Foubert and Douglas 1948.

Historical: Formerly *V. alcalescens,* now attached to *Micrococcus* because of their Gram-positive character which is evident before the cultures are 12 hours old, after which they appear Gram-negative.

Habitat: Tonsils (normal or diseased).

Morphology: Cocci, 0.5 to 0.75μ, occurring singly, in pairs, tetrads or irregular masses of large size. Gram-positive in young cultures, becoming Gram-negative upon ageing.

Physiology: Strict anaerobe; opt. t $= 37°$. Very slight reducing powers.

Cultural characteristics: Gas produced, but no fetid odor.

Deep agar: Colonies, 0.5 to 1.0 mm, round, glistening, slightly convex, opaque, greyish-white, viscous.

Gelatin: No liquefaction.

Litmus milk: Unchanged; reduced.

Coagulated proteins: Not attacked.

Carbohydrates: Not fermented, but abundant gas produced from lactate, pyruvate and malate.

Biochemistry: H_2, CO_2, acetate and propionate produced from lactate. Fermentation of Vf broth gives rise to NH_3, acetic and propionic acids, volatile amines, SH_2. Indole not formed. Nitrates and nitrites are reduced.

Pathogenicity, natural: Lung abscesses, purulent rhinitis.

Pathogenicity experimental: Non-pathogenic.

APPENDIX

As an addendum to the genus *Micrococcus,* we may place here the physiological sub-genus proposed by Groeneweg in 1920 and suggested anew in 1936 by Kluyver and van Niel for the methane-producing coccus described by Mazé in 1915 and studied again by Barker in 1936.

Methanococcus (Groeneweg) Kluyver and van Niel 1936.

Cocci occurring singly or in irregular masses. Gram-variable. Chemo-heterotrophic; methane-producing anaerobe. Two species:

1. Produces CH_4 from acetate and butyrate.
>   1. *Methanococcus mazei,* page 89
2. Produces CH_4 from formate.
>   2. *Methanococcus vannieli,* page 90

1. *Methanococcus mazei* Barker 1936.

Synonym: Pseudosarcina Mazé 1915.

Habitat: Garden soil; H_2S—producing black mud of sewage, rivers and stagnant waters; feces of herbivorous animals.

Morphology: Cocci of small size, occurring singly or irregular masses which may sometimes attain large sizes, sometimes in regular cysts. Non-motile. Gram-variable. Stain easily with erythrosin.

Physiology: Strict anaerob opt. t=30-37°. Does not utilize organic nitrogen.

Cultural characteristics: 1) Enrichment on media containing calcium acetate. 2) *Agar + 2% mud extract:* Slow growth, abundant gas produced.

Biochemistry: CH_4 produced by fermentation of acetate or butyrate in the presence of CO_2. Ethanol and butanol not attacked. The most active methane producer in nature.

Pathogenic: Non-pathogenic.

2.   *Methanococcus vannieli* Stadtman and Barker 1951.

Habitat: Soil.

Morphology: Slightly ellipsoidal cocci, often occurring in pairs, sometimes with one cell larger than the other giving the illusion of budding yeast; mean diameter 1 to 2 μ; small forms 0.5 μ and large-sized cells 3 to 4 μ. Motile but no flagella. Can be stained only in liquid media upon a slide.

Physiology: Strict anaerobe; opt. pH = 8 (7.4-9). Produces CH_4 under certain conditions.

Deep agar: Lenticular colonies 0.5 to 1.0 mm, brownish, regular, sometimes lobate.

Cultural characteristics: No growth on the usual media. A favorable medium contains 0.1% Na formate, 0.001% SO_4 $(NH_4)_2$, 0.2% NA_2-MNO_4, 0.001% $CaCl_2$, 0.001% $Frecl_3$, 0.0001% SO_4 Mm, 0.003% PO_4K_2H and 0.05% Thioglycollate.

Biochemistry: Attacks formate (maximum growth occurs with 1.5% Na formate while inhibition is seen with 5%). Final pH = 9-9.4. Acetate, propionate, butyrate, succinate, glucose, ethanol and methanol not attacked. In 1% Na formate buffered with 0.25% CO_3Na_2, gas is produced in 90 hours at 30° according to the equation:

$$4 \text{ NaCOOH} + H_2O — CO_3Na_2 + 2 \text{ } CO_3NaH + CH_4$$

Pathogenicity: Non-pathogenic.

CHAPTER 4

ORDER II: *BACTERIALES*

Definition: Non-sporeforming *Eubacteriales,* cylindrical, elongated, straight or slightly-curved.

The anaerobic species of this order may be grouped into three families:

1. Gram-negative *Bacteriales:*
   a) of small size; *Parvobacteriaceae,* p. 91
   b) of average size or larger: *Ristellaceae,* p. 96
2. Gram-positive Bacteriales: *Bacteriaceae,* p. 152

FAMILY I: *PARVOBACTERIACEAE* Rahn 1937.

Gram-negative *Bacteriales* of small size.

The anaerobic species belonging to this family may be allotted to two tribes:

1. Rods showing bipolar staining: *Pasteurelleae,* p. 91
2. No bipolar staining. Require for isolation and first generations one or several growth factors from blood or vegetable tissues: *Hemophileae,* p. 94

TRIBEI. *PASTEURELLEAE* Castellani and Chalmers 1919.

One single genus of this tribe has anaerobic species:

GENUS I: *Pasteurelleae* Trevisan 1885.

Small Gram-negative rods, ovoid or elongated, showing bipolar staining.

This genus comprises actually five well-described anaerobic species; we shall not retain here the species insufficiently described such as: *Pasteurella anaerobiontica* Levinthal 1928 which cannot be classified.

Here is the key to the five species (four described by Eggerth and Gagnon):

1. Broth turbid: little gas formed; gelatin liquefied; milk coagulated; saccharolytic: H_2S formed.
   1. *Pasteurella vulgata,* page 92

2. Broth turbid; gas, indole formed; gelatin liquefied, milk coagulated; saccharolytic; H₂S formed.

    2. *Pasteurella ovata,* page 92

3. Broth turbid; gas produced; indole not formed; gelatin liquefied, milk coagulated; saccharolytic, H₂S formed.

    3. *Pasteurella convexa,* page 93

4. Broth turbid; gas and indole produced; getlatin liquefied; milk coagulated and digested; non-saccharolytic.

    4. *Pasteurella coagulans,* page 93

5. Obligate serophile; little gas produced; gelatin unchanged; milk coagulated.

    5. *Pasteurella serophila,* page 93

1. **Pasteurella vulgata** (E. and G.) Prévot 1938.

Synonym: Bacteroides vulgatus Eggerth and Gagnon 1933.

Habitat: Human intestine. Quite frequent.

Morphology: Oval rods, 0.7 by 2.5 μ, occurring singly or in pairs, rarely in chains; filaments of 10 μ; pleomorphic; shuttle-like and swollen forms. Non-motile. No endospores. Gram-negative; bipolar staining.

Physiology: Strict anaerobe. Opt. T=37°.

Cultural characteristics: Slight gas formation.

Deep agar: No colonies.

Blood agar: Colonies greyish, opaque.

Blood agar: Translucent colonies with hemopeptonization.

Glucose broth: Diffuse turbidity; little gas; acid; H₂S.

Peptone water: Weak growth; indole not formed.

Gelatin: Liquefied in 4-20 days.

Milk: Acidified and coagulated.

Carbohydrates: Acid and gas from glucose, levulose, maltose, sucrose galactose, lactose, arabinose, xylose, inulin, dextrin and starch.

Biochemistry: Nitrites not produced from nitrates. H₂S formed.

Pathogenicity: Non-pathogenic.

2. **Pasteurella ovata** (E. and G.) Prévot 1938.

Synonym: Bacteroides ovatus E. and G. 1933.

Habtitat: Human intestine. Quite uncommon.

Morphology: Ovoid rods; 1 by 0.5 μ. Non-motile. No endospores. Gram-negative.

Physiology: Strict anaerobe. t = 37°.

Cultural characteristics: Gas formed.

Deep agar: No colonies.

Glucose broth: Diffuse turbidity, gas, acid, H₂S.

Peptone water: Turbid, gas, indole.

Gelatin: Liquefied in 15 days.

Milk: Acidified and coagulated in 4 days.

Carbohydrates: Acid and gas from glucose, levulose, maltose, lactose, sucrose, galactose, xylose, glycogen, inulin, and starch.

Pathogenicity: Non-pathogenic.

3. *Pasteurella convexa* (E. and G.) Prévot 1938.

Synonyms: Bacteroides convexus E. and G. 1933; *Eggerthella convexa* (E. and G.) Beerens.

Habitat: Human intestine. Quite frequent.

Morphology: Ovoid rods, 1.5 to 3 μ by 0.8 μ, occurring singly or in pairs. Non-motile. No endospores. Gram-negative.

Physiology: Sitrct anaerobe. t=37°. Requires bile.

Cultural characteristics: Gas formed.

Deep agar: Greyish colonies of 1 to 1.5 mm.

Glucose broth: Diffuse turbidity, gas, H_2S; final pH 4. 8.

Peptone water: Turbid, little gas, indole not formed.

Gelatin: Liquefied in 20 to 30 days.

Milk: Acidified and coagulated in 4 days.

Carbohydrates: Acid and gas from glucose. levulose, maltose, galactose, sucrose, lactose, xylose, glycerol, dextrin, inulin.

Pathogenicity: Non-pathogenic.

4. *Pasteurella coagulans* (E. and G.) Prévot 1938.

Synonym: Bacteroides coagulans E. and G. 1933.

Habitat: Human intestine. Quite uncommon.

Morphology: Ovoid rods, 1 to 2 μ by 0.5 μ. Non-motile. No endospores. Gram-negative; bipolar staining.

Physiology: Strict anaerobe. t= 37°.

Cultural characteristics: Gas formed.

Deep agar: Rare punctiform colonies.

Glucose broth: Diffuse turbidity; gas.

Peptone water: Turbid, gas, indole.

Gelatin: Liquefied in 8 to 12 days.

Milk: Coagulated in 8 days, then digested.

Carbohydrates: Not attacked.

Pathogenicity: Non-pathogenic.

5. *Pasteurella serophila* Bokkenhauser 1951.

Habitat: Probably human intestinal tract. Quite uncommon.

Morphology: Ovoid rods, 1.8 to 2 by 0.5 to 0.5 μ. Shuttle-like forms showing bipolar staining. Non-motile. No spores. Gram-negative.

Physiology: Strict anaerobe; obligate serophile; opt. t = 37°; not thermoresistant. Reduces neutral red and phenosafranin.

Cultural characteristics: Slight gas production; light H₂S odor.

Deep: Agar + Serum: Lenticular colonies; no gas produced.

Glucose Vf Broth: + Serum: Abundant turbidity which settles slowly. No spontaneous gas production but gas bubbles appear upon tapping.

Gelatin + Serum: No liquefaction.

Milk: Coagulated. Slight retraction of the clot, little lactoserum apparent

Coagulated proteins: Not attacked.

Carbohydrates: Marked acidity from glucose, levulose, lactose and sucrose, less marked with maltose, galactose, glycerol and starch.

Biochemistry: Nitrites not formed from nitrates. Sulfides not formed from sulfites. Produces NH_3, H_2S, volatile amines, aldehydes, ketones, indole, scatol, acetic and propionic acids.

Pathogenicity, natural: Isolated in pure culture from a peri-anal abscess.

Pathogenicity, experimental: Non-pathogenic. No toxin nor hemolysin.

TRIDE II: **Hemophilae** Winslow *et al.* 1920.

Small Gram-negative rods requiring for primary isolation and first transfers a growth factor from hemoglobin, ascitic fluid or vegetable tissue. A single genus of this tribe shows anaerobic species:

GENUS I: *Dialister* Bergey *et al.* 1923.

Very small rods, non-motile, no endospores, Gram-negative, filtering through Berkefeld V and Chamberland L2. This genus comprises two anaerobic species and one variety:

1. Strict anaerobe; obligate serophile; lenticular colonies; no gas; slightly saccharolytic; pathogenic.

1. *Dialister pneumosintes,* page 94

1. *bis.* Similar to the above, but with fluffy colonies, saccharolytic.

1. *bis. D. pneumosintes* var *septicemiae.* page 95

2. Microaerophilic anaerobe: punctiform colonies; no gas; saccharolytic, pathogenic; granular growth.

2. *Dialister granuliformans,* page 95

1. **Dialister pneumosintes** (Olitsky and Gates) Bergey *et al.*

Synonym: Bacterium pneumosintes Olitsky and Gates 1921.

Habitat: Nasopharyngeal cavity of man and animals. Respiratory tract. Quite frequent.

Morphology: Very short and slender rods, 0.3 by 0.15 μ, occurring singly or in pairs, and short chains. Non-motile. No endospores. Gram-negative.

Physiology: Strict anaerobe. t = 37°. Resists drying and freezing. Killed at 56°. Longevity quite marked (2 years); filters through Berkefeld V and Chamberland L2; pH 7 to 8.

Cultural characteristics: Grows only in the presence of fresh animal proteins. No gas produced.

Deep agar + ascitic fluid: Lenticular colonies. No gas produced.

Deep agar + blood: Transparent colonies. No hemolysis.

Smith-Noguchi medium: Cloudy growth after 9 to 15 days. No gas or odor produced.

Glucose broth + testicle: Cloudy growth. No gas produced.

Coagulated proteins: Not attacked.

Carbohydrates: Glucose only is fermented.

Pathogenicity, natural: Pulmonary complications of epidemic influenza.

Pathogenicity, experimental: The intratracheal injection to the rabbit and guinea-pig gives rise to hemorrhagic congestion of the lungs. Inoculation gives rise to reactions of active immunity (antibodies).

1 *bis.* **Dialister pneumosintes** var. **septicemiae** Prévot and Raynaud 1947.

Habitat: Probably the natural cavities of man.

Morphology: Absolutely like the type-species.

Physiology: Strict anaerobe, obligate serophile. Serum may be replaced by brain extract. Longevity more than one year if transferred once a month. Killed at 70°. Reduces neutral red and phenosafranin.

Cultural characteristics: No gas or odor formed.

Deep agar + serum: Fluffy colonies, translucid, very small.

Gelatin + serum: Liquefied in 48 hours.

Milk + serum: Coagulated in 48 hours.

Coagulated proteins: Not attacked.

Carbohydrates: Glucose, levulose, maltose, galactose, lactose and arabinose fermented.

Biochemistry: Nitrites not formed from nitrates. Produces small quantities of NH_3; acetic, butyric and lactic acids.

Pathogenicity, natural: Isolated from a fatal case of recurring septicemia with brain and lung abscesses.

Pathogenicity, experimental: Non-pathogenic. Serology: Agglutinated at 1/200 by the homologous serum.

2. **Dialister granuliformans** (Pavlovic) Bergey *et al.*

Synonym: Bacterium granuliformans Pavlovic 1929.

Habitat: Nasopharynx man. Quite frequent.

Morphology: Rods similar to *D. pneumosintes.* Non-motile. No endospores. Gram-negative.

Physiology: Microaerophilic anaerobe. Filters through candles.

Cultural characteristics: No gas produced.

Deep agar: Small transparent colonies; no gas produced.

Glucose broth: Granular growth.

Milk: Unchanged.

Carbohydrates: Glucose, sucrose and mannitol fermented.

Pathogenicity, experimental: The intratracheal injection into the rabbit produces pulmonary congestion and sensitizes the lung to other bacteria.

Agglutination: Agglutinated by the anti-*pneumosintes* serum.

Note: We are dealing with two quite similar species.

FAMILY II: *Ristellaceae* Prévot.

Gram-negative Bacteriales of average or large size.

This family comprises three genera:

Here is the key to the genera of this family:

A) Non-motile forms:

    a) Not encapsulated.

        1. Straight rods, short, average or long.

        Genus I: *Ristella,* page 96

    b) Encapsulated:

        Genus II: *Capsularis,* page 122

B) Motile forms:

Not encapsulated.

        Genus III: *Zuberella,* page 125

GENUS I: *Ristella* Prévot 1938.

Definition: Non-motile rods without endospores, straight or slightly curved, no capsules, Gram-negative.

This genus comprises 35 anaerobic species of which here is the key:

A) Rods predominantly short or of average length:

    a) Gazogenous species:

        1. Lenticular colonies; non-proteolytic, but saccharolytic, fragile growth (dies in 8 to 10 days); pathogenic.

        1. *Ristella fragilis,* page 99

        2. Black colonies; hemoglobinophilic, fetid odor, slightly-proteolytic, saccharolytic, indole formed; pathogenic.

        2. *Ristella melaninogenica,* page 100

        3. Lenticular colonies surrounded by a halo; serophile; fragile growth, fetid odor (H_2S); indole produced; non-proteolytic; pathogenic.

        3. *Ristella haloseptica,* page 101

4. Arborescent colonies; fetid odor (H_2S); indole produced; proteolytic, non saccharolytic; toxic.

5. Irregularly-rounded colonies; non-proteolytic; saccharolytic; pathogenic.

6. Forked rods; small lenticular colonies; non-proteolytic; saccharolytic; pathogenic.

7. Lenticular colonies; proteolytic; lipolytic; non-saccharolytic; fetid odor (H_2S); non-pathogenic.

8. Rods with pointed ends; lenticular colonies; non-proteolytic; no fetid odor; non-pathogenic.

9. Lenticular colonies; non-proteolytic; saccharolytic; non-pathogenic.

10. Thermophilic; punctiform colonies; milk coagulated and digested; saccharolytic; non-pathogenic.

11. Thermophilic; punctiform colonies; milk coagulated then digested; saccharolytic; pathogenic.

12. No fetid odor produced; gelatin liquefied; milk unchanged; saccharolytic; indole not formed; H_2S produced.

13. No fetid odor produced; gelatin not liquefied; milk coagulated; indole formed; H_2S produced; saccharolytic.

14. Fetid odor produced; indole not formed; saccharolytic.

15. Requires a minimum of 4% NaCl in the culture medium; broth turbid; indole not formed; non-proteolytic; saccharolytic.

b) Species producing no gas:

16. Rods with pointed ends; non-proteolytic; saccharolytic; non-pathogenic.

17. Obligate serophile; isolated from lichen planus.

18. Obligate serophile; lenticular colonies; milk coagulated, then digested; non-saccharolytic; isolated from "foot rot" of the lamb.
   18. *Ristella nodosa.* page 108

19. Mucoid colonies; thermophilic; pathogenic (bronchitis).
   19. *Ristella destillationis,* page 109

20. Punctiform colonies; indole not formed; gelatin liquefied; milk coagulated; saccharolytic; H_2S formed.
   20. *Ristella uniformis,* page 109

21. Punctiform colonies; indole not formed; gelatin liquefied; milk coagulated; saccharolytic; H_2S formed.
   21. *Ristella distasonis,* page 109

22. Punctiform colonies; gelatin liquefied; milk unchanged; saccharolytic; H_2S not formed; indole not produced.
   22. *Ristella uncata,* page 110

23. Broth turbid; gelatin liquefied; milk unchanged; saccharolytic; indole not formed; H_2S produced.
   23. *Ristella tumida,* page 110

24. Punctiform colonies; broth turbid; gelatin liquefied; milk coagulated; saccharolytic; indole not formed; H_2S not formed.
   24. *Ristella exigua,* page 111

B) Cells predominatingly elongated, filamentous.

   a) Gazogenous:
   25. Lenticular colonies; fecal odor; H_2S produced; non-proteolytic; saccharolytic; pathogenic.
      25. *Ristella trichoides,* page 111

   26. Thick, coherent lenticular colonies; viscous growth in broth; gelatin liquefied; milk coagulated.
      26. *Ristella glutinosa,* page 112

   b) Not gasogenous:
   27. Fine, granular, non-coherent colonies; gelatin not liquefied; non-proteolytic; feebly saccharolytic; non-pathogenic; milk unchanged.
      27. *Ristella capillosa,* page 112

   28. Small, round, non-granular colonies; gelatin not liquefied; non-proteolytic; saccharolytic; non-pathogenic.
      28. *Ristella cylindroides,* page 113

C) Rather irregular forms, sometimes swollen, sometimes accompanied by spheroids; formerly linked with the genus *Sphaerophorus;* the basal composition of their DNA recalls that of the *Ristella.*

   a) gas-producing species:
   29. Punctiform colonies; broth turbid; gelatin liquefied; milk

coagulated; carbohydrates fermented; indole produced; H_2S formed; weakly pathogenic.

    29. *Ristella gulosa,* page 113

  30. Obligate serophile; lenticular colonies; flaky growth; fetid odor; gelatin not liquefied; milk coagulated; carbohydrates fermented; indole produced; H_2S formed; highly pathogenic.

    30. *Ristella freundii,* page 114

  b) species producing no gas:

  31. Obligate serophile; punctiform colonies; broth turbid; gelatin not liquefied; milk unchanged; carbohydrates feebly fermented; weakly pathogenic.

    31. *Ristella abscedens,* page 114

  32. Obligate serophile; punctiform and lenticular colonies; broth turbid; gelatin slowly liquefied; milk rapidly clotted and partially digested; carbohydrates fermented; pathogenic.

    32. *Ristella glycolytica,* page 115

D) Fusiform rods with pointed ends, formerly attached to the genus *Fusiformis;* the basic composition of their DNA is that of the *Ristella.*

  a) gas-producing species:

  33. Non-serophilic; lenticular colonies; broth turbid; gas not fetid; milk clotted; proteins not attacked; carbohydrates fermented; indole not produced; little or no H_2S formed; feebly pathogenic.

    33. *Ristella biacuta,* page 116

  b) species producing no gas:

  34. Nonserophilic; lenticular colonies; gelatin not liquefied; milk partly clotted; carbohydrates fermented; nitrites not formed from nitrates; little or no indole formed.

    34. *Ristella polymorpha,* page 116

  35. Serophile; red ochre colonies; broth turbid with red ochre sediment; fetid odor; gelatin not liquefied; milk unchanged; carbohydrates fermented; feebly pathogenic.

    35. *Ristella ochracea,* page 117

Species *incertae sedis, Ristella vesca,* page 117

Ristella corrodens, page 118

1. *Ristella fragilis* (Veillon and Zuber) P. 1938.

Synonym: Bacillus fragilis V. and Z. 1898; *Bacteroides fragilis* (V. and Z.) C., and C.; *Fusiformis fragilis* (V. and Z.) Topley.

Habitat: Natural cavities of man, especially digestive tract. Contaminated sea water. Frequent.

Morphology: Short rods with rounded ends staining more intensely than the central portion; 1 to 2 x 0.5 μ. Non-motile. No endospores. Gram-negative.

Physiology: Strict anaerobe. t = 23° to 37°; killed at 56°. Short-lived, dying in 8 to 10 days. Reduces neutral red.

Cultural characteristics: Slightly gasogenous.

Deep agar: Lenticular colonies, appearing slowly.

Glucose broth: Slightly turbid; little gas formed; slight acidity; no H_2S nor indole formed.

Peptone water: Meager growth; indole not formed.

Milk: Unchanged.

Gelatin: No liquefaction.

Coagulated proteins: Not attacked.

Carbohydrates: Acid and gas, from glucose, maltose, sucrose, galactose, levulose, arabinose.

Pathogenicity, natural: Gangrenous suppuration; pulmonary gangrene; appendicitis; urinary and peri-urethral infections; septicemia with purulent metastases.

Pathogenicity, experimental: Weak or marked; abscesses, fatal cachexia. In association: Gangrenous suppurations.

No toxin, nor hemolysin.

2. *Ristella melaninogenica* (Oliver and Wherry) P. 1938.

Synonym: Bacterium melaninogenicum O. and W.; *Hemophilus mela-ninogenicus* (O. and W.) Bergey (3rd); *Bacteroides melaninogenicus* (O. and W.) Bergey (5th); *Fusiformis nigrescens* Schwabacher *et al.,* 1947.

Habitat: Buccal cavity; respiratory tract; digestive tract; urogenital tract. Frequent.

Morphology: Short rods staining more deeply in the ends; 1 to 3 x 0.8 μ. Non-motile. No endospores. Gram-negative.

Physiology: Strict anaerobe. t = 37°. Killed at 56°. Dies rapidly in pure culture; survives a long period of time in fresh blood media. Hemoglobinophilic.

Cultural characteristics: Fetid gas produced.

Deep agar + human blood: Punctiform colonies becoming black.

Glucose broth: Meager growth; autolysis; fetid gas and indole formed.

Gelatin: Flaky growth; gas with fetid odor; liquefaction variable.

Milk: Acidification, gas; digestion variable.

Coagulated serum: Abundant growth; liquefaction.

Carbohydrates: Glucose, levulose, maltose, sucrose, lactose and mannitol fermented.

Black pigment: formed from hemoglobin (melanin group).

Pathogenicity, natural: Buccal, pumonary, intestinal suppuration; alveolar pyorrhea; puerperal fever.

Pathogenicity, experimental: Weak or marked; in the rabbit: gangrene of the tissues.

Toxin: Produces the Schwartzmann phenomenon.

3. *Ristella haloseptica* (Wyss) P. 1938.

Synonym: Bacterium halosepticum Wyss 1904.

Habitat: Human bones; Respiratory tract. Uncommon.

Morphology: Short thin rods with pointed ends; 1 x 0.5 μ. Non-motile. No endospores. Gram-negative.

Physiology: Strict anaerobe, t $= 38°$ (40° to 42°). Killed at 56°. Short-lived.

Cultural characteristics: Slightly gasogenous and fetid. Requires ascitic fluid or serum.

Glucose Deep agar: Punctiform colonies; no gas.

Ascitic fluid agar: Starred lenticular colonies, surrounded by a halo; gas.

Ascitic fluid broth: Flaky growth, greyish yellow, causing no turbidity; gas; fetid odor (H_2S); indole formed; acidification.

Glucose broth: Meager growth; little gas; weak odor.

Peptone water: No growth.

Ascitic gelatin: Flaky growth; no liquefaction.

Milk: Unchanged.

Coagulated proteins: Not attacked.

Pathogenicity, natural: Osteomyelitis; fatal septicemia with purulent metastasis. Purulent pleurisy.

Pathogenicity, experimental: In the rabbit, necrotic abscesses and fatal cachexia, liver abscess. In the guinea-pig: necrotic abscess. Injection into the bone marrow of the rabbit produces fatal osteomyelitis. No toxin.

4. *Ristella putredinis* (Heyde) W.N.P. 1937.

Synonym: Bacillus putredinis Heyde 1911.

Habitat: Human appendix: quite frequent.

Morphology: Straight elongated rods with rounded ends, 3 to 5 x 0.8 μ. Non-motile. No endospores. Gram-negative.

Physiology: Strict anaerobe. t $= 37°$; not thermoresistant. pH 6 to 8. Short-lived.

Cultural characteristics: Gasogenous; highly fetid.

Deep agar: Small round arborescent colonies; no gas produced.

Glucose broth: Turbid; fetid odor (H_2S); indole formed as well as products of putrefaction.

Gelatin: Liquefied; fetid odor.

Milk: Digested; gas and fetid odor.

Coagulated serum: Digested, fetid odor.

Coagulated ascitic fluid: Digested, fetid odor.

Carbohydrates: Not fermented.

Pathogenicity, natural: Appendicitis when associated with other germs.

Pathogenicity, experimental: Non-pathogenic in pure culture; when associated, fetid localized abscesses. Weak cachectic toxin.

5. *Ristella terebrans* (Brocard and Pham) P. 1938.

Synonym: Bacillus terebrans B. and P. 1934.
Habitat: Human skin; uncommon.
Morphology: Straight rods with rounded ends; pleomorphic evolution forms. Non-motile. No endospores. Gram-negative.
Physiology: Strict anaerobe; t = 37°; killed at 56°. Longevity quite marked. Reduces neutral red.
Cultural characteristics: Slightly gasogenous and fetid.
Deep agar: Colonies of 1 mm.: irregularly rounded; little gas.
Glucose broth: Turbid; gas and fetid odor; no H_2S formed.
Gelatin: No liquefaction.
Milk: Acidified, not coagulated.
Coagulated proteins: Not attacked.
Carbohydrates: Acid and gas from glucose levulose, maltose, lactose, sucrose and mannitol.
Pathogenicity, natural: Gangrene of the skin consecutive to erysipelas.
Pathogenicity, experimental: The intramuscular injection of pus into the rabbit gives rise to a dissecting abscess of the skin. In pure culture: Non-pathogenic; no toxin, nor hemolysin.
Agglutination: Specific.

6. *Ristella furcosa* (Veillon and Zuber) P. 1933.

Synonym: Bacillus furcosus V. and Z. 1898; *Bacteroides furcosus* (V. and Z.) Hauduroy.
Habitat: Appendix, lung. Quite frequent.
Morphology: Small, forked rods. Non-motile. No endospores. Gram-negative.
Physiology: Strict anaerobe, t = 37°; killed at 56°. Survives for 15 to 20 days.
Cultural characteristics: Slow meager growth; little gas produced.
Deep agar: Fine lenticular colonies; no gas.
Plain broth: Slow growth, fine precipitate, little gas; slightly fetid tart odor.
Gelatin: No liquefaction.
Milk: Unchanged.
Coagulated proteins: Not attacked.
Smith-Noguchi Medium: Clotty growth; fetid gas and odor.
Carbohydrates: Acid and acid from glucose, maltose, sucrose and mannitol.
Biochemistry: Produces NH_3, volatile amines, aldehydes, ketones, traces of indole, acetic, propionic and lactic acids.

Pathogenicity, experimental: In the guinea-pig; subcutaneous abscess, cachexia, death.

7. Ristella putida (Tissier and Martelly) P. 1938.

Synonym: Bacillus gracilis putidus Tissier and Martelly 1902; *Bacillus putidus* W.N.P. 1937.

Habitat: Putreying butcher's meat. Quite frequent.

Morphology: Short thin rods. Non-motile. No endospores. Gram-negative.

Physiology: Strict anaerobe. t $= 18°$ to $37°$. Killed at $100°$. Survives for 15 days.

Cultural characteristics: Slightly gasogenous; putrid odor.

Deep agar: Lenticular colonies; no gas.

Plain broth: Turbid in 48 hours; no gas; putrid odor.

Gelatin: No liquefaction.

Milk: Unchanged.

Casein: Not attacked.

Fibrin: Digested with formation of gas.

Coagulated proteins: Digested with formation of amines and H_2S.

Sterile urine: Abundant growth; urea decomposed.

Carbohydrates: Not attacked.

Lipides: Saponified by a lipase.

Pathogenicity: Non-pathogenic.

8. Ristella clostridiiformis (Burri and Ankersmit) P. 1938.

Synonym: Bacterium clostridiiformis Angersmit 1906.

Habitat: Digestive tract of man and cattle. Quite common.

Morphology: Straight rods with pointed ends; 2 to 3 x 0.75 μ. Non-motile. No endospores. Gram-negative.

Physiology: Strict anaerobe. t $= 37°$. Killed at $80°$. Reduces neutral red and safranin.

Cultural characteristics: Large amounts of gas produced.

Deep agar: Lenticular colonies of 1 mm. Abundant gas.

Glucose broth: Becomes rapidly and heavily turbid. Gas, acid.

Gelatin: No liquefaction.

Milk: Unchanged.

Carbohydrates: Acid and gas from glucose, levulose, maltose, galactose, sucrose and arabinose.

Coagulated proteins: Not attacked.

Pathogenicity, natural: Isolated in appendicitis and coccygeal abscess.

Pathogenicity, experimental: Some strains are pathogenic for laboratory animals. No toxin nor hemolysin.

Biochemistry: Nitrates not formed from nitrites. Produces NH_3, indole, volatile amine, traces of aldehydes, acetylmethylcarbinol, ethanol, formic, acetic and lactic acids.

9. *Ristella perfoetens* (Tissier) P. 1938.

Synonym: Coccobacillus anaerobius perfoetens Tissier 1900; *Bacterium perfoetens* (Tissier) W.N.P. 1937; *Bacteroides perfoetens* (T). Hauduroy *et al.*

Habitat: Large intestinal tract of the nursling. Intestinal tract of the horse. Quite uncommon.

Morphology: Short oval rods, 0.8 to 1 x 0.6 μ, occurring singly or in pairs. Non-motile. No endospores. Gram-negative.

Physiology: Strict anaerobe. t $= 37°$; killed at 60°. Survives for a long period of time. Reduces neutral red.

Cultural characteristics: Quite gasogenous and fetid.

Deep agar: Lenticular colonies of 1 mm. Abundant fetid gas.

Glucose broth: Rapid growth with gas and fetid odor.

Gelatin: No growth at 20°.

Milk: Unchanged.

Coagulated proteins: Not attacked.

Carbohydrates: Acid and gas from glucose and sucrose

Biochemistry: Volatile acids, aldehydes, butyric, valerianic and lactic acids. H_2S, CO_2 and NH_3 produced. Indole not formed.

Pathogenicity: Non-pathogenic. Some strains can produce in the quineapig a serous peritonitis with visceral congestion.

Ristella perfoetens var. lacticus (Tissier).

This variety differs from the above by:

1. the slightly greater length of its cells;
2. the lesser production of fetid gas;
3. the possibility of growing, even feebly, at 20°;
4. the fermentation of lactose.

10. *Ristella thermophila* β (R. Veillon) P. 1938.

Habitat: Horse dung. Quite uncommon.

Morphology: Long and slender rods. Non-motile. No endospores. Gram-negative. In chains sometimes.

Physiology: Strict anaerobe. t$=37°$ to 55°. Killed at 58°.

Cultural characteristics: Gas produced.

Deep agar: At 37°: Small, round, punctiform colonies; at 50°: powder-puff colonies; abundant gas.

Glucose broth: Turbid. Gas. Rapidly-forming sediment. H_2S and NH_3 produced.

Gelatin: No liquefaction.

Milk: Coagulated, then peptonised. At 55°: completely digested, becoming brown.

Coagulated proteins: Not attacked.

Cellulose: Not attacked.

Carbohydrates: Acid and gas from glucose, maltose, levulose, galactose, sucrose and lactose. Production of acetic and propionic and CO_2 acids.

Pathogenicity: Non-pathogenic.

11. *Ristella thermophila* γ (R. Veillon) P. 1938.

Habitat: Horse dung. Quite uncommon.

Morphology: Short slender rods. Non-motile. No endospores. Gram-negative. In chains, sometimes in long filaments.

Physiology: Strict anaerobe. t = 37° to 55°. Killed at 58°. Cultural characters: gas produced.

Deep agar: At 37°, small circular punctiform colonies; at 55°, powder-puff colonies; gas.

Glucose broth: Turbid. Gas.

Gelatin: No liquefaction.

Milk: Coagulated then digested.

Coagulated proteins: Not attacked.

Cellulose: Not attacked.

Carbohydrates: glucose, maltose, levulose, galactose, sucrose and lactose fermented with production of gas and propylic alcohol, acetic, propionic and CO_2 acids, NH_3.

Pathogenicity, experimental: Small subcutaneous abscesses in the guinea-pig; suppuration with healing.

12. *Ristella incommunis* (Eggerth and Gagnon) P. 1938.

Synonym: Bacteroides incommunis Eggerth and Gagnon 1933.

Habitat: Human intestine. Uncommon.

Morphology: Isolated rods of 1 to 2 x 0.5 μ; swollen forms of 1 to 3 x 0.7 to 1.5 μ. Non-motile. No endospores. Gram-negative.

Physiology: Strict anaerobe. t = 37°. Killed at 56°. Reduces neutral red and phenosafranin. Longevity: several years.

Cultural characteristics: Gas produced, but not fetid.

Deep agar: Lenticular colonies; gas.

Agar slant in vacuo: Yellowish colonies, 2 mm. in diameter.

Glucose broth: Diffuse turbidity; gas, acid; H_2S.

Peptone water: Turbid. No gas; indole not formed.

Gelatin: No liquefaction.

Milk: Acidified but not coagulated.

Coagulated proteins: Not attacked.

Carbohydrates: Acid and gas form glucose, maltose, levulose, sucrose galactose, lactose, raffinose, arabinose, xylose, dextrin and inulin.

Biochemistry: Nitrites not formed from nitrates. Produces NH_3, H_2S, volatile amines, alcohol, ketones, aldehyde, acetylmethylcarbinol, formic, butyric, and lactic acids.

Pathogenicity, natural: Isolated from a case of acute appendicitis.
Pathogenicity, experimental: Non-pathogenic.

13. *Ristella insolita* (E. and G.) P. 1938.

Synonym: Bacteroides insolitus E. and G. 1933.

Habitat: Human intestine; lungs. Quite frequent.

Morphology: Rods, 1 to 2 x 0.4 μ; straight and curved forms may sometimes reach from 2 to 3 μ. Non-motile. No endospores. Gram-negative.

Physiology: Strict anaerobe. t $= 37°$, killed at 56°. Longevity: several years. Reduces neutral red and phenosafranin.

Cultural characteristics: Gas produced, not fetid.

Deep agar: Punctiform colonies, becoming lenticular. Little gas produced.

Glucose broth: Diffuse turbidity; gas; acid; H_2S.

Peptone water: Turbid; gas; indole.

Gelatin: No liquefaction.

Milk: Slowly coagulated.

Coagulated proteins: Not attacked.

Carbohydrates: Acid and gas from glucose, maltose, levulose, galactose, lactose, mannose and glycerin.

Biochemistry: Nitrites not formed from nitrates. Produces NH_3, H_2S, aldehyde, volatile amines, acetone, alcohol, acetylmethylcarbinol; formic, propionic and lactic acids.

Pathogenicity, natural: Isolated from acute appendicitis, peritonitis and pulmonary abscess.

Pathogenicity, experimental: Non-pathogenic for guinea-pig and mice.

14. *Ristella pseudo-insolita* Beerens and Aladame 1949.

Habitat: Human intestinal tract. Very frequent.

Morphology: Rods with rounded ends, straight or slightly curved, 1 to 5 x 0.6 μ, occurring singly or in small irregular masses. Non-motile. No endospores. Gram-negative.

Physiology: Strict anaerobe; opt. t $= 37°$; not thermoresistant.

Longevity: More than 15 days, may attain several years by serial transfer. Reduces phenosafranin and neutral red.

Cultural characteristics: Slightly fetid gas produced.

Deep agar: Punctiform colonies; little gas produced.

Peptone water: Abundant turbidity in 24 hours; gas.

Glucose Vf broth: Heavy growth; gas.

Gelatin: Heavy growth; no liquefaction.

Milk: Coagulated in 24 hours; slight retraction.

Coagulated proteins: Not attacked.

Carbohydrates: Glucose, levulose, maltose, galactose, sucrose and lactose actively fermented.

Biochemistry: Nitrites not formed from nitrates. Production of NH_3, SH_2, volatile amines, ketones, acetic, propionic, lactic and succinic acids.

Pathogenicity, natural: Acute appendicitis and post-appendicular suppuration; purulent pleurisy; salpingitis.

Pathogenicity, experimental: Non-pathogenic. No toxin nor hemolysin.

15. Ristella halosmophila (Baumgartner) P. 1938.

Synonym: Bacteroides halosmophilus Baumgartner 1937.

Habitat: Sea water and salted anchovies from the Mediterranean. Uncommon.

Morphology: Rods with rounded ends, 2 to 3 $\times$ 0.5 μ, occurring singly or in pairs, occasionally in chains; sometimes curved; pleomorphic. Non-motile. No endospores. Gram-negative.

Physiology: Strict anaerobe; t $=$ 22° to 35°; killed at 56°. pH 5.5 to 8.5. Halophilic: requires more than 4% NaCl in culture medium; optimum is 12.5 to 15%.

Cultural characteristics: Gas produced.

Deep agar salt: Lenticular colonies, 2 to 3 mm.

NaCl broth: Turbid; granular sediment; indole not formed; traces of H_2S produced.

Gelatin + NaCl: No liquefaction.

Carbohydrates: Acid and gas from glucose, maltose and glycerin. Starch not hydrolyzed.

Biochemistry: Nitrites not formed from nitrates.

Meat medium + NaCl: Gas produced; the medium becomes red; light fetid odor.

Pathogenicity: Non-pathogenic.

16. Ristella naviformis (Jungano) P. 1938.

Synonym: Bacillus naviformis Jungano 1909.

Habitat: Large intestine of the rat. Quite uncommon.

Morphology: Rods with pointed ends, 3 to 4 x 1 μ, occurring singly, in pairs or in filaments. Non-motile. No endospores. Gram-negative.

Physiology: Strict anaerobe. t $=$ 37°; killed at 55°.

Cultural characteristics: No gas produced.

Deep agar: Lenticular colonies.

Glucose broth: Turbid, acidified.

Gelatin: No liquefaction.

Milk: Unchanged.

Proteins: Not attacked.

Carbohydrates: Glucose only is fermented.

Pathogenicity: Non-pathogenic.

17. Ristella lichenis-plani (Jacob and Helmbold) P. 1938.

Habitat: Human skin. Quite uncommon.

Morphology: Straight rods, 2.5 to 3.5 x 0.5 to 0.7 μ. Non-motile. No endospores. Gram-negative.

Physiology: Strict anaerobe. t $= 37.5°$; killed at 55°. Short-lived.

Cultural characteristics: No gas produced. Does not grow on ordinary media.

Jacob and Helmbold Medium (4% semi-solid agar containing human serum, glucose and fresh tissue): The fragment of skin taken aseptically from the lesion of lichen planus is placed in the medium which is then recovered with oil of Vaseline: the medium becomes turbid.

Pathogenicity, experimental: By scarification, the papules of lichen planus are reproduced from which the same germ can be isolated.

Agglutination: Not specific.

18. *Ristella nodosa* (Beveridge) P. 1948.

Synonym: Fusiformis nodosus Beveridge 1941.

Habitat: Foot-rot in lambs of South Australia. Quite frequent.

Morphology: Rods with swollen ends (0.8 to 1.2 mm), 3 to 10 x 0.6 to 0.8 μ. Occurring singly or in pairs; may occasionnally show a swollen center. Non-motile. No endospores. Gram-negative.

Physiology: Strict anaerobe. Opt. t $= 37°$. Not thermoresistant.

Longevity: 5 weeks in culture, 2 years when dried. Opt. pH 7.4 to 7.6. Obligate serophile (horse serum).

Cultural characteristics: Grows in media containing 10% CO_2 and serum. No gas formed. No fetid odor produced.

Isolation: In Vf broth containing horse blood.

Vf deep agar with 10% horse serum: Cream-white lenticular colonies, 0.5 mm.

1% Cystein ClH-Vf agar with serum on surace: Circular, convex, smooth colonies with regular edges, 1 mm in diameter. Tart odor.

Veal infusion broth: No growth.

Milk: Slowly coagulated, then digested.

Broth with heart: Abundant growth with formation of tyrosine. No gas nor odor produced.

Carbohydrates: Glucose, maltose, galactose, lactose, sucrose and mannitol are not fermented.

Pathogenicity; natural: Isolated from foot-rot of the lamb, in association with *Tr. pernortha* or with a motile fusiform (*Zuberella pedipedis*).

Pathogenicity, experimental: By sub-cutaneous injection, feebly or non-pathogenic; by intravenous injection; sudden death. No toxin, no hemolysin.

Biochemistry: Nitrites not formed from nitrates. Production of H_2S; indole not formed.

Serology: The antiserum agglutinates the homologous strain at 1/3.200 and at 1/6.400, the heterologous strain at 1/600.

19. *Ristella destillationis* (Tunnicliff) P. 1938.

Synonym: Bacterium destillationis (T.) W.N. P. 1937.
Habitat: Bronchi. Uncommon.
Morphology: Straight rods, 2 × 0.3 μ. Occurring singly or in masses; filamentous forms. Non-motile. No endospores. Gram-negative.
Physiology: Strict anaerobe. t = 37°. Killed at 55°.
Cultural characteristics: Serophile. Slow growth. No gas produced.
Deep agar + blood or ascitic fluid: Lenticular colonies, hard, coherent, mucoid.
Loeffler serum: Smooth colonies.
Potato: Smooth, moist, adherent colonies.
Glucose broth: Irregular mucoid zooglea; no turbidity.
Pathogenicity, natural: Isolated from chronic bronchitis.
Pathogenicity, experimental: In the guinea-pig, pulmonary congestion and broncho-pneumonia, with atelectasis of the lung.

20. *Ristella uniformis* (E. and G). P. 1938.

Synonym: Bacteroides uniformis Eggerth and Gagnon 1933.
Habitat: Intestinal tract of man. Quite uncommon.
Morphology: Small rods with rounded ends, quite regular and uniform, 1.5 x 0.8 μ, occurring singly. Non-motile. No endospores. Gram-negative, staining more deeply at the poles.
Physiology: Strict anaerobe. t = 37°; killed at 56°.
Cultural characteristics: No gas produced.
Deep agar: Punctiform colonies.
Glucose broth: Diffuse turbidity, acid; traces of H_2S.
Peptoned water: Diffuse turbidity. Indole produced.
Gelatin: Slowly liquefied.
Milk: Acid and coagulated in 3 to 12 days.
Carbohydrates: Acid but no gas from glucose, levulose, maltose, galactose, sucrose, lactose, xylose, arabinose, dextrin, glycogen, inulin and starch.
Pathogenicity, natural: Isolated from a human case of ulcerative colitis.
Pathogenicity, experimental: Not pathogenic for laboratory animals.
Biochemistry: Nitrates not formed from nitrates. Sulfites not attacked. Produces NH_3, H_2S, acetoin, indole, acetic and propionic acids.

21. *Ristella distasonis* (E. and G.) P. 1938.

Synonym: Bacteroides distasonis Eggerth and Gagnon 1933.
Habitat: Intestinal tract of man. Quite frequent.
Morphology: Straight rods with rounded ends, 1.5 to 2.5 × 0.5 to 0.8μ. Non-motile. No endospores. Gram-negative.
Physiology: Strict anaerobe. t = 37°. Reduces neutral red.

Cultural characteristics: No gas produced.

Deep agar: Punctiform colonies.

Glucose broth: Diffuse turbidity; no gas produced; acid and H_2S formed.

Peptone water: No gas but indole formed.

Gelatin: No liquefaction (or very slowly liquefied).

Milk: Acid and coagulated.

Carbohydrates: Acid from glucose, levulose, maltose, sucrose, galactose, lactose, xylose, inulin and starch.

Pathogenicity, natural: Isolated in a fatal case of post-appendicular purulent peritonitis.

Pathogenicity, experimental: Non-pathogenic for laboratory animals.

Biochemistry: Nitrates and sulfites not attacked. Produces NH_3, H_2S, volatile amines, ethanol, ketones, sometimes traces of indole, acetic, valerianic and lactic acids.

22.   *Ristella uncata* (E. and G.) P. 1938

Synonym: Bacteroides uncatus Eggerth and Gagnon 1933.

Habitat: Human intestinal tract. Quite uncommon.

Morphology: Rods, 0.5 to 2 $\times$ 0.3μ; filamentous forms with swellings. Ends in the form of a hook. Non-motile, No endospores. Gram-negative.

Physiology: Strict anaerobe. t $= 37°$.

Cultural characteristics: No gas produced.

Deep agar: Punctiform colonies.

Glucose broth: Slow, cloudy growth; no gas produced; acid.

Peptone water: Turbid; no gas produced; indole not formed; no H_2S produced.

Gelatin: Liquefied in 16 days.

Milk: Unchanged.

Carbohydrates: Acid from glucose, levulose, maltose, galactose, sucrose lactose, dextrin and starch.

Pathogenicity: Non-pathogenic.

23.   *Ristella tumida* (Eggerth and Gagnon) P. 1938

Synonym: Bacteroides tumidus E. and G. 1933.

Habitat: Human intestinal tract. Uncommon.

Morphology: Slender rods, 1 to 1.5μ; filamentous forms, 4 to 10μ. Swollen forms with irregular staining. Non-motile. No endospores. Gram-negative.

Physiology: Strict anaerobe. t $= 37°$. Longevity: Several years. Neutral red not reduced.

Cultural characteristics: No gas produced.

Deep agar: Punctiform colonies; no gas produced.

Agar slant: Soft grayish colonies, 2 mm. in diameter.

Glucose broth: Diffuse turbidity; no gas; acid and H_2S produced.
Peptone water: Diffuse turbidity; no gas nor indole formed.
Gelatin: Liquefied in 12 to 20 days.
Milk: Acid, not coagulated.
Coagulated proteins: Not attacked.
Carbohydrates: Glucose, levulose, maltose, galactose, raffinose, sucrose, glycogen, inulin, dextrin and starch are fermented.
Pathogenicity, natural: Isolated from a case of acute appendicitis.
Biochemistry: Nitrites not formed from nitrates. Produces NH_3, H_2S, aldehydes, acetylmethylcarbinol, acetic, butyric and lactic acids.

24. *Ristella exigua* (E. and G.) P. 1938

Synonym: Bacteroides exiguus Eggerth and Gagnon 1933.
Habitat: Human intestinal tract. Quite uncommon.
Morphology: Short slender rods, 0.5 to 1μ. Non-motile. No endospores. Gram-negative.
Physiology: Strict anaerobe. t $= 37°$.
Cultural characteristics: No gas produced.
Deep agar: Punctiform colonies.
Glucose broth: Diffuse turbidity; H_2S, formed.
Peptone water: Diffuse turbidity; indole not formed.
Gelatin: Liquefied in 16 to 20 days.
Milk: Coagulated in 35 to 40 days.
Carbohydrates: Glucose, levulose, maltose, galactose, lactose, sucrose, and raffinose are fermented.
Pathogenicity: Non-pathogenic.

25. *Ristella trichoides* (Potez and Compagnon) P. 1938

Synonym: Bacillus trichoides P. and C. 1922; *Bacteroides trichoides* (P. and G.) Hauduroy *et al.*
Habitat: Human digestive tract. Uncommon.
Morphology: Slender filamentous rods, $0.3 \times 5\ \mu$ (up to 70 μ). Non-motile. No endospores. Gram-negative.
Physiology: Strict anaerobe. t $= 37°$; killed at $56°$ Longevity: over 7 weeks. Decolorizes neutral red.
Cultural characteristics: Gas and fecaloid odor produced.
Deep agar: Lenticular, coherent colonies.
Glucose broth: Abundant turbidity; flaky sediment in 5 days; H_2S produced.
Gelatin: No liquefaction.
Milk: Coagulated in 4 to 5 days.
Coagulated proteins: Not attacked.
Carbohydrates: Acid and gas from glucose, maltose, levulose, sucrose and mannitol.

Pathogenicity, natural: Cholescystis and fatal pericarditis.

Pathogenicity, experimental: Sub-cutaneous injection of 2 cc. of pus into the rabbit produces a voluminous enkysted abscess. Injection into the gall bladder produces a purulent cholecystis. No toxin, nor hemolysin.

26. *Ristella glutinosa* (Guillemot and Hallé) P. 1938

Synonym: Bacillus glutinosus G. and H. 1904; *Bacteroides glutinosus* (G. and H.) Hauduroy *et al.*

Habitat: Respiratory tract. Pleura. Uncommon.

Morphology: Long filamentous rods, 6 to 8 $\times$ 0.8μ (may reach 32μ); entangled clumps; discrete swellings. Bipolar staining with middle portion barely visible. Metachromatic granules. Non-motile. No endospores. Gram-negative.

Physiology: Strict anaerobe. t = 37°; killed at 55°. Survives for 4 days only in agar. Obligate serophile on primary isolation. Slight reducing power.

Cultural characteristics: No gas produced by most strains. A few strains produce slight fetid gas.

Deep agar: Lenticular colonies appearing slowly, highly cohesive on account of an abundant intermediary substance which forms a network embedding the bacterial cells.

Peptone water: Very meager growth; no gas produced.

Glucose Vf broth: Highly cohesive colonies sticking to the wall of the tube, causing no turbidity and not dissociated by shaking, 1 to 2 mm. in diameter. They are constituted by cell bodies imbedded in a network of viscous material. Very little gas formed.

Gelatin: Liquefied in 3 to 5 days.

Milk: Coagulated in 3 days.

Coagulated proteins: Not attacked.

Carbohydrates: Glucose, levulose, and lactose are fermented.

Biochemistry: Nitrites not formed from nitrates. Produces NH_3, H_2S, indole, volatile amines, aldehydes, ketones, formic and butyric acids as well as a trace of a third undetermined acid.

Pathogenicity, natural: Purulent pleurisy, pulmonary gangrene, fatal perinephritic phlegmon with metastatic abscesses in the brain.

Pathogenicity, experimental: Fetid suppuration in the guinea-pig.

27. *Ristella capillosa* (Tissier) P. 1938.

Synonym: Bacillus capillosus Tissier 1908.

Habitat: Large intestinal tract of children. Uncommon.

Morphology: Long thick filamentous rods, 4 to 5 $\times$ 1μ; may reach 20 to 30μ. Entangled clumps. Non-motile. No endospores. Gram-negative.

Physiology: Strict anaerobe. t = 37°; killed at 55°. Survives for 10 to 15 days.

Cultural characteristics: No gas produced.

Deep agar: Fine irregular colonies.
Glucose broth: Turbid. Indole not formed.
Gelatin: No liquefaction.
Milk: Unchanged.
Coagulated proteins: Not attacked.
Proteoses: Digested. Indole not formed or H₂S.
Carbohydrates: Glucose feebly fermented.
Pathogenicity: Non-pathogenic.

28. *Ristella cylindroides* (Rocchi) P. 1938.

Synonym: Bacterium cylindroides Rocchi 1908.
Habitat: Intestinal tract of man. Uncommon.
Morphology: Long, thick, filamentous rods, 6 to 8μ in length, with swellings; non-motile; no endospores; Gram-negative.
Physiology: Strict anaerobe. Growth at 18° C. Killed at 56° C. Survives 15 days at the most.
Cultural characters: No gas produced.
Deep agar: Small, circular colonies.
Glucose broth: Turbid; light sediment.
Gelatin: No liquefaction.
Milk: Unchanged.
Coagulated proteins: Not attacked.
Carbohydrates: Acid but no gas from glucose and sucrose.
Proteoses: Feebly attacked.
Pathogenicity: Non-pathogenic.

29. *Ristella gulosa* (Eggerth and Gagnon) Sébald 1962.

Synonyms: Bacteroides gulosus Eggerth and Gagnon 1933; *Sphaerophorus gulosus* (E. and G.) Prévot 1938.
Habitat: Intestinal tract of man; other natural cavities. Quite frequent.
Morphology: Pleomorphic rods: short oval forms, 1 to 2μ × 0.8μ; swollen forms, 3 to 4μ × 2 to 3μ; spheroids; long filamentous forms. Non-motile; no endospores. Gram-negative. Bipolar staining.
Physiology: Strict anaerobe. Opt. T = 37°C. Slight reducing power (neutral red and phenosafranin not decolorized). Serophile upon isolation and primary cultures; becomes adapted to media without serum.
Cultural characters: Slightly fetid gas produced.
Deep agar: Punctiform colonies, becoming lenticular.
Glucose broth: Diffuse turbidity; gas, acid; H₂S formed.
Peptone water: Turbid. Indole formed.
Gelatin: Liquefied in 2 to 3 weeks.
Milk: Acid, clotted.
Coagulated proteins: Not attacked.
Carbohydrates: Acid and gas from arabinose, glucose, levulose, galac–

tose, maltose, lactose, sucrose, xylose, inulin, dextrin, starch and glycogen.

Biochemistry: Produces NH_3, H_2S, volatile amines, acetylmethylcarbinol, formic, butyric and lactic acids.

Pathogenicity, natural: Frequently isolated from septicemic cases, either fatal or very severe, of appendicular or post-abortal origin, with multiple metastases: purulent cystitis, purulent peritonitis, purulent pleurisy, gangrenous phlegmon, suppurative arthritis, brain abscess. No hemolysin.

Pathogenicity, experimental: Injection of pus to the guinea pig produces a rapidly fatal disease; in laboratory cultures ,the germ rapidly loses its virulence.

30. *Ristella freundii* (Freund) Sébald 1962.

Synonym: Bacteroides freundii (Freund) Hauduroy *et al., Sphaerophorus freundii* (F.) Prévot 1938.

Habitat: Intestinal tract of man. Buccal cavity. Frequent.

Morphology: Short rods: 0.8 to 1.0 × 0.3 to 0.4μ; oval forms with clear center; coccoid forms; spheroids; very long filaments; metachromasia; swellings; non-motile; no endospores; Gram-negative.

Physiology: Strict anaerobe. Opt. T. $= 37°$C. Killed at $100°$C. Survives for 26 to 30 days. Obligate serophile upon isolation; adapts itself slowly to media without serum. Reduces neutral red.

Cultural characters: Fetid gas produced.

Serum-Deep Agar: Lenticular colonies 1 mm. in diameter; gas.

Serum-glucose broth: Turbid; gas; flaky, powdery sediment; fetid odor; acid; H_2S; indole.

Peptone water: No growth.

Gelatin: Not liquefied.

Milk: Coagulated in 3 days.

Carbohydrates: Butyric acid and gas from glucose, maltose, sucrose, mannitol.

Biochemistry: Produces NH_3, volatile amines, H_2S; aldehydes; ketones; acetic, butyric and lactic acids. Nitrites not formed from nitrates.

Pathogenicity, natural: Fatal purulent meningitis. Puerperal septicemia. Necrotizing ileitis. Retropelvic abscess. Post- appendicular septicemia with multiple metastases. Septicemia following cholecystitis, dental infection.

Pathogenicity, experimental: Injection of 1 ml. to the guinea pig by the subcutaneous route gives rise to an abscess; 2 ml. produce death after necrotic phlegmous abscess and septicemia. The injection of 0.5 ml. to the rabbit by the intravenous route produces necrosis and miliary abscesses of the viscera, especially of the liver.

31. *Ristella abscedens* (Tardieux and Monteverde) Sébald 1962.

Synonym: Sphaerophorus abscedens Tardieux and Monteverde 1951.

Habitat: Buccal cavity of certain mammals (dog and calf).

Morphology: Pleomorphic rods: shuttle-like forms with clear center,

2 to 3μ: elongated forms, flexuous, with metachromatic granules: pseudo-branching; lateral swellings in the shape of clubs or handbells; spheroids. Non-motile. No endospores. Gram-negative.

Physiology: Strict anaerobe. Survives 2 to 3 months. Resists at 60°C for a few minutes. Marked reducing powers (neutral red and safranin permanently or temporarily reduced).

Cultural characters: Obligate serophile. No gas nor fetid odor produced.

Serum-deep agar: Slow growth. Punctiform colonies, becoming lenticular.

Serum-peptone water: Very slight turbidity; indole formed.

Serum-glucose Vf broth: Diffuse turbidity in 24 to 48 hours.

Gelatin: Not liquefied.

Milk Unchanged.

Coagulated proteins: Not attacked.

Carbohydrates: Very slight fermentation of glucose and galactose.

Biochemistry: Nitrites not formed from nitrates. Produces NH_3, H_2S, indole, sometimes cresol and acetoin. No amines, no alcohol, no ketones. Fermentation type: acetic, butyric and lactic.

Pathogenicity, natural: Abscess of the cow's mammary glands; osteitis of the calcaneum in man (necrotic type lesion); abdominal abscess; infected wounds.

Pathogenicity, experimental: Non-pathogenic for guinea pigs and mice.

32. *Ristella glycolytica* (Tardieux and Ernst) Sébald 1962.

Synonym: Sphaerophorus glycolyticus Tardieux and Ernst 1951.

Habitat: Genital tract of the woman; intestinal tract of man. Frequent.

Morphology: Pleomorphic rods: shuttle-like forms with clear center, long forms, flexuous, with metachromatic granules; spheroids. Gram-negative. Non-motile. No endospores.

Physiology: Strict anaerobe. Survives 1 to 2 months. Not thermoresistant. Slight reducing powers (neutral red and phenosafranin reduced temporarily).

Cultural characters: Obligate serophile. No gas produced, but a slightly fetid odor.

Serum-deep agar: Punctiform and lenticular colonies.

Serum-peptone water: Very slight turbidity.

Serum-glucose-VF broth: Abundant diffuse turbidity.

Gelatin + serum: Slowly liquefied (3 to 4 weeks).

Coagulated proteins: Not attacked.

Milk: Rapidly clotted with partial digestion.

Carbohydrates: Glucose, levulose, galactose, sucrose, glycerol and starch strongly fermented.

Biochemistry: Nitrites not formed from nitrates. Produces NH_3, H_2S, acetone, traces of aldehydes and scatole; acetic, butyric and lactic acids.

Pathogenicity, natural: Isolated from pyosalpinx, puerperal septicemia, purulent pleurisy following perforative appendicitis, adnexitis, ulcer, granuloma of the apex of the tooth, brain abscess following otitis, purulent pleurisy following a liver abscess in a case of chronic polyarthritis, suppurative otitis.

Pathogenicity, experimental: Injection of the culture to the guinea pig produces wasting and cachexia, followed by death in 10 to 15 days without any local lesion visible at necropsy.

33. *Ristella biacuta* (Weinberg and Prévot) Sébald 1962.

Synonyms: Fusobacterium biacutum Weinberg and Prévot 1926; *Fusiformis biacutus* (W. and P.) Prévot 1938.

Habitat: Appendix. Frequent.

Morphology: Straight rods with pointed ends, 1.5 to $3.0\mu \times 0.5\mu$; occurring singly, in pairs or in short chains; numerous spheroids, 1.0 to 1.5μ, inserum broth. Gram-negative. Non-motile. No endospores.

Physiology: Strict anaerobe. Opt. T. $= 22\text{-}37°C$. Killed at $60°C$ after one hour. Survives for several years in tubes sealed under *vacuo*. Reduces neutral red.

Cultural characters: Abundant gas produced, but not fetid.

Deep agar: Lenticular colonies; abundant gas.

Glucose broth: Abundant growth; diffuse turbidity; gas; final pH 4.5. Indole not formed, but traces of H_2S.

Peptone water: Meager growth; some gas formed; indole not formed.

Gelatin: Not liquefied.

Milk: Acidified and clotted in 48 hours to 8 days.

Coagulated proteins: Not attacked.

Carbohydrates: Acid and gas from flucose, levulose, maltose, lactose and galactose.

Biochemistry: Nitrites not formed from nitrates; produces NH_3, H_2S, propionic and acetic acids, alcohol, ketones and aldehydes, acetylmethylcarbinol.

Pathogenicity, natural: Isolated from severe cases of appendicitis, salpingitis, and phlegmons.

Pathogenicity, experimental: In pure culture, gives rise in the guinea pig to hemorrhagic gelatinous edema and death. No toxin nor hemolysin.

Agglutination: Specific at 1-2,500.

34. *Ristella polymorpha* (Knorr) Sébald 1962.

Synonyms: Fusobacterium polymorphum Knorr 1923; *Fusiformis polymorphus* (Knorr) Bergey *et al.*

Habitat: Buccal cavity; intestinal tract. Quite uncommon.

Morphology: Rods with pointed ends: 8 to 16 $\mu \times$ 0.2 to 0.5 μ; occurring often in pairs or in short chains; highly pleomorphic: undulating filaments; one single chromatinic body per cell. Gram-negative. Non-motile. No endospores.

Physiology: Strict anaerobe. Opt. T. $= 30\text{-}37\,^{\circ}$C. Resists at $56\,^{\circ}$C for 5 minutes. Opt. pH $= 7.0\text{-}8.2$. Reduces neutral red and safranin. Survives for several years.

Cultural characters: Not serophilic. No gas produced.

Serum-deep agar: Lenticular colonies.

Broth: Highly coherent viscous sediment. Indole irregularly produced. No odor nor H_2S.

Gelatin: No liquefaction.

Milk: Partly clotted.

Coagulated proteins: Not attacked.

Carbohydrates: Glucose, levulose and sucrose fermented.

Biochemistry: Nitrites not formed from nitrates. Produces NH_3, H_2S, indole, volatile amines, ketones, aldehydes, acetylmethylcarbinol, acetic and propionic acids.

Pathogenicity, natural: Isolated from dental saburra in a case of gingivitis, and in a case of appendicitis; actinomycosis of the cat.

Pathogenicity, experimental: Not pathogenic.

35.   *Ristella ochracea* (Prévot *et al.*) Sébald 1962.

Synonym: Fusiformis nucleatus var. *ochraceus* Prévot *et al.*

Habitat: Natural cavities of man and cat. Quite uncommon.

Morphology: Non-motile Gram-negative rods with pointed ends; nucleus visible without special staining procedure.

Physiology: Strict anaerobe. Opt. T. $= 33\text{-}37\,^{\circ}$ C. Opt. pH $= 7\text{-}8$. Slight reducing powers (neutral red not reduced). Slight odor or none.

Cultural characters: Slow growth.

Deep agar: Fluffy or lenticular colonies, slowly taking on an ochre-red color.

Glucose VF broth: Diffuse turbidity which sediments as an ochre-red powder.

Biochemistry: Nitrites not formed from nitrates. Indole not formed. Fermentation type: propionic-formic-lactic.

Pathogenicity, natural: Isolated in a case of bronchial infection, in a case of gangrenous pleurisy and in an ulcer-like wound of the cat.

Pathogenicity, experimental: Not pathogenic.

Species *incertae sedis:*

Ristella vesca (Eggerth and Gagnon) Sébald 1962.

Synonyms: Bacteroides vescus (Eggerth and Gagnon) 1933; *Fusiformis vescus* (E. and G.) Prévot 1938; *Fusobacterium vescum* (E. and G.) Hoffman *et al.*

Habitat: Intestinal tract. Quite uncommon.

Morphology: Slender rods, 1 to 3μ long, with pointed ends; filaments measuring 15μ, sometimes slightly curved; metachromatic granules; bipolar staining. Non-motile. No endospores. Gram-negative.

Physiology: Strict anaerobe. Opt. T. $= 37°$C.

Cultural characters: No gas produced, but a slightly fetid odor.

Deep agar: Small lenticular colonies.

Glucose broth: Cloudy, diffuse turbidity; acid and H_2S produced. Indole not formed.

Peptone water: Turbid; no gas; indole not formed.

Gelatin: Liquefied in 8 to 25 days.

Milk: Unchanged.

Coagulated proteins: Not attacked.

Carbohydrates: Acid but no gas from dextrin, glucose, maltose, mannose, rhamnose and cellobiose (30 days). Some strains ferment a larger number of carbohydrates.

Pathogenicity: Non-pathogenic. One strain isolated by Brocart was hemolytic.

Ristella corrodens (Eiken) nov. comb.

Synonym: Bacteroides corrodens Eiken 1958.

Habitat: Natural cavities of man.

Morphology: Gram-negative rods, $0.4\mu \times 2.0\mu$, occurring singly or in chains of 2 to 4 cells, sometimes in filaments measuring 50μ. Non-motile. No endospores.

Physiology: Strict anaerobe. Opt. T $= 32$-$43°$C. Not thermoresistant. Opt. pH $=7$-8.

Cultural characters: Slow growth; no gas or fetid odor produced.

Blood-agar: Umbonate colonies.

Gelatin: No liquefaction.

Carbohydrates: Not fermented.

Biochemistry: Nitrites produced from nitrates. H_2S produced.

Pathogenicity: Unknown.

APPENDIX

1.   The generic term *Methanobacterium* proposed by Kluyver and van Niel in 1936 does not cover a homogeneous group. If we eliminate the motile Gram-positive sporeformers, which will be reclassed further on in the appropriate genera, there remains a group of 3 homogeneous species which answer well to the definition originally submitted for the genus *Methanobacterium,* which we consider to be a sub-genus of *Ristella.*

Sub-genus *Methanobacterium* Kluyver and van Niel 1936

Definition.—Non-motile, Gram-negative rods, strictly anaerobic, producing methane from CO_2 or formates. Three species:

1. *Methanobacterium soehngenii* Barker 1936, page 119
2. *Methanobacterium formicicum* Schnellen 1947, page 119
3. *Methanobacterium ruminantium* Smith and Hungate, page 119.

1. *Methanobacterium soehngenii* Barker 1936.

Synonym: Ristella soehngeni (Barker) Prévot 1947.

Habitat: River mud, sewage.

Morphology: Gram-negative rods, straight or slightly-curved, of average length. In fluid cultures, may form long parallel chains which become bundled. Non-motile. No endospores.

Physiology: Strict anaerobe. Chemo-heterotrophic or chemo-autotrophic, capable of oxidizing several organic or inorganic compounds, or of reducing CO_2 to CH_4.

Enrichment cultures: Media containing acetate or butyrate as a source of carbon are fermented with production of CO_2 and CH_4. Ethanol and butanol are not fermented.

2. *Methanobacterium formicicum* Schnellen 1947.

Habitat: Mud from soft waters; caecum of herbivorous animals; waste waters; sludge from domestic sewage. Frequent.

Morphology: Gram-negative rods, $0.4\mu \times 4$ to 5μ, often in chains. Non-motile. No endospores.

Physiology: Strict anaerobe. Opt. T. $= 38\text{-}45°C$. Opt. pH $= 7.8$. Requires an atmosphere containing 80% H_2 and 20% CO_2 with a palladium catalyzer.

Cultural characters: Na_2S may serve as a reducing agent.

Deep agar: Arborescent, villous colonies.

Biochemistry: Produces CH_4 from formates.

3. *Methanobacterium ruminantium* Smith and Hungate 1958.

Habitat: Rumen of cattle; domestic sludge. Quite frequent.

Morphology: Gram-negative rods, 0.7 to 0.8 $\mu \times 1.8$ μ, encapsulated. Non-motile: No endospores.

Physiology: Strict anaerobe. Opt. T. $= 39°C$. Requires an atmosphere containing 80% H_2 and 20% CO_2.

Cultural characters: Requires a mineral medium containing 20% rumen.

Deep agar: Yellowish, round colonies.

Biochemistry: Produces CH_4 from formates or by reduction of CO_2 by H_2.

Note.—Since pure cultures of *M. suboxydans* and *M. propionicum* have yet to be obtained, these species cannot figure in this manual.

Desulforistella hydrocarbonoclastica Hwid Hansen 1951.

Habitat: Subsoil water from the hydrogen sulfide region of Sjaelland (Denmark).

Morphology: Gram-negative rods, with pointed ends, 0.7 to 1.0 μ x 1 to 2 μ, occurring often in pairs. Non-motile. No endospores.

Physiology: Strict anaerobe. Opt. T. $= 30°$C.

Cultural characters: No growth on heterotrophic media.

Autotrophic agar: Primary black colonies do not survive when transferred unless CH_4 and H_2 are present as hydrogen donors. May utilize as hydrogen donors: formic, acetic, propionic and lactic acids from which is produced a bituminous oil soluble in ether.

Genus *incertae sedis:*

Ruminobacter Kaars Syperstein 1948.

Definition: Oval or coccoid cells, occurring singly.
Gram-negative. Non-motile. No endospores. Chemo-heterotrophic fermenting cellulose. Anaerobic.

Type-species: R. parvum.

Ruminobacter parvum Kaars Syperstein 1948.

Habitat: Rumen of cattle; caecum of herbivorous animals.

Morphology: Gram-negative, ovoid cells, o.5 $\times$ 0.8 μ, occurring singly. in older cultures, cells may measure 1.5 μ. Non-motile. No endospores.

Physiology: Strict anaerobe. Chemo-heterotrophic. Cellulose fermented. Catalase production uncertain. No pigment. Mesophilic. Probably identical or related with *Micrococcus ruminantium* and *M. pygmaeus* Henneberg 1922-1946, and the cocci described by Backer (1947) and Hungate (1947).

Ruminobacter amylogenes (Doetsch *et al.*) nov. comb.

Synonym: Bacteroides amylogenes Doetsch, Howard, Mann and Oxford 1957 [1].

Habitat: Rumen of sheep.

Morphology: Gram-negative, curved rods, 0.5 $\mu \times$ 2.5 μ. Non-motile. No endospores. After growth on sugar media, presence of an iodophilic granule.

Physiology: Strict anaerobe. Growth on media containing rumen and bicarbonate. From a number of carbohydrates, including the pentoses, produces an intracellular iodophile polysaccharide (glucose polymer) as a reserve substance used up later on.

Biochemistry: Butyric acid is the main fermentation product of xylose.

---

[1] J. Gen Microb., 1957, *16*, 156.

Ruminobacter amylophilum Hamlin and Hungate.

Synonym: Bacteroides amylophilus Hamlin and Hungate 1956.

Habitat: Caecum of sheep and cattle. Frequent.

Morphology: Gram-negative rods, 0.9 to 1.6 μ x 1.6 to 4.0 μ, pleomorphic, with rounded ends; noniodophilic intracellular granules; oval and coccoid forms. Non-motile. No endospores.
Long swollen forms.

Physiology: Strict anaerobe. Opt. T. = 35-45°C. Opt. pH = 6.8-7.8. Requires CO_2. Survives 3 to 4 days.

Cultural characters: Growth only in mineral media added with soluble starch, maize starch, rumen, yeast extract, or extract of *Medigo sativa*. Gas produced.

Agar plate in vacuo: Large colonies, white, convex, translucent, smooth, brilliant.

Enriched deep agar: White lenticular colonies. Gas.

Enriched gelatin: Liquefaction.

Carbohydrates: Maltose and starch fermented.

Biochemistry: Nitrites formed from nitrates. In enriched medium, produces formic, acetic, lactic and succinic acids, ethanol and CO_2. Intense proteolysis.

Pathogenicity: Non-pathogenic.

Ruminobacter ruminocola (Bryant et al.) nov. comb.

Synonym: Bacteroides ruminicola Bryant, Small, Bouma and Chu 1958.

Habitat: Rumen of cattle.

Morphology: Gram-negative straight rods, 0.8 to 1.0 μ x 1.2 to 6.0 μ; pleomorphic: oval forms, shuttle-like, with bipolar staining; filaments measuring 50 μ; swollen forms, spheroids, coccoid forms, rare branching forms. Noniodophilic metachromatic granules. Some cells may be encapsulated. presence of cytochrom b. Non-motile. No endospores.

Physiology: Strict anaerobe. Opt. T. = 30-37°C. Final pH = 5.4-5.8. No catalase.

Cultural characters: Growth only in media added with sterile rumen. No gas nor odor produced.

Agar slant in vacuo: Tan-colored colonies, smooth, convex opaque.

Deep agar: Lenticular colonies.

Glucose fluid media: Turbid; viscous sediment. Heavy bacteriogloea.

Enriched gelatin: Liquefaction.

Carbohydrates: Xylose, arabinose, glucose, galactose, levulose, lactose, cellobiose, maltose, sucrose, dextrin, inulin, xylane, salicin, pectin, and esculin fermented. Starch hydrolyzed.

Biochemistry: May utilize enzymatic hydrolysate of casein and NH_4. Produces NH_3, formic, acetic and succinic acids from peptone. Nitrites not formed from nitrates.

Pathogenicity: Non-pathogenic.

Ruminobacter succinogenes (Hungate) nov. comb.

Synonym: Bacteroides succinogenes Hungate 1950.

Habitat: Rumen of cattle.

Morphology: Gram-negative rods, with pointed ends, 0.3 to 0.4 μ x 1 to 2 μ, slightly-curved, occurring singly or in pairs. Pleomorphic in glucose media: spherical and ellipsoidal forms, rosette shapes. Non-motile. No endospores. Bipolar staining.

Physiology: Strict anaerobe. Opt. T. $= 40°C$. pH $= 5.5$.

Cultural characters: No gas nor odor produced.

Cellulose agar: Zones of clearing.

Cellobiose agar: Lenticular colonies, colorless or yellowish.

Sterile rumen + glucose or cellobiose: Turbid.

Gelatin: No liquefaction.

Gasein: Digested.

Carbohydrates: Glucose, cellobiose, cellulose and pectin are fermented. Some strains ferment in addition: maltose, lactose, trehalose, dextrin and starch.

Biochemistry: Nitrites not formed from nitrates. Requires fatty acids (aliphatic or with side-chains), NH_3 in the presence of amino acids. Produces CO_2, acetic and succinic acids.

GENUS II: *CAPSULARIS* Prévot 1938.

Definition: Gram-negative, simple, straight rods; encapsulated; non-motile; no endospores.

This genus actually comprises four species:

1. Long slender rods; encapsulated; serophilic; viscous zoogloea in broth; saccharolytic; no gas produced.
   1. *Capsularis zoogleiformans,* page 123
2. Short pleomorphic rods; encapsulated; microaerophilic; serophilic; gas produced; fetid; indole formed; pathogenic.
   2. *Capsularis mucosus,* page 123
3. Pleomorphic rods; encapsulated; not serophilic; saccharolytic; non-proteolytic; indole formed; non-pathogenic.
   3. *Capsularis variabilis,* page 124
4. Short rods; encapsulated; not serophilic; saccharolytic; indole not formed; pathogenic; stable.
   4. *Capsularis stabilis,* page 124

1. Capsularis zoogleiformans (Prausnitz) P. 1938.

Synonym: Bacillus mucosus capsulatus [1] Prausnitz 1922; *Bacteroides prausnitzi* Hauduroy; *Bacterium zoogleiformans* W.N.P. 1937.

Habitat: Respiratory tract. Uncommon.

Morphology: Fine slender rods with pointed ends; 0.5 μ x 5 to 14 μ; encapsulated (very thick, highly mucoid, easily stainable capsule); non-motile; no endospores. Gram-negative.

Physiology: Strict anaerobe. Opt. T. $= 37°C$. Killed at 56°C. Survives 2 weeks.

Cultural characters: No gas produced. Require fresh animal albumin (Tarrozzi's medium).

Ascite-broth + fresh kidney: Delicate cloudy turbidity with coherent viscous sediment after one week. No gas produced.

Semi-solid horse serum + fresh kidney: Delicate turbidity followed by viscous, coherent, mucoid mass. No gas produced.

Carbohydrates: Glucose and maltose actively fermented. Levulose, galactose, sucrose and lactose lightly fermented. No gas or odor produced.

Pathogenicity, natural: Isolated from a pleural abscess.

Pathogenicity, experimental: Non-pathogenic.

Serology: The patient's serum will fix complement. Intradermal reaction positive.

2. Capsularis mucosus (Klinger) P. 1938.

Synonym: Coccobacterium mucosum capsulatum Klinger 1912; *Bacteroides viscosus* Hauduroy; *Bacterium mucosum* W.N.P. 1937.

Habitat: Respiratory tract. Uncommon.

Morphology: Short ovoid rods with rounded ends; 0.4 μ x 1 to 2 μ, encapsulated; pleomorphic: swollen forms and filaments measuring 6 μ. Presence of glycogen in the swellings. Non-motile. No endospores. Gram-negative. Bipolar staining.

Physiology: Microaerophilic. Opt. T. $= 37°C$. Killed at 56°C. Survives 5 weeks.

Cultural characters: Serophilic. Gas produced.

Serum-deep agar: Lenticular colonies. Gas with fetid odor (H_2S).

Serum-broth: Turbid; mucous zoogloea; fetid gas; indole and H_2S formed.

Serum-gelatin: Flaky growth. Liquefaction.

Serum-milk: Coagulated, then digested. H_2S produced.

Coagulated serum: Not attacked.

Pathogenicity, natural: Found in association with a fusiform bacillus in a case of bronchiectasis with brain abscess and fatal meningitis.

---

[1] Name abandoned because of homonymy, priority being given to Klinger's homonym described in 1912.

Pathogenicity, experimental: Subcutaneous abscess in the mouse; phlegmon in the guinea pig; purulent hemorrhagic inflammation in the rabbit.

3. Capsularis variabilis (Distaso) P. 1938.

Synonym: Bacillus variabilis Distaso 1912; *Bacteroides variabilis* C. and C.

Habitat: Intestinal tract of man. Quite frequent.

Morphology: Short rods, with rounded ends; 1 to 2 μ, wide clear capsule. Pleomorphic: may produce filaments measuring 10 to 12 μ, swellings. Non-motile. No endospores. Gram-negative.

Physiology: Strict anaerobe. Opt. T. $= 37°$C. Survives 10 days at the most.

Cultural characters: Gas produced.

Deep agar: Round, transparent colonies; gas produced.

Glucose broth: No turbidity; white sediment; gas produced; odor of scatole; H_2S produced.

Peptone water: Indole produced.

Carbohydrate-gelatin: Turbid; H_2S produced; no liquefaction.

Milk: Acidified but not clotted.

Coagulated proteins: Not attacked.

Carbohydrates: Acid and gas from glucose, levulose, sucrose, lactose, arabinose and starch (butyric odor).

Pathogenicity: Non-pathogenic.

4. Capsularis stabilis Patocka and Prévot 1947.

Habitat: Genital tract of the woman (Czecho-Slovakia). Uncommon.

Morphology: Short rods with rounded ends, 0.5 to 0.6 μ x 1.4 μ; occurring singly; short and long forms may be seen; encapsulated; non-motile; no endospores. Gram-negative.

Physiology: Strict anaerobe. Opt. T. $= 37°$C. Not thermoresistant. Survives more than 2 years. Opt. pH $= 7.4$. Not obligate serophile. Neutral red and phenosafranin not reduced.

Cultural characters: Gas produced (slightly fetid).

Deep agar: Puntiform colonies; gas produced.

Peptone water: Slight turbidity.

Glucose VF broth: Uniform turbidity; gas produced with slightly fetid odor; acid.

Gelatin: Liquefaction in 24 hours.

Milk: Massive coagulation in 3 days.

Coagulated proteins: Not attacked.

Carbohydrates: Glucose, levulose, maltose, sucrose, galactose, lactose, arabinose, starch, mannitol and glycerol fermented.

Biochemistry: Nitrites not formed from nitrates. Produces NH_3, formic, butyric and lactic acids; volatile amines, acetone, acetylmethylcarbinol; indole not formed.

Pathogenicity, natural: Isolated from a case of purulent salpingitis and from a fatal septicemia following gangrenous appendicitis.

Pathogenicity, experimental: Edema and abscess in the guinea pig, followed by death in 2 to 3 weeks; germ found in the blood and spleen. Serology: In the rabbit, produces a serum with an agglutinating titer of 1 to 360 for heterologous strains as well.

GENUS III: *ZUBERELLA* Prévot 1938.

Definition: Straight rods, unencapsulated; non-motile; no endospores; Gram-negative.

This genus actually comprises eleven species:

A) Species producing gas:
1. Thick rods; milk clotted; gelatin liquefied; saccharolytic.
    1. *Zuberella serpens,* page 126
2. Short rods with pointed ends; milk unchanged; gelatin not liquefied; indole not formed; fat saponified.
    2. *Zuberella praeacuta,* page 126
3. Rods of average length, with pointed ends; milk unchanged; gelatin not liquefied.
    3. *Zuberella clostridiiformis-mobilis,* page 127
4. Rods with pointed ends; spinning movement; milk clotted; gelatin liquefied.
    4. *Zuberella nova,* page 127
5. Long rods with 6 to 8 peritrichous flagella; milk unchanged; gelatin not liquefied; saccharolytic.
    5. *Zuberella aquatilis,* page 128
6. Short rods with giratory movement; milk partly clotted; gelatin not liquefied; saccharolytic; fat saponified; nitrites formed from nitrates; produces acetic acid.
    6. *Zuberella constellata,* page 128
7. Rods with pointed ends; spinning movement; not serophilic; lenticular colonies; gas produced; gelatin not liquefied; milk clotted.
    7. *Zuberella girans,* page 129
8. Fusiform rods; highly motile; not obligate serophile; gas produced; lenticular colonies; milk unchanged.
    8. *Zuberell pedipedis,* page 130

B) Species producing no gas.

9. Not serophilic; highly pleomorphic; milk clotted; indole formed; saccharolytic.

9. *Zuberella variegata,* page 130

10. Serophilic; long, slender rods with refringent corpuscules.

10. *Zuberella rhinitis,* page 131

11. Long, slender rods; slowly motile; difficult to grow; obligate serophile; fluffy colonies; no gas produced; non-pathogenic.

11. *Zuberrella shmaninei,* page 131

1. *Zuberella serpens* (Veillon and Zuber) P. 1938.

Synonym: Bacillus serpens Veillon and Zuber 1898; *Bacillus radiiformis* Rist and Guillemot 1904; *Bacteroides serpens* (V. and Z.) Hauduroy *et al.*

Habitat: Digestive tract, especially appendix. Respiratory tract. Middle ear. Contaminated sea water. Frequent.

Morphology: Straight rods with rounded ends, 0.8 μ $\times$ 1.5 to 2.0 μ, occurring in pairs or in short chains. Slowly motile, proceeding by undulation and reptation; peritrichous flagella. Unencapsulated. No endospores. Gram-negative.

Physiology: Strict anaerobe. Opt. T. = 22-37°C. Killed at 56°C. Survives 25 to 30 days. Opt. pH = 7. Neutral red reduced.

Cultural characters: Gas and fetid odor produced.

Deep agar: Very small colonies, lenticular or mulberry-shaped, which degenerate to show divergent offshoots. Gas produced.

Glucose broth: Abundant turbidity; whitish sediment. Gas and fetid odor produced. No H_2S formed.

Peptone water: Indole not formed.

Coagulated proteins: Not attacked.

Gelatin: Turbid; liquefied in a few days; gas produced.

Milk: Acidified, then clotted; gas produced.

Coagulated ascitic fluid or hydrocele fluid: Gaseous growth; no liquefaction.

Brain medium: Blackened.

Carbohydrates: Acid and gas from glucose, levulose, maltose, galactose and lactose.

Biochemistry: Nitrites not formed from nitrates. Produces NH_3, H_2S, volatile amines; aldehydes, ethanol, ketones, acetic and propionic acids.

Pathogenicity, natural: Found associated with other organisms in cases of appendicitis, mastoiditis and pulmonary gangrene.

Pathogenicity, experimental: Putrid pleurisy, fetid suppuration.

2. *Zuberella praecuta* (Tissier) P. 1938.

Synonym: Coccobacillus praeacutus Tissier 1908.

Habitat: Large intestine of the child. Quite frequent.

Morphology: Short rods with pointed ends, occurring in pairs or in chains of 8 to 10 cells. Quite motile. Unencapsulated. No endospores. Gram-negative.

Physiology: Strict anaerobe. Opt. T. = 22-37°C. Killed at 56°C. Survives 8 to 10 days. Neutral red and safranin reduced.

Cultural characters: Gas produced.

Deep agar: Lenticular colonies 1 to 2 mm.; gas and acid produced.

Glucose broth: Turbid; indole not formed.

Gelatin: No liquefaction.

Milk: Unchanged.

Coagulated proteins: Not attacked.

Proteoses: Not assimilated.

Carbohydrates: Glucose only is fermented.

Lipids: Cream is saponified.

Biochemistry: Nitrites formed from nitrates; produces NH_3, H_2S, volatile amines, ethanol, acetic and butyric acids.

Pathogenicity: Non-pathogenic.

3. *Zuberella clostridiiformis-mobilis* (Choukévitch) P. 1938.

Synonym: Bacterium clostridiiformis-mobilis Choukévitch 1911.

Habitat: Large intestine of the horse. Large intestine of man. Uncommon.

Morphology: Rods with pointed ends, 0.75 μ x 2 to 3 μ, occurring in pairs or in short chains. Motile in young cultures. No endospores. Gram-negative.

Physiology: Strict anaerobe. Opt. T. = 37°C. Killed at 80°C. Survives several years. Neutral red reduced.

Cultural characters: Gas produced, but no fetid odor.

Deep agar: Smooth lenticular colonies.

Glucose broth: Abundant turbidity; acid.

Gelatin: No liquefaction.

Milk: Unchanged.

Carbohydrates: Glucose, levulose, galactose, sucrose, arabinose and maltose are fermented.

Potato: No growth.

Biochemistry: Nitrites not formed from nitrates; produces NH_3, volatile amines; ethanol; acetic and formic acids.

Pathogenicity, natural: Isolated from acute appendicitis.

Pathogenicity, experimental: Non-pathogenic for laboratory animals.

4. *Zuberella nova* Prévot 1946.

Habitat: Intestinal tract of man. Uncommon.

Morphology: Rods with pointed ends, 0.6 μ x 2 to 3 μ, occurring singly, in pairs or in short chains; motile; distribution of flagella unknown; spinning movement. No endospores. Gram-negative.

Physiology: Strict anaerobe. Opt. T. $= 37°$C. Killed at 56°C. Opt. pH $= 7.4$. Survives several years when transferred annually. Neutral red and phenosafranin reduced.

Cultural characters: Gas produced, but no odor.

Deep agar: Lenticular colonies, showing eventually a fluffy halo; gas produced.

Peptone water: Slightly turbid.

Glucose VF broth: Abundant turbidity; gas produced.

Gelatin: Liquefaction in 3 weeks.

Milk: Clotted in 8 days.

Coagulated proteins: Not attacked.

Carbohydrates: Glucose, levulose, maltose, galactose and lactose actively fermented; sucrose and sorbitol weakly fermented.

Biochemistry: Nitrites not formed from nitrates; produces NH_3, H_2S, formic, butyric and lactic acids; aldehydes, alcohol; acetyl-methyl-carbinol.

Pathogenicity, natural: Isolated from a case of acute appendicitis.

Pathogenicity, experimental: Non-pathogenic for guinea pig or mouse. No toxin nor hemolysin.

5. *Zuberella aquatilis* (Spray and Laux) P. 1938.

Habitat: Water. Uncommon.

Morphology: Rods, 0.6 μ x 6 to 8 μ, occurring singly or in pairs; filamentous forms; actively motile by means of several peritrichous flagella. Gram-negative. No endospores.

Physiology: Strict anaerobe. Killed at 56°C. Survives 2 to 3 days.

Cultural characters: Gas produced.

Deep agar: No growth.

Egg glucose broth: Abundant growth, broth becoming clear; gas produced; no proteolysis.

Gelatin: Cloudy, spherical colonies; no liquefaction.

Milk: Unchanged.

Coagulated serum: Meager growth; no proteolysis.

Carbohydrates: Acid and gas from glucose, levulose, maltose, galactose, sucrose, lactose, raffinose, xylose, arabinose, mannose, rhamnose, trehalose, salicin, dextrin and starch.

Pathogenicity: Non-pathogenic.

6. *Zuberella constellata* Martres, Brygoo and Thouvenot 1952.

Habitat: Tear gland (Vietnam). Uncommon.

Morphology: Rods measuring 0.5 μ x 1.8 μ; giratory movement; distribution of flagella unknown. Unencapsulated. No endospores. Gram-negative.

Physiology: Strict anaerobe. Opt. T. $= 37°$C. Not thermoresistant. Opt. pH $= 7.4$. Survives 8 to 10 days. Obligate serophile (red blood cell extract may replace serum). Neutral red and safranin reduced.

Cultural characters: Gas but no odor produced.

Serum-deep agar: Punctiform colonies 1 to 2 mm. made up of a lenticular, opaque center surrounded by a constellation of small colonies.

Serum-peptone water: Slightly turbid.

Serum-glucose VF broth: Turbid; sediment; gas produced.

Serum-gelatin: No liquefaction.

Serum-milk: Slow, partial coagulation; fat saponified.

Coagulated proteins: Not attacked.

Carbohydrates: Glucose, maltose and starch actively fermented. Levulose, galactose, sucrose, lactose and glycerol weakly fermented.

Biochemistry: Nitrites formed from nitrates; sulfides not attacked. Fermentation of glucose broth produces pure acetic acid, NH_3, H_2S, aldehydes, ketones and ethanol.

Pathogenicity, natural: Phlegmon of the tear gland in a Vietnamese, accompanied by dacryocystitis.

Pathogenicity, experimental: Non-pathogenic. No toxin nor hemolysin. Fluid cultures will hemolyse red blood cells incorporated in deep agar.

7. *Zuberella girans* (Prévot) Sébald 1962.

Synonym: Fusocillus girans Prévot 1940.

Habitat: Intestinal tract of man; cat. Frequent.

Morphology: Rods with pointed ends, 0.5 to 0.8 μ x 1.5 to 3.0 μ, occurring often in pairs, short chains or filaments; spheroids measuring 1.0 μ x 1.5 μ; metachromatic granules. Giratory motility by spinning movement; no flagella could be demonstrated by special staining methods; the electron microscope shows a reticular membranous expansion which could explain the girations. No endospores. Gram-negative.

Physiology: Strict anaerobe: Opt. T. = 37°C. Resists at 80°C., for 5 minutes. Opt. pH = 6-8. Neutral red reduced.

Cultural characters: Abundant gas formed. Tart odor.

Deep agar: Lenticular colonies, sometimes surrounded by a halo or a constellation of smaller colonies. Agar ruptured by gas production.

Glucose VF broth: Abundant turbidity; inflammable gas (H_2). Tart odor. Acid.

Peptone water: Turbid; gas produced; indole not formed.

Gelatin: No liquefaction.

Milk: Clotted in 2 to 4 days followed by retraction.

Coagulated proteins: Not attacked.

Carbohydrates: Acid and gas from glucose, levulose, lactose, maltose, galactose and arabinose. Three strains out of 5 ferment also sucrose.

Biochemistry: Nitrites not formed from nitrates; produces NH_3; volatile amines; acetylmethylcarbinol; formic and acetic acids; ethanol.

Pathogenicity, natural: Isolated from cases of appendicitis and enterocolitis; gangrenous suppurative processes; actinobacterioses; gangrenous wounds; in the cat, infections with this germ are frequent and may reach the subcutaneous cellular tissue, peritoneum, maxillary bone, thus recalling white-grained actinomycosis.

Pathogenicity, experimental: The guinea pig dies from cachexia after intramuscular injection. No toxin nor hemolysin. Serology: Two serological types without cross-reactions.

8. *Zuberella pedipedis* (Beveridge) Sébald 1962.

Synonym: Fusocillus pedipedis (Beveridge) Prévot 1948.

Habitat: Isolated from foot-rot of sheep. Quite frequent.

Morphology: Slightly curved or spindle-shaped rods, 0.4 to 0.7 μ x 2 to 7 μ, occurring singly, in pairs, short chains or filaments. Actively motile by means of peritrichous flagella. No endospores. Gram-negative.

Physiology: Strict anaerobe. Opt. T. $= 26\text{-}37°$C. Requires atmosphere of CO_2 (5%). Not obligate serophile.

Cultural characters: Gas produced.

Serum-VF deep agar: Lenticular colonies; gas produced.

Blood-VF agar CO_2: Greyish-white surface growth.

Semi-solid agar: Cloudy, flaky turbidity.

Milk: Unchanged.

Biochemistry: No H_2S nor indole formed.

Pathogenicity, experimental: The subcutaneous injection into the rabbit or guinea pig gives rise to inflammation with a nodule persisting 1 month. In association with *Sph. necrophorus* and *Treponema pernortha,* produces foot-rot in the sheep. No hemolysin.

Serology: The homologous serum agglutinates up to 1-120.

9. *Zuberella variegata* (Distaso) P. 1938.

Synonym: Bacillus variegatus Distaso 1912; *Bacteroides variegatus* (Distaso) C. and C.

Habitat: Intestinal tract of man.

Morphology: Pleomorphic rods: short and regular, or long and undulating filaments. Motile. No endospores. Gram-negative.

Physiology: Strict anaerobe. Opt. T. $= 37°$C.

Cultural characters: No gas produced.

Deep agar: Lenticular colonies surrounded by smaller colonies which produce a rosette of lenses. No gas produced.

Glucose broth: Turbid; no gas produced; indole formed.

Gelatin: No liquefaction.

Milk: Massive clot which does not retract.

Coagulated proteins: Not attacked.

Carbohydrates: Glucose and lactose weakly fermented.

Pathogenicity: Not pathogenic.

10. *Zuberella rhinitis* (Tunnicliff) P. 1938.

Synonym: Bacillus rhinitis Tunnicliff 1915.

Habitat: Rhino-pharyngeal cavity of man and animals. Frequent.

Morphology: Long, slender, flexuous rods, 0.3 to 0.5 μ x 5 to 8 μ, curved, undulating or straight. Refringent corpuscules, either free or sessile. Motile in young cultures. No endospores. Gram-negative.

Physiology: Strict anaerobe. Opt. T. $= 37°$C. Killed at 56°C.

Cultural characters: No gas produced. Requires blood or serum. Slow growth.

Deep agar: Small round colonies in 5 days to 1 month.

Glucose broth: Flaky growth.

Milk: No growth.

Loeffler's serum: Growth in the water of condensation.

Potato: Whitish, creamy growth.

Pathogenicity, natural: Isolated from the mucous secretions of acute coryza and rhinitis.

Pathogenicity, experimental: Slight rhinitis by instillation.

Serology: Patient's serum will fix complement.

11. *Zuberella shmaminei* (Shmanine) Sébald 1962.

Synonym: Fusocillus shmaminei (Shmanine) Prévot 1938.

Habitat: Buccal cavity. Quite frequent.

Morphology: Rods with pointed ends, slender, straight, needle-shaped, sometimes curved or slightly undulating. Weakly motile. No endospores. Gram-negative.

Physiology: Strict anaerobe. Opt. T. $= 37°$C. Not thermoresistant. Survives 1 to 2 months.

Cultural characters: Growth has been obtained by a very small number of workers, among which Séguin. Obligate serophile. No gas produced, nor fetid odor.

Serum-deep agar: Flaky colonies. No gas produced.

Serum broth: Turbid; sediment; acid odor, but not fetid.

Serum gelatin: No liquefaction.

Serum milk: Unchanged.

Coagulated proteins: Not attacked.

Carbohydrate: Glucose only is fermented.

Biochemistry: Nitrites not formed from nitrates; produces NH_3, H_2S; volatile amines; aldehydes, ketones; traces of indole; formic and propionic acids.

Pathogenicity: Non-pathogenic.

We can relate to the genus *Zuberella* the following two sub-genera which differ only by the distribution of the flagella.

SUB-GENUS **Zymomonas** (Kluyver and van Niel 1936) emend P. 1960.

Definition.—Gram-negative rods, sometimes ellipsoidal; motile by means of lophotricous flagella. Ferments glucose under anaerobic conditions with the production of CO_2, ethanol and lactic acid. Isolated from fermenting beverages: pulque, palm wine, cider and beer.

Zymomonas anaerobiae (Shimwell 1937) Kluyver 1957.

Synonym: Achromobacter anaerobium Shimwell 1937; *Saccharomonas anaerobia* Shimwell 1950.

Habitat: Plant juice or extract containing glucose; beer and cider.

Morphology: Rods with rounded ends, 1.0 to 1.5 μ $\times$ 2 to 3 μ; rosette-like clusters. Young cells are actively motile by means of lophotrichous flagella. Gram-negative.

Physiology: Strict anaerobic, microaeroduric. Opt. T. $= 30°$C. Killed at $60°$C after 5 minutes. Opt. pH $= 3.4$-7.5.

Beer-glucose agar: (in the presence of CO_2): Irregularly round colonies, 2 mm., in diameter, convex, creamy-yellow to brownish, granular, butyrous.

Glucose beer: Abundant turbidity, heavy sediment.

Glucose yeast extract broth: Growth sedimenting on the walls and bottom of tube.

Glucose beer gelatin: Dense filiform growth; no surface growth. No liquefaction.

Carbohydrates: Glucose and levulose rapidly fermented.

Biochemistry: Nitrites not formed from nitrates. Indole not formed or acetoin.

SUB-GENUS **Succinomonas** nov. gen. Bryant *et al.* 1958.

Definition.—Nonsporeforming anaerobic Gram-negative rods with rounded ends, motile by means of a single polar flagellum, fermenting carbohydrates with production of succinic acid.

Type species: *S. amylolytica nov. sp.*

Succinomonas amylolytica Bryant *et al.* 1958.

Habitat: Rumen of cattle.

Morphology: Rods with rounded ends, 1.0 to 1.5 μ x 1.2 to 3.0 μ, oval, coccoid; intracellular granules showing a bipolar distribution. Motile by means of a single polar flagellum. Gram-negative.

Physiology: Strict anaerobe. Opt. T. $= 30$-$37°$C. Catalase negative.

Cultural characters: No gas produced, or odor.

Deep agar: Lenticular colonies of 0.7 to 1.0 mm.

Agar slant: Smooth, convex, translucent colonies, tan-colored.

Glucose fluid media: Turbid.

Gelatin: No liquefaction.

Yeast extract trypticase: Abundant growth.

Carbohydrates: Glucose, maltose and dextrin are fermented; starch is hydrolyzed.

Biochemistry: Nitrites not formed from nitrates. Produces succinic, acetic and traces of propionic acids.

Taxonomical position: Bryant *et al.* relate this species to the *Pseudo-monadaceae.* As far as we are concerned, they represent a sub-genus of *Zuberella.*

FAMILY III: *SPHAEROPHORACEAE* Prévot 1938.

Definition.—Pleomorphic Gram-negative rods: short forms, filaments, swollen forms, numerous spheroids. No endospores. Three genera:

1. Highly pleomorphic rods, straight or curved; in exudates: ovoid forms showing bipolar staining; in cultures: highly varied shapes: filaments, swollen forms, sausage-shaped forms, branching forms with the constant presence of spheroids of varying size, sometimes quite large, free or sessile, chromaffinic; metachromasia in the elongated cells and especially in the filamentous forms. Non-motile. No endospores. Gram-negative.

    1. *Sphaerophorus[1],* page 134

2. Rods with pointed ends, occurring as a long spindle; spheroids of small size, chromaffinic; metachromasia. Non-motile. No endospores. Gram-negative.

    2. *Fusiformis,* page 146

3. Very long, filamentous rods with rounded or pointed ends; no branching; finely vacuolar cytoplasm; ovoid, spherical or fusiform swellings staining purple with iodine; non-motile; no endospores. Generally Gram-negative, but the metachromatic granules may be Gram-positive in young cultures.[2]

    3. *Leptotrichia,[2]* page 149

---

[1] The use of the term *Sphaeorophorus* for a bacterial genus has been criticized by Breed who recalled that this paronym had been used previously for a lichen. But, according to the legal code of botanical nomenclature, the legal name of a lichen is made up of the botanical names of each of the symbionts: the name of the algae and that of the fungus. Therefore, the term *Sphaerophorus* remains free, since the protistologists do not use it and we shall continue to use it as a generic term in bacteriology.

[2] In 1938, we had proposed the term: *Pseudoleptothrix* for this genus. In 1939, Thjotta, Hartman and Boe published a well-documented study of this genus and established the fact that is corresponds well with *Leptotrichia* Trevisan 1879. We accept this part of their conclusions and adopt the term originally proposed by Trevisan. On the other hand, we cannot accept the unicity of the species of this genus, nor the species proposed in Bergey's 5th edition.

GENUS I: *Sphaerophorus* Prévot 1938.

Highly pleomorphic rods, straight or slightly-curved; ovoid forms showing bipolar staining; swollen, pseudo-branched filamentous forms; free or sessile spheroids of variable size containing masses of nuclear substance; metachromasia in the elongated forms. Non-motile. No endospores. Gram-negative.

This important genus presently comprises 17 anaerobic species of which here is the determinative key:

I. Species producing gas:

A) Not obligate serophiles:

a) Hemolytic (β-hemolysis in deep agar-red blood cells).

1. Lenticular colonies; broth turbid; putrid odor; gelatin not liquefied; milk clotted; nonproteolytic; saccharolytic; indole formed; little or no H_2S formed; pathogenic (agent of necrosis in the muscles and tendons of mammals); weak soluble toxin; hemagglutinating; specific antitoxin.

1. *Sphaerophorus necrophorus,* page 136

2. Lenticular colonies; flaky growth leaving the broth clear; quite fetid odor; gelatin not liquefied; milk slowly clotted; nonproteolytic; saccharolytic; little or no H_2S formed; indole formed; pathogenic (agent of visceral necrosis in man); non-hemagglutinating.

2. *Sphaerophorus funduliformis,* page 132

3. Small, fine colonies; gas produced; broth turbid; fetid odor; milk unchanged; gelatin not liquefied; indole formed; nonproteolytic; saccharolytic; not hemolytic; pathogenic.

3. *Sphaerophorus pseudonecrophorus,* page 138

4. Punctiform colonies; gelatin not liquefied; milk unchanged; pathogenic (agent of avian necrosis).

4. *Sphaerophorus necrogenes,* page 138

5. Spheroids appearing late; lenticular colonies; viscous zooglea in glucose broth which becomes turbid; fetid odor; indole not formed; gelatin not liquefied; milk unchanged; not proteolytic; saccharolytic; feebly pathogenic.

5. *Sphaerophorus necroticus,* page 139

6. Spheroids appearing late; gelatin not liquefied; milk unchanged; abundant formation of H_2S; hydrocele fluid slowly digested; indole formed; lactic acid and ethanol produced; not pathogenic for laboratory animals.

6. *Sphaerophorus peritonitis,* page 139

7. Punctiform colonies; broth turbid; gelatin not liquefied; milk unchanged; indole formed; H_2S produced; saccharolytic; pathogenic.

7. *Sphaerophorus inaequalis,* page 140

8. Lenticular colonies; broth turbid; gelatin not liquefied; milk unchanged; saccharolytic; indole formed; H_2S produced; non-pathogenic.

   8. *Sphaerophorus varius,* page 140

9. Broth not turbid; indole not formed; gelatin not liquefied; milk unchanged; saccharolytic; H_2S produced.

   9. *Sphaerophorus siccus,* page 141

10. Highly complex morphology, exhibiting numerous grotesque forms; broth turbid; gelatin not liquefied; milk clotted; saccharolytic.

    10. *Sphaerophorus ridiculosus,* page 141

B) Obligate serophilic:

11. Lenticular or irregular colonies; sometimes surrounded by a swarm of smaller colonies; fecaloid odor; broth uniformly turbid with viscous sediment; traces of indole formed; H_2S produced; gelatin not liquefied; milk unclotted but digested; pathogenic (viscous lesions); no toxin; causes browning of hemoglobin.

    11. *Sphaerophorus mortiferus,* page 142

12. Lenticular colonies; flaky growth in broth; fetid odor; gelatin not liquefied; proteins not attacked; milk clotted; saccharolytic; indole and H_2S formed; ethanol and butyric acid produced; pathogenic.

    12. *Sphaerophorus pyogenes,* page 142

13. Punctiform colonies; flaky growth with clear broth; no fetid odor; milk unchanged; proteins not attacked; not saccharolytic; pathogenic.

    13. *Sphaerophorus gonidiaformans,* page 143

    II. Species producing no gas:

A) Not obligate serophiles:

14. Cloudy colonies; curdled browth in broth; fetid odor; gelatin not liquefied; milk unchanged; not proteolytic; not saccharolytic; hemolytic; pathogenic.

    14. *Sphaerophorus floccosus,* page 144

15. Lenticular colonies surrounded by smaller satellite colonies; broth turbid; fetid odor; H_2S formed; gelatin not liquefied; milk slowly clotted; proteins not attacked; little or no indole formed; ethanol, butyric and lactic acids produced; pathogenic.

    15. *Sphaerophorus influenzaeformis,* page 144

B) Obligate serophiles:

16. Lenticular colonies; broth not turbid; curdled growth; not fetid; indole not formed, nor H_2S; gelatin not liquefied; milk unchanged; proteins not attacked; not saccharolytic; pathogenic.

    16. *Sphaerophorus caviae,* page 145

17. Broth turbid; gelatin not liquefied; milk clotted; proteins not attacked; saccharolytic; not pathogenic.
17. *Sphaerophorus hypermegas,* page 145

1. *Sphaerophorus necrophorus* (Schmorl) P. 1938

Synonym: Bacille de Schmori; *Bacillus necrophorus* (S.) Flugge; *Streptothrix cuniculi* Schmorl; *Actinomyces cuniculi* Gasparini; *Oospora diphteria vitulorum* L. and N. 1896; *Actinomyces necrophorus* (Flugge) L. and N. 1901; *Streptothrix necrophora* Kitt; *Corynebacterium necrophorum* L. and N.; *Cladothrix cuniculi Macé Bacterium necrophorum* L. and N.

Habitat: Digestive tract and genital organs of herbivorous animals and pigs, necrotic lesions in cattle, ulcerative dermatitis of horses, liver abscess of cattle and pigs. Very frequent.

Morphology: Highly pleomorphic rods; short, straight, oval forms, long filamentous forms, 10-30μ, even 100μ $\times$ 0.7 to 1.0μ swellings, branching, free or sessile spheroids, metachromatic granules; non-motile[1], no endospores; Gram-negative.

Physiology: Strict anaerobe. Opt. T $= 37°C$ (30-40). Killed at 55°C. Opt. pH $= 6$-8.4. Survives 1 to 2 months. Neutral red reduced.

Cultural characters: Gas and fetid odor produced.

Deep agar: Lenticular colonies; gas.

Blood-deep agar: Delicate colonies showing β-hemolysis.

Glucose broth: Turbid; gas; putrid odor; acidified; H_2S not produced or very slight amounts.

Peptone water: Meager growth; indole formed.

Gelatin: No liquefaction.

Milk: Generally coagulated, but not digested.

Coagulated proteins: Not attacked.

Carbohydrates: Acid and gas from glucose, fructose, maltose, lactose, sucrose, galactose, arabinose, mannose, xylose and sorbose.

Biochemistry: Nitrites not formed from nitrates; produces ketones (traces), aldehydes (traces), butyric, acetic, succinic and tartric acids (traces).

Pathogenicity, natural: Necrotic suppurative processes in mammals, especially cattle; ulcerous sore on horse's pastern; diphteria of calves, necrobacillosis of pigs, sheep, etc.

Pathogenicity, experimental: Highly pathogenic. In the guinea pig, subcutaneous injection produces soft edema, eschar and necrosis of the tissues; intravenous injection produces rapid death (12 hours); small doses produce necrotic abscesses of the viscera (especially liver). In the rabbit: local edema, metastases, death. The mouse is highly susceptible: necrosis and death.

---

[1] Schmorl has supposedly observed some motility in young and short forms, but no other worker has been able to confirm this.

Toxin: Exotoxin, endotoxin and β-hemolysin, hemagglutinin.

Serology: Specific agglutination at 1-500; 2 serological groups.

Immunization: Specific by means of soluble toxin.

Antigenicity: Boivin and Mesrobeanu type of lipido-polysaccharide complete antigen shared also by *Sph. funduliformis.*

1. *bis.* **Sph. necrophorus** var. **thermophilus** Sartory and Meyer.

Differential characters: Opt. T $= 45°$C. Nitrites formed from nitrates.

2. *Sphaerophorus funduliformis* (Hallé) P. 1938.

Synonym: Bacillus funduliformis Hallé 1898; *Bacillus thetoides* Rist 1898; *Bacteroides funduliformis* (Hallé) Bergey *et al.*

Habitat: Natural cavities of man, especially female genital organs, contaminated sea water, necrotic lesions and blood of spontaneously infected humans. Very frequent.

Morphology: Highly pleomorphic rods: short, ovoid forms with clear center; long filamentous forms with swellings; sausage-shaped forms; free spheroids of large size; metachromasia; branching; non-motile; unencapsulated; no endospores; Gram-negative.

Physiology: Strict anaerobe. Opt. T $= 26$-$37°$C. Killed at $56°$ C. Opt. pH $= 6.5$-8.0 Survives 3 to 4 weeks. Neutral red reduced.

Cultural characters: Gas and fetid odor produced.

Deep agar: Lenticular colonies; gas.

Glucose broth: Flaky growth which sediments rapidly leaving a clear broth; fetid odor; gas; acidified; indole formed; little or no H_2S produced.

Peptone water: Meager growth; indole formed.

Gelatin: No liquefaction.

Milk: Slow coagulation (8-10 days).

Coagulated proteins: Not attacked.

Bile: Prevents growth of some strains.

Carbohydrates: Acid and gas from glucose, maltose, fructose, galactose, sucrose, arabinose, mannose, xylose and sorbose.

Biochemistry: Nitrites not formed from nitrates; produces compounds with ketonic and aldehyde groups, butyric, acetic, succinic and tartric (traces) acids.

Pathogenicity, natural: Necrotic suppurative processes: otitis, mastoiditis, angina, brain abscess, pulmonary abscess and suppuration, hepatic abscess, acute appendicitis, uro-genital suppuration, peritonitis, purulent arthritis, fatal septicemia with tonsil, intestinal tract, genital tract as starting point.

Pathogenicity, experimental: Subcutaneous injection into the guinea pig produces necrotic abscess; intravenous injection produces fatal septicemia with necrotic abscesses of the viscera, especially of the liver. Subcutaneous injection into the rabbit produces fatal fetid abscess; intraperitoneal injection causes fatal peritonitis. Injection into the monkey produces multiple abscesses of the viscera (necrosis). Intravenous injection into the dog causes fatal septicemia.

Toxin: No soluble toxin; hemolysin active *in vitro:* β-hemolysis around the colonies in blood-deep agar. No hemagglutinin (major differential character with *Sph. necrophorus*).

Serology: Specific agglutination at 1-5,000.

Antigenicity: Boivin and Mesrobeanu type of lipido-polysaccharide complete antigen shared with *Sph. necrophorus.*

3. **Sphaerophorus pseudonecrophorus** (Harris and Brown) P. 1930.

Synonym: Actinomyces pseudonecrophorus Harris and Brown 1927.

Habitat: Natural cavities of man and animals, especially female genital organs. Frequent.

Morphology: Long, slender, irregular, filamentous rods of variable length; isolated elements average 3μ in length; branching; metachromatic granules; non-motile; no endospores; Gram-negative.

Physiology: Strict anaerobe. Opt. T. $= 37°$C. Phenosafranin and neutral red reduced.

Cultural characters: Gas and fetid odor produced.

Deep agar: Punctiform colonies, becoming lenticular and translucent; gas.

Blood deep agar: Small, transparent colonies; no hemolysis.

Serum-broth: Good growth: turbid; fetid odor; indole formed.

Gelatin: No liquefaction.

Milk: Good growth; no coagulation.

Coagulated serum: Not attacked.

Meat: Not attacked.

Carbohydrates: Acid and gas from glucose, fructose, sucrose, maltose and salicin.

Biochemistry: Nitrites not formed from nitrates; produces NH_3, H_2S, volatile amines, aldehydes, ketones, acetylmethylcarbinol, butyric, propionic and lactic acids.

Pathogenicity, natural: Puerperal infections of the woman, post-appendicular suppuration, post-anginal septicemia, brain abscess, purulent arthritis, purulent pleurisy, cervical phlegmon, urinary abscess, lung abscess.

Pathogenicity, experimental: Pathogenic for guinea pig and rabbit (fluid culture, filtrates, washed cells). No hemolysin.

4. **Sphaerophorus necrogenes** (Kawamura) P. 1938.

Synonym: Bacillus necrogenes (Kawamura) W. N.P. 1937

Habitat: Domestic fowl. Quite uncommon.

Morphology: Rods and very long filaments, with swellings; metachromasia; closely resembles *Sph. necrophorus;* non-motile; no endospores; Gram-negative.

Physiology: Strict anaerobe. Opt. T. $= 37°$C. Killed at $58°$C.

Cultural characters: Gas produced. Facultatively serophilic.

Deep agar: Small, punctiform colonies; gas.

Glucose broth: Turbid; gas; sediment and clarification.

Gelatin: No liquefaction; gas.

Milk: No coagulation; cheesy odor.

Pathogenicity, natural: Cause of suppurative necrosis of epizootic nature in domestic fowl, especially hen.

Pathogenicity, experimental: Mouse, guinea pig and rabbit are susceptible: Subcutaneous injection of 0.1 ml. produces local edema and necrotic metastatic abscesses of lung and liver. Intramuscular injection of 0.1 ml. into the pigeon and hen produces purulent inflammation, followed by necrosis and death. Injection into the foot pad reproduces the necrotic phlegmon seen in the epizootic disease.

5. *Sphaerophorus necroticus* (Nativelle) P. 1938.

Synonym: Bacillus necroticus Nativelle 1936.

Habitat: Appendix. Very uncommon.

Morphology: Highly pleomorphic rods: short and slender forms, often with clear center; long forms with ovoid swellings; eventually, very numerous free spheroids make up the entire population of old cultures; metachromasia; nonmotile; no endospores; Gram-negative.

Physiology: Strict anaerobe. Opt. T. $= 37°$ C. Killed at $100°$ C. Survives several months. Neutral red reduced.

Cultural characters: Gas and highly fetid odor produced.

Deep agar: Lenticular colonies; gas.

Glucose broth: Turbid; formation of a very coherent viscous mass; gas; foul odor.

Peptone water: Abundant growth; fetid odor; indole not formed.

Gelatin: No liquefaction.

Milk: Unchanged.

Coagulated proteins: Not attacked.

Carbohydrates: Acid and gas from glucose, fructose, lactose, sucrose, galactose and maltose.

Pathogenicity, natural: Isolated in a case of appendicitis.

Pathogenicity, experimental: Injection of 1.5 ml. into the guinea pig produces a marked edema which invades the thorax and brings about necrosis, followed by an eschar. No toxin. No hemolysin.

6. *Sphaerophorus peritonitis* (Ghon and Sachs) P. 1938.

Habitat: Intestinal tract. Uncommon.

Morphology: Entirely similar to *Sph. funduliformis;* however, the swollen forms, pyriform, barrel-shaped, yeast-like, spermatozoidal, appear later; non-motile; Gram-negative.

Physiology: Strict anaerobe. Opt. T. $= 27$-$37°$C. Survives 8 days.

Neutral red reduced.

Cultural characters: Gas produced.

Deep agar: Lenticular colonies; gas.

Glucose broth: Flaky growth; abundant H_2S formed.

Peptone water: Meager growth; no gas.

Gelatin: No liquefaction.

Milk: Unchanged.

Coagulated hydrocele fluid: Slowly liquefied.

Carbohydrates: Acid and gas from glucose.

Biochemistry: Produces indole, ethanol and acetic acid.

Pathogenicity, natural: Isolated in a case of peritonitis.

Pathogenicity, experimental: Non-pathogenic.

7. *Sphaerophorus inaequalis* (Eggerth and Gagnon) P. 1938.

Synonym: Bacteroides inaequalis E. and G. 1933.

Habitat: Intestinal tract. Very uncommon.

Morphology: Highly pleomorphic rods, either ovoid forms, $1\mu \times 2\mu$, or filaments, 3 to 12μ; slightly curved, winding, swollen; free spheroids, 0.5 μ; non-motile, no endospores; Gram-negative (bipolar staining).

Physiology: Strict anaerobe. Opt. T. $= 37°C.$

Cultural characters: Gas produced.

Deep agar: No growth.

Blood agar: Punctiform colonies;

Glucose broth: Diffuse turbidity; gas; acidified, H_2S formed.

Peptone water: Turbid; gas; indole formed.

Gelatin: No liquefaction.

Milk: Unchanged.

Carbohydrates: Acid and gas from arabinose, galactose, glucose, fructose, lactose, maltose, sucrose and xylose.

Pathogenicity: Non-pathogenic.

8.   *Sphaerophorus varius* (Eggerth and Gagnon) P. 1938.

Synonym: Bacteroides varius E. and G. 1933.

Habitat: Intestinal tract and buccal cavity. Quite uncommon.

Morphology: Rods measuring 1 to 2 μ; ovoid forms; free spheroids; long forms with or without swellings; non-motile; no endospores; Gram-negative (irregular staining).

Physiology: Strict anaerobe. Opt. T. $= 37°C.$ Survives several months. Neutral red reduced.

Cultural characters: Gas and fetid odor produced.

Deep agar: Lenticular colonies, 1 to 2 mm.

Glucose broth: Uniform turbidity; gas; acidified; H_2S formed.

Peptone water: Turbid; gas; indole formed.

Gelatin: No liquefaction.

Milk: Unchanged.

Coagulated proteins: Not attacked.

Carbohydrates: Acid and gas from glucose, fructose, mannose, sucrose, lactose, sorbitol and glycerol.

Biochemistry: Nitrites not formed from nitrates; produces NH_3, H_2S, indole, traces of skatole, volatile amines, aldehydes, ketones, alcohols, acetylmethylcarbinol, acetic, butyric and lactic acids.

Pathogenicity, natural: Isolated from severe fetid sinusitis, abscess, necrotizing peritonitis, purulent pleurisy, septicemia.

Pathogenicity, experimental: Non-pathogenic for guinea pig and rabbit. No hemolysin.

9. *Sphaerophorus siccus* (Eggerth and Gagnon) P. 1938.

Synonym: Bacteroides siccus E. and G. 1933.

Habitat: Intestinal tract. Very uncommon.

Morphology: Short, thick rods, 1μ in length; spheroids; chains of 6 elements; non-motile; no endospores; Gram-negative.

Physiology: Strict anaerobe. Opt. T. $= 37°C$.

Cultural characters: Gas produced.

Deep agar: Hard, coherent colonies, 1mm. in diameter.

Glucose broth: Powdery sediment; clear fluid; H_2S formed.

Peptone water: Turbid; gas; indole not formed.

Gelatin: No liquefaction.

Milk: Unchanged.

Carbohydrates: Acid from fructose.

Pathogenicity: Not pathogenic.

10. *Sphaerophorus ridiculosus* Prévot 1948.

Habitat: Buccal cavity, pleura, intestinal tract, urinary bladder, gall-bladder. Quite frequent.

Morphology: Extremely pleomorphic rods: shuttle-shaped rods: 0.8μ $\times$ 2.5 to 10μ, filaments, spheroids, grotesque forms such as propellers, cup-and-ball spermatozoa; metachromatic granules; non-motile; no endospores; Gram-negative.

Physiology: Strict anaerobe. Opt. T. $= 37°C$. Not thermoresistant. Survives more than 3 months. Neutral red and phenosafranin reduced in 3 days.

Cultural characters: Abundant gas formed; slightly fetid odor.

Deep agar: Lenticular colonies; abundant gas formed.

Peptone water: Turbid; gas.

Glucose broth: Very abundant growth; gas; fetid odor.

Gelatin: No liquefaction.

Milk: Coagulated in 5 days, without retraction of the clot.

Coagulated proteins: Not attacked.

Carbohydrates: Glucose, fructose, sucrose, lactose, maltose and galactose are actively fermented; starch is feebly fermented.

Biochemistry: Nitrites not formed from nitrates; indole not formed, nor skatole; produces NH_3, H_2S (traces), acetic, butyric and lactic acids. Acetoin not formed.

Pathogenicity, natural: Isolated in a secondary infection of an epithelioma of the gum propagating to the maxillary bone; appendicitis; purulent cystitis; cholecystitis; purulent pleurisy; perianal abscess; puerperal and post-appendicular septicemia.

Pathogenicity, experimental: Non-pathogenic for guinea pig and mouse. No toxin. No hemolysin, nor darkening of red blood cells.

11. *Sphaerophorus mortiferus* (Harris) P. 1938.

Synonym: Bacillus mortiferus Harris 1901.

Habitat: Digestive tract of man. Uncommon.

Morphology: Straight rods, $0.6\mu \times 2.0\mu$; coccoid forms with swollen ends; filaments; globular forms; branching; spheroids; metachromasia; non-motile; no endospores; Gram-negative.

Physiology: Strict anaerobe. Opt. T. $= 36.5°C$. Killed at $56°C$. Survives 6 weeks. Neutral red and phenosafranin not reduced.

Cultural characters: Gas and fetid odor produced. Obligate serophile.

Serum-deep agar: Lenticular or irregular colonies; gas. The colonies are sometimes surrounded by a swarm of smaller colonies.

Blood-deep agar: Same aspect; hemoglobin is browned.

Hydrocele fluid-agar: Turbid; viscous, flaky sediment; fetid gas; fecaloid odor; H_2S.

Blood-broth: Turbid; viscous sediment; traces of indole; H_2S.

Hydrocele fluid-gelatin: No liquefaction.

Hydrocele fluid-milk: No coagulation, but digestion.

Coagulated proteins: Not attacked.

Carbohydrates: Glucose, fructose, maltose, galactose, lactose, sucrose, mannitol, sorbitol, glycerol and starch are fermented.

Biochemistry: Produces NH_3, H_2S, volatile amines, aldehydes, acetylmethylcarbinol, acetic, valerianic and lactic acids.

Pathogenicity, natural: Necrotic abscess of the liver, septicemia, purulent pleurisy.

Pathogenicity, experimental: Subcutaneous injection into the rabbit produces a necrotic abscess of the liver with viscous fluid. No toxin.

12. *Sphaerophorus pyogenes* (Buday) P. 1938.

Synonym: Bacillus pyogenes anaerobius Buday 1916; Bela Johan 1922; *Bacteroides pyogenes* (Buday-Bela Johan) Hauduroy.

Habitat: Intestinal tract of man, epidemic necrotic liver abscess among wounded soldiers. Frequent in Hungary.

Morphology: Short, oval rods with clear center; filamentous forms, swollen, fusiform; metachromasia; spheroids; non-motile; no endospores; Gram-negative (bipolar staining).

Physiology: Strict anaerobe. Opt. T. $= 37°$ C. Survives 1 year. Neutral red partly reduced.

Cultural characters: Gas, and slightly fetid odor produced. Obligate serophile.

Serum-deep agar: Punctiform colonies; gas.

Ascitic fluid-glucose broth: Flaky growth, sedimenting rapidly with clear fluid; gas, small amounts of H_2S.

Peptone water: Discrete homogeneous turbidity.

Gelatin: No liquefaction.

Milk: Coagulated.

Liver-broth: Abundant growth; virulent.

Carbohydrates: Glucose, fructose, maltose, galactose, lactose, sucrose, xylose and starch are fermented.

Biochemistry: Nitrites not formed from nitrates; produces NH_3 volatile amines, indole (traces), acetic, iso-butyric and lactic acids.

Pathogenicity, natural: Epidemic of severe septicemia with visceral purulent metastases with a necrotic character, especially hepatic and pulmonary, among wounded soldiers in a Hungarian hospital; post-appendicular septicemia.

Pathogenicity, experimental: Intravenous injection into the rabbit produces septicemia with liver abscess characterized by necrosis and odorless pus. Hemolysin active *in vitro* on sheep red blood cells.

13. *Sphaerophorus gonidiaformans* (Tunnicliff and Jackson) P. 1938.

Synonym: *Bacillus gonidiaformans* T. and J. 1925; *Bacteroides gonidiaformans* (T. and J.) Hauduroy *et al.; Actinomyces gonidiaformans* (T. and J.) Bergey *et al.*

Habitat: Tonsils. Uncommon.

Morphology: Short, pleomorphic rods, $0.5\mu \times 1$ to 3μ, with clear center; round or oval chromaffinic corpuscules (spheroids); metachromasia; filamentous, swollen, branched forms; non-motile; no endospores; Gram-negative.

Physiology: Strict anaerobe. Opt. T. $= 24\text{-}36°$C. Killed at $55°$C after 30 minutes. Resists 4 hours to drying.

Cultural characters: Gas produced. Obligate serophile.

Serum-deep agar: Lenticular colonies, 1 to 5 mm. in diameter.

Glucose broth: Meager growth; gas.

Ascticif fluid-broth: Flaky growth.

Coagulated serum: No liquefaction.

Gelatin: No growth.

Milk: No growth.

Carbohydrates: Generally not fermented. One strain ferments glucose, fructose and maltose.

Biochemistry: Nitrites not formed from nitrates; produces NH_3, H_2S, aldehydes, ketones, indole, skatole, formic and butyric acids.

Pathogenicity, natural: Cryptic tonsillitis, retropharyngeal abscess.

Pathogenicity, experimental: Injection of 1 to 2 ml. into the guinea pig produces a fibrous peritonitis, followed by death in 2 to 3 days.

14. *Sphaerophorus floccosus* (Courmont and Cade) P. 1938.

Synonym: Streptobacillus pyogenes floccosus Courmont and Cade 1900; *Bacteroides floccosus* (Courmont and Cade) Hauduroy *et al.*

Habitat: Natural cavities of man. Quite uncommon.

Morphology: Short, ovoid rods, with clear center; filamentous forms; swollen metachromasia; non-motile; no endospores; Gram-negative.

Physiology: Strict anaerobe. Opt. T. = 37° C. Killed at 55° C. Survives 30 days.

Cultural characters: No gas produced.

Deep agar: Cloudy colonies.

Blood-deep agar: Hemolysis.

Glucose broth: Flaky growth, which leaves a clear fluid; slightly fetid odor.

Blood-broth: Abundant, flaky growth; fetid odor; no gas.

Gelatin: No liquefaction.

Milk: Unchanged.

Coagulated serum: Not digested.

Carbohydrates: Not fermented.

Pathogenicity, natural: Malignant angina with septicemia, lung abscess, and death.

Pathogenicity, experimental: Intravenous injection into the rabbit produces a fulminating septicemia, fatal in 2 days, with visceral congestion, necrotic abscess of the liver with viscous fluid. Injection into the guinea pig produces voluminous pleural abscess, peritonitis. Injection into the dog produces lung and pancreatic abscesses.

15. *Sphaerophorus influenzaeformis* (Russ) P. 1938.

Synonym: Bacillus influenzaeformis Russ 1905; *Bacteroides russii* (Russ) Hauduroy *et al.*

Habitat: Human body. Quite uncommon.

Morphology: Short, oval rods, with clear center; coccoid forms; very long filaments with swellings; highly pleomorphic; spheroids; branching; metachromasia; unencapsulated; non-motile; no endospores; Gram-negative.

Physiology: Strict anaerobe. Opt. T. = 21-37°C. Killed at 55°C. Opt. pH = 6.5-8. Survives 3 to 4 weeks. Neutral red reduced.

Cultural characters: No gas produced.

Deep agar: Lenticular colonies, sometimes surrounded by a swarm of smaller satellite colonies.

Glucose broth: Diffuse turbidity; sediment; H_2S.

Peptone water: Very meager growth; traces of indole.

Brain-medium: Slight blackening.

Gelatin: No liquefaction.

Milk: Slowly Coagulated.

Coagulated hydrocele fluid: No liquefaction.

Carbohydrates: Glucose and mannitol are fermented.

Biochemistry: Produces ethanol, butyric and lactic acids.

Pathogenicity, natural: Perianal abscess, otitic meningitis.

Pathogenicity, experimental: Injection into the rabbit and guinea pig produces an ulcerative local inflammation, followed by wasting and death.

16. *Sphaerophorus caviae* (Vinzent) P. 1938.

Synonym: Streptobacillus caviae Vinzent 1928; *Bacteroides caviae* (Vinzent) hauduroy *et al.*

Habitat: Guinea pig. Frequent.

Morphology: Short rods, 0.3 to 0.5 μ x 1.0 to 1.5 μ, with clear center; very long filaments, with swellings, either free or laterally-sessile; pseudo-branching; metachromasia; non-motile; no endospores; Gram-negative.

Physiology: Strict anaerobe. Opt. T. $= 37°C$. Killed at $55°C$. Survives several months in serum gelatin. Neutral red reduced.

Cultural characters: No gas produced. Obligate serophile.

Serum-deep agar: Lenticular colonies; no gas.

Serum-glucose broth: Clotty growth, with clear fluid; no gas, or odor; no H_2S formed.

Serum-peptone water: Same aspect; indole not formed.

Serum-gelatin: Abundant growth; no liquefaction.

Milk: Unchanged.

Coagulated egg-white: Not attacked.

Carbohydrates: Not fermented.

Pathogenicity, natural: Epizootic, cervival, purulent adenitis of the guinea pig.

Pathogenicity, experimental: Injection into the guinea pig produces a hard, enkysted abscess which opens and eventually heals. Injection into the rabbit produces multiple abscesses, followed by wasting and death.

17. *Sphaerophorus hypermegas* Harrison and Hanson nov. comb.

Synonym: Bacteroides hypermegas Harrison and Hanson 1963.

Habitat: Intestinal tract of the turkey. Quite frequent.

Morphology: Rods of large size, $2\mu \times 15\mu$; highly pleomorphic: swellings, spheroids, filaments, sometimes Gram-positive metachromatic granules and inclusions of volutin. Non-motile. No endospores. Gram-negative.

Physiology: Strict anaerobe. Opt. T. $= 37\text{-}42°C$; slow growth at $45°C$; killed at $49°C$. after some hours, at $60°C$ after 10 minutes. Opt. pH $= 4.8\text{-}8.6$. Catalase-negative.

Cultural characters: No gas produced, or fetid odor. Requires a fermentable carbohydrate.

Glucose broth: Abundant uniform turbidity.

Gelatin: Not liquefied.

Milk: Clotted.

Coagulated proteins: Not attacked.

Carbohydrates: Arabinose, xylose, sorbitol, mannitol, fructose, glucose, mannose, galactose, sucrose, trehalose, maltose, cellobiose, melibiose, lactose, raffinose, and salicin are fermented. (dextrin slowly).

Biochemistry: Nitrites not formed from nitrates; no H_2S formed; produces acetic, propionic and lactic acids, some alcohol and acetone.

Pathogenicity: Non-pathogenic.

Variety described by Goldberg, Barnes and Charles 1964.

Habitat: Cecum of the chick.

Morphology: Slightly smaller size.

Carbohydrates: Glucose, galactose, xylose and mannitol only are fermented.

GENUS II: *FUSIFORMIS* Hoelling emend. 1910.

Definition.—Straight or slightly-curved rods, with pointed ends, appearing as long spindles; spheroids of small size, free in cultures; non-motile; no endospores; Gram-negative; metachromatic granules.

This genus comprises actually 3 anaerobic species:

1. Obligate serophile upon isolation; lenticular or budding colonies; serum-broth turbid; gas and fetid odor produced; not proteolytic; saccharolytic; indole and H_2S formed; pathogenic.
   1. *Fusiformis fusiformis,* page 146

2. Serophile; lenticular colonies; no gas formed; H_2S produced; fetid odor; saccharolytic; chromatinic bodies stainable by fuchsin.
   2. *Fusiformis nucleatus,* page 147

3. Large size; not serophilic; gas and fetid odor produced; hemolytic; pathogenic for the rabbit.
   3. *Fusiformis hemolyticus,* page 148

1. *Fusiformis fusiformis* (Vincent) Topley and Wilson.

Synonym: Bacillus *fusiformis* Vincent 1896; *Fusiformis vincenti* Hauduroy *et al.; Fusobacterium plauti-vincenti* Knorr.

Habitat: Human body; especially buccal cavity, tonsils, lungs and genital organs. Quite frequent.

Morphology: Pleomorphic rods with pointed ends, appearing as long spindles; granular and vacuolar cytoplasm; short forms measuring 2 to 3 μ, long forms 6 to 7 μ and more. Non-motile. No endospores. Gram-negative. Metachromatic granules. Free spheroids measuring 2 to 3 μ.

Physiology: Strict anaerobe. Opt. T. $= 37°$C. Not thermoresistant. Neutral red reduced. Survives 8 to 15 days.

Cultural characters: Some gas produced; obligate serophile on isolation; may become adapted eventually; highly fetid.

Serum-deep agar: Budding, lenticular colonies with branching; very little gas produced.

Glucose broth: Abundant turbidity; granular sediment leaving the supernatant clear; little gas formed; indole; H_2S.

Peptone water: Very meager, flaky growth; indole formed.

Gelatin: No liquefaction.

Milk: Often clotted, but not digested.

Coagulated proteins: Not attacked.

Carbohydrates: Glucose, lactose, maltose and mannitol are fermented by practically all strains; fructose, galactose, arabinose and xylose by a few strains only.

Biochemistry: Nitrites not formed from nitrates; produces NH_3, H_2S, volatile amines; aldehyde, indole, acetic, butyric and lactic acids.

Pathogenicity, natural: In association with the *Treponema,* constitute the fuso-treponemal symbiosis which causes Vincent's angina, hospital gangrene, pyorrhea alveolaris, certain forms of pulmonary gangrene, lung abscess, putrid pleurisy, purulent meningitis, brain abscess; it is also found in association with *Actinobacterium* in human and animal actinobacterioses. During the past several years, the pathogenicity of *Fusiformis per se* has been recognized through finding pure cultures in the same types of infection, preceeded or followed by a septicemic phase in which *F. fusiformis* was found alone.

Pathogenicity, experimental: In association, produces abscesses and gangrenous suppurative processes. Boe has realized an experimental infection in man with the use of pure cultures, obtaining a hot abscess. No lipid-carbohydrate antigen. No toxin nor hemolysin. In pure culture, most of the strains lose their virulence for laboratory animals. But a few strains may still produce local or generalized infections in the mouse, in particular a fatal sero-fibrinous peritonitis.

2. **Fusiformis nucleatus** (Knorr) Bergey *et al.*

Synonym: Fusobacterium nucleatum Knorr 1923. Well individualized, this species has nothing in common with *Sphaerophorus funduliformis.*

Habitat: Buccal cavity; intestinal tract of man. Quite frequent.

Morphology: Rods with pointed ends, 1 to 4 μ; long forms, 0.4 μ $\times$ 7 to 15 μ; occurring singly; 1 to 2 nuclear bodies present in the bacillary body. Non-motile; No endospores. Gram-negative.

Physiology: Strict anaerobe. Opt. T. $=$ 35-37°C. Killed at 60°C after 10 minutes. Opt. pH $=$ 6.8-8.2. Serophilic. Neutral red reduced.

Cultural characters: No gas produced; disagreeable, fetid odor.

Serum-agar: Lenticular or irregularly constellated colonies.

Serum-VF glucose broth: Diffuse turbidity.

Serum-broth liver: Flaky sediment on the pieces of liver after 1 to 3 days. Indole irregularly produced; H_2S formed.

Gelatin: Not liquefied.

Milk: Unchanged.

Coagulated proteins: Not attacked.

Carbohydrates: Glucose fructose, sucrose, lactose and galactose fermented.

Biochemistry: Nitrites formed from nitrates; produces NH_3, H_2S, indole, volatile amines; aldehydes, ketones, acetylmethylcarbinol; valerianic, propionic and lactic acids.

Pathogenicity, natural: Similar to that of *F. fusiformis.* Isolated in pure culture or in association from cases of pyorrhea alveolaris, phlegmon of the floor of the mouth, cellulitis and cervico-facial actinobacterioses, tonsillitis, dental phlegmon, purulent ascitic fluid, pulmonary abscess; putrid and purulent pleurisy, liver abscess following septicemia (fatal case).

Pathogenicity, experimental: Several strains lose their virulence in artificial culture. But others may remain virulent and produce in the mouse and guinea pig local or generalized infections which may be fatal. No toxin, nor hemolysin.

3. *Fusiformis hemolyticus* Beerens and Gaumont 1953.

Habitat: Rabbit. Quite uncommon.

Morphology: Fusiform rods of large size, 8 to 12 μ in length, often filamentous (15 to 20 μ); swellings; free or sessile spheroids; metachromatic granules; non-motile; no endospores; Gram-negative.

Physiology: Strict anaerobe. Opt. T. $=$ 37°C. Not thermoresistant. Survives more than 1 month on Rosenow's medium. Neutral red reduced, phenosafranin partly reduced.

Cultural characters: Slight amounts of gas and slightly fetid odor. Not serophilic.

Deep agar: Irregular and opaque colonies, 3 mm. in diameter.

VF broth: Diffuse turbidity; slightly fetid odor; small amounts of gas.

Rosenow's medium: Abundant growth; gas.

Peptone water $+$ proteose $+$ glucose $+$ pyruvate $+$ brain extract: Slight turbidity; gas.

Gelatin: No liquefaction.

Milk: Unchanged.

Coagulated proteins: Not attacked.

Carbohydrates: Glucose, fructose, sucrose and galactose are fermented.

Biochemistry: Nitrites not formed from nitrates; produces NH_3, H_2S, volatile amines, aldehydes, ethanol, ketones, indole, acetic, butyric and lactic acids. Acetoin not formed. Catalase-negative. Grows in the presence of 1-100,000 gentian violet. Cystein reduced in iron media containing no other carbon source.

Pathogenicity, natural: Single abscess of large size in the rabbit (dorso-lumbar region); may heal spontaneously or produce death through wasting.

Pathogenicity, experimental: Abscess may be reproduced by intravenous injection into the rabbit; Subcutaneous injection into the guinea pig causes purulent pleurisy and pericarditis. No toxin. No hemolysin, but a bone of β-hemolysin may be seen around the colonies on blood agar.

GENUS III: *LEPTOTRICHIA* Trevisan 1879.

Definition.—Long, straight, filamentous rods with rounded or pointed ends; finely vacuolar cytoplasm; no branching; ovoid, fusiform or spherical swellings; stain blue with iodine; metachromatic granules; non-motile; no endospores; Gram-negative. (Not to be confused with *Leptothrix,* an algobacteria of the class *Chlamydobacteriales;* we had proposed the term *Pseudo-Leptothrix* for this genus in 1938; since publication of Thjotta, Hartmann and Boe's work in 1939, who place the following species with the genus Trevisan *Leptotrichia* 1879, we accept this denomination. In addition to the aerobic species, this genus comprises 4 anaerobic species:

1. Serophilic; microaerophilic; ramified, irregular colonies; gas produced; flaky growth in broth; gelatin not liquefied; milk unchanged; saccharolytic.

   1. *Leptotrichia innominata,* page 150

   1. bis. Ochre-colored species.

   1. bis. *L. innominata* var. *ochracea,* page 150

2. Not serophilic; strict anaerobe; circular, flaky colonies; broth turbid; no gas produced; milk unchanged; pathogenic.

   2. *Leptotrichia tenuis,* page 150

3. Facultatively serophilic; very strict anaerobe; lenticular colonies; no gas produced; gelatin not liquefied; milk unchanged.

   3. *Leptotrichia vaginalis,* page 151

4. Small-sized rods; not serophilic; no gas produced; hemolytic; pathogenic.

   4. *Leptotrichia haemolytica,* page 151

1. *Leptotrichia innominata* (Miller) P. 1940.

Synonym: Pseudo-Leptothix innominata (Miller) P. 1938. (This species should not be confused with *Leptotrichia buccalis* (Robin) Trevisan, well-described by Thjotta, Hartmann and Boe, and which is facultatively anaerobic.)

Habitat: Buccal cavity; dental saburra. Frequent.

Morphology: Long rods, 0.8 to 1.4 μ × 5 to 14 μ; occurring in short chains of 2 to 8 elements, winding, irregular, interwined; rounded or pointed ends; vacuolar cytoplasm; no branching; ovoid or fusiform terminal swellings; metachromatic granules; non-motile; no endospores; Gram-negative (with disseminate Gram-positive islets).

Physiology: Microaerophilic. Opt. T = 37°C. Not thermoresistant.

Cultural characters: Gas produced. Obligate serophile.

Ascitic fluid-deep agar: Irregular, medusa-shaped colonies.

Ascitic fluid-glucose broth: Flaky growth; gas.

Smith-Noguchi medium: Turbid; large amounts of gas; foul odor.

Ascitic fluid-gelatin: No gelatin.

Serum-milk: Unchanged.

Carbohydrates: Acid and gas from glucose, fructose, galactose, lactose, sucrose, maltose, inulin, dextrin, raffinose and mannose.

Pathogenicity: Non-pathogenic.

1. bis. *L. innominata* var *ochracea* Mazurek 1955.

Habitat: Bronchial tract of man.

Morphology: Similar to *L. innominata*.

Physiology: Similar to *L. innominata,* except for the following:

Serum-deep agar: Ochre, cottony colonies with opaque center.

Serum-VF broth: Ochre flakes which sediment.

Carbohydrates: Galactose, sucrose and starch are feebly fermented.

Biochemistry: Nitrites not formed from nitrates; produces NH_3, volatile amines, indole, acetoin, acetic, propionic and lactic acids.

Pathogenicity, natural: Isolated in a case of bronchial suppuration and in a case of human bronchial actinobacteriosis.

Pathogenicity, experimental: Non-pathogenic.

2. *Leptotrichia tenuis* (Lewkowicz) P. 1938.

Synonym: Leptothrix anaerobius tenuis Lewkowicz 1901.

Habitat: Buccal cavity of nurslings. Uncommon.

Morphology: Rods measuring 0.2 to 0.3 μ × 2 to 3 μ, forming long filaments (18 to 25 μ), with rounded or pointed ends; swellings at first fusiform, then spherical; no branching; metachromatic granules; spheroids stained blue by iodine; non-motile; no endospores; Gram-negative.

Physiology: Strict anaerobe. Opt. T. = 37°C. Killed after 5 minutes at 60°C.

Cultural characters: No gas produced.

Deep agar: Circular colonies flaky; no gas.

Glucose broth: Uniform turbidity; slow, flaky sediment; disagreeable odor.

Milk: Unchanged.

Pathogenicity, experimental: Non-pathogenic for rabbit and mouse. Injection of 0.2 ml. under the skin of the guinea pig causes death in 3 days, without any lesions.

3. *Leptotrichia vaginalis* Patocka and Reynes 1947.

Habitat: Genital tract of women (Czecho-Slovakia). Uncommon.

Morphology: Long rods, 0.8 μ × 8 μ; occurring singly, in pairs, in long chains, or as very long, slender, winding filaments; pointed ends; granular cytoplasm, giving a vacuolar aspect; Gram-positive metachromatic granules; non-motile; no endospores; Gram-negative.

Physiology: Strict anaerobe. Opt. T. = 37°C. Killed at 65° C. Survives 2 to 3 weeks. Neutral red and safranin are reduced.

Cultural characters: No gas, but fetid odor produced. Facultatively serophilic.

Deep agar: Punctiform, translucent colonies, becoming lenticular, finally budding.

Glucose VF broth: Abundant turbidity; fetid odor.

Peptone water: Slight turbidity. Indole formed.

Gelatin: No liquefaction.

Milk: Unchanged.

Coagulated serum: Partly digested.

Coagulated egg-white: Not attacked.

Fibrin: Partly digested.

Carbohydrates: Glucose, fructose, sucrose, galactose and sorbitol are fermented.

Biochemistry: Nitrites not formed from nitrates; produces NH_3, H_2S, indole, cresol, acetylmethylcarbinol, acetic, butyric and lactic acids.

Pathogenicity, experimental: Non-pathogenic for guinea pig and mouse.

4. *Leptotrichia hemolytica* Bezjak 1952.

Habitat: Intestinal tract of man and female genital organs. Very uncommon.

Morphology: Long, straight rods, 0.6 μ × 1.5 to 3 μ; elongated forms: 6 μ; ovoid swellings on blood agar; rounded or pointed ends; bipolar staining with Giemsa; metachromatic granules in the long forms; non-motile; unencapsulated; no endospores; Gram-negative.

Physiology: Microaerophilic. Opt. T. = 37°C. Short-lived. Not serophilic.

Cultural characters: No gas produced, or odor.

Deep agar: Lenticular colonies.

Blood agar: Small, circular colonies, surrounded by a zone of β-hemolysis.

Glucose broth: Slight, flaky growth; no gas, or odor.

Tryptophane broth: Turbid; indole not formed.

Gelatin: No liquefaction.

Pathogenicity, natural: Isolated in fatal purulent peritonitis following post-abortum septicemia.

Pathogenicity, experimental: Injection of the mouse causes death in 1 month with hepatic, pulmonary and mesenteric abscesses from which the germ may be retrieved. No toxin. β-hemolysin.

FAMILY III.   *BACTERIACEAE* Cohn emend.

Definition.—Gram-positive *Bacteriales.* This family comprises several anaerobic species which may be grouped in four genera:

A) NON-MOTILE SPECIES:

1. Straight or slightly-curved rods; non-motile; unencapsulated; no endospores; Gram-positive; occurring singly, in pairs or in very short chains, and never show pseudo-branching.

   Genus I. *Eubacterium,* page 152

2. Straight or slightly-curved rods; non-motile; no endospores; unencapsulated; Gram-positive; occurring in long chains or filaments.

   Genus II: *Catenbacterium,* page 167

3. Straight or slightly-curved rods; non-motile; unencapsulated; no endospores; Gram-positive; show pseudo-branching.

   Genus III. *Ramibacterium,* page 174

B) MOTILE SPECIES:

4. Straight or slightly-curved rods; motile; unencapsulated; no endospores; Gram-positive.
   Genus IV. *Cillobacterium,* page 178

GENUS I.   *EUBACTERIUM* Janke 1930 emend.

Straight or slightly-curved rods, occurring singly, in pairs or in short chains; non-motile; unencapsulated; no endospores; Gram-positive; never show pseudo-branching. This genus comprises actually 23 anaerobic species of which here is the key for their determination:

A) Gas-producing species:

a) Fetid:

   1. Gelatin not liquefied; milk unchanged; non-proteolytic; non-pathogenic.
      1. *Eubacterium foedans,* page 154

   2. Gelatin not liquefied; milk clotted; non-proteolytic; pathogenic.
      2. *Eubacterium niosii,* page 154

   3. Non-proteolytic, saccharolytic; milk clotted; hemolytic; non-pathogenic.
      3. *Eubacterium rectale,* page 155

   4. Non-proteolytic; saccharolytic; hemolytic; pathogenic.
      4. *Eubacterium obsti,* page 156

   5. Proteolytic (gelatin and milk digested); pathogenic.
      5. *Eubacterium quartum,* page 156

b) Not fetid:

   6. Proteolytic; not fetid; pathogenic.
      6. *Eubacterium quintum,* page 157

   7. Non-proteolytic; saccharolytic; milk clotted; gelatin not liquefied; produces abundant ethanol; pathogenic.
      7. *Eubacterium ethylicum,* page 157

   8. Non-proteolytic; milk clotted; saccharolytic; non-pathogenic; produces abundant butyric acid.
      8. *Eubacterium cadaveris,* page 158

   9. Non-proteolytic; saccharolytic; non-pathogenic; winding.
      9. *Eubacterium torutosum,* page 158

  10. Winding; gelatin liquefied; nitrites formed from nitrates.
      10. *Eubacterium pseudo-tortuosum,* page 159

  11. Non-proteolytic; saccharolytic; milk clotted; feebly pathogenic.
      11. *Eubacterium aerofaciens,* page 159

  12. Non-proteolytic; saccharolytic; milk clotted; feebly pathogenic.
      12. *Eubacterium biforme,* page 160

  13. Non-proteolytic; saccharolytic; gelatin liquefied; non-pathogenic.
      13. *Eubacterium limosum,* page 160

  14. Non-proteolytic; milk unchanged; gelatin not liquefied; saccharolytic; nitrites formed from nitrates.
      14. *Eubacterium nitritogenes,* page 161

B) Non-proteolytic species producing no gas:

  15. Milk clotted; very small size; gelatin not liquefied; pathogenic.
      15. *Eubacterium disciformans,* page 161

  16. Gelatin not liquefied; milk unchanged; toxic, pathogenic.
      16. *Eubacterium poeciloides,* page 162

17. Serophilic; saccharolytic; gelatin not liquefied; pathogenic.
    17. *Eubacterium typhi-exanthematici,* page 162
18. Gelatin not liquefied; milk unchanged; saccharolytic; non-pathogenic.
    18. *Eubacterium ventriosum,* page 163
19. Difficult to grow; non-saccharolytic; pathogenic.
    19. *Eubacterium minutum,* page 163
20. Milk clotted; gelatin not liquefied; saccharolytic; non-pathogenic.
    20. *Eubacterium parvum,* page 164
21. Gelatin not liquefied; milk unchanged; non-saccharolytic; non-pathogenic.
    21. *Eubacterium lentum,* page 164
22. No fetid odor; milk slowly coagulated and partly digested; non-pathogenic.
    22. *Eubacterium crispatum,* page 165
23. Utilizes creatinin as sole source of carbon and nitrogen; produces sarcosin.
    23. *Eubacterium sarcosinogenum,* page 165

1. *Eubacterium foedans* (Klein) P. 1938.

Synonym: Bacillus foedans Klein.

Habitat: Putrefying salted ham; soil of Central Africa. Quite uncommon.

Morphology: Straight or slightly curved rods, 0.4 μ $\times$ 3 to 5 μ; occurring in short chains and sometimes in filaments. Non-motile. No endospores. Gram-positive.

Physiology: Strict anaerobe. Opt. T. $=$ 20-37°C. Difficult to grow. Neutral red not reduced; phenosafranin reduced.

Cultural characters: Gas and fetid odor produced.

Deep agar: Lenticular colonies, becoming fluffy and arborescent.

Glucose broth: Clotty growth with alkaline reaction; gas and fetid odor produced.

Glucose-gelatin: Cloudy colonies; no liquefaction.

Milk: Unchanged; fetid odor.

Coagulated proteins: Not attacked.

Carbohydrates: Glucose, fructose, maltose and galactose are fermented.

Biochemistry: Nitrites formed from nitrates; produces NH_3, H_2S, volatile amines, ethanol, acetone, acetylmethylcarbinol, formic, propionic and lactic acids.

Pathogenicity: Non-pathogenic.

2. *Eubacterium niosii* (Niosi) P. 1938.

Synonym: Bacteroides niosii (N.) Hauduroy *et al.* 1911.

Habitat: Respiratory tract of man. Quite uncommon.

Morphology: Short thick rods, 0.8 to 1.2 μ × 1.0 to 1.5 μ; oval forms with rounded ends; occurring singly, in pairs, in V-formation, in short chains or in clumps. Unencapsulated. Non-motile. No endospores. Gram-positive in young cultures and in pus.

Physiology: Strict anaerobe. Opt. T. = 20-37°C. Neutral red and safranin reduced. Survives 12 to 14 days.

Cultural characters: Gas and fetid odor produced.

Deep agar: Small lenticular colonies, becoming mulberry-shaped. Gas formed.

Glucose broth: Turbid; small quantities of gas; fetid odor; indole not formed.

Tarozzi broth: Abundant turbidity; highly fetid odor.

Gelatin: No growth.

Milk: Clotted in 5 days with retraction of the clot.

Coagulated proteins: Not attacked.

Carbohydrates: Glucose, fructose, maltose, lactose, galactose, sucrose, arabinose and mannitol actively fermented.

Biochemistry: Nitrites not formed from nitrates; sulfites reduced; produces NH_3, volatile amines, acetic, propionic and lactic acids, sometimes ethanol.

Pathogenicity, natural: Putrid purulent pleurisy, dental caries with pulp gangrene.

Pathogenicity, experimental: In the guinea pig and rabbit: fatal purulent pleurisy by intrapleural inoculation; peritonitis by intraperitoneal injection.

3. *Eubacterium rectale* (Grooten) P. 1938.

Synonym: Bacteroides rectalis Hauduroy *et al.*

Habitat: Rectum. Very uncommon.

Morphology: Straight or slightly-curved rods with rounded ends, 0.8 μ × 3 μ. Winding filaments may reach 20 μ. Non-motile. No endospores, Gram-positive.

Physiology: Strict anaerobe. Opt. T. = 37°C. Killed at 56°C. Neutral red and safranin reduced. Longevity marked.

Cultural characters: Gas and slightly fetid odor produced.

Deep agar: Arborescent, spherical colonies measuring 1 to 2 mm.; agar broken up by gas production.

Glucose broth: Abundant turbidity which sediments rapidly; fetid gas and H_2S produced.

Blood broth: Hemolysis in 24 hours; H_2S produced.

Gelatin: No liquefaction.

Milk: Acidified and clotted in 3 weeks; gas produced.

Coagulated proteins: Not attacked.

Carbohydrates: Acid and gas from glucose, maltose, lactose, fructose, galactose, sucrose and glycerol.

Biochemistry: Nitrites not formed from nitrates; sulfites not reduced; produces NH_3 H_2S, indole, formic, butyric and lactic acids.

Pathogenicity, natural: Isolated in mixed culture from a case of ulcerative rectitis and in a case of cervical actinomycosis.

Serology: Specific agglutination at 1-1,000.

4. *Eubacterium obsti* (Obst) P. 1938.

Habitat: Sea water; intestinal tract of Copepods, Schizopods and shrimps, sea fish; may be isolated from canned cheese. Quite common.

Morphology: Short, straight rods. Non-motile. No endospores. Gram-positive.

Physiology: Strict anaerobe. Opt. T. $= 37.5\,°C$. Killed at $65\,°C$. Neutral red and safranin reduced.

Cultural characters: Gas and slightly fetid odor produced.

Deep agar: Discoid colonies, sometimes fluffy, transparent; gas produced.

Blood agar: Discoid colonies; hemolysis.

Blood media: Abundant growth; fetid gas produced.

Peptone water: Slight turbidity.

Glucose VF broth: Abundant turbidity; gas produced.

Gelatin: Liquefied in 3 to 5 days.

Milk: Unchanged.

Coagulated proteins: Not attacked.

Carbohydrates: Gas from glucose by some strains; other strains non-saccharolytic.

Biochemistry: Nitrites not formed from nitrates; sulfites not reduced; produces NH_3, free nitrogen, amines, H_2S, aldehydes, ketones, acetic and butyric acids; indole not formed.

Pathogenicity, natural: Death of marine fish which swell from the gas produced.

Pathogenicity, experimental: Intraperitoneal injection to the guinea pig produces NH_3, free nitrogen, amines, H_2S, aldehydes, ketones, acetic and Mouse: killed in 48 hours by injection of 0.1 ml. Active hemolysin.

5. *Eubacterium quartum* (Rodella) P. 1938.

Habitat: Intestinal tract of the child; pulp gangrene; canned processed cheese; soil of French Guinea. Quite frequent.

Morphology: Thick rods of variable length, with rounded ends; may show coccoid corpuscules. Non-motile. No endospores. Gram-positive.

Physiology: Strict anaerobe. Opt. T. $= 37\,°C$. Killed at $70\,°C$. Neutral red and safranin reduced.

Cultural characters: Gas and fetid odor produced.

Deep agar: Small, round, arborescent colonies.

Glucose broth: Turbid; sediment; abundant gas formed.

Gelatin: Liquefied in 6 to 9 days; sediment.

Milk: Digested in 3 to 5 days; cheesy odor.

Coagulated serum: No liquefaction.

Carbohydrates: Glucose, fructose, maltose and glycerol fermented.

Biochemistry: Nitrites not formed from nitrates; sulfites usually reduced to sulfides, produces NH_3, H_2S, volatile amines, ethanol, formic, propionic, butyric and lactic acids.

Pathogenicity, experimental: Guinea pig killed in 24 hours by intraperitoneal injection.

6. *Eubacterium quintum* (Rodella) P. 1938.

Habitat: Intestinal tract of the child. Uncommon.

Morphology: More or less thick rods of variable length, with rounded ends. Non-motile. No endospores. Gram-positive.

Physiology: Strict anaerobe. Opt. T. $= 37°C$. Not thermoresistant.

Cultural characters: Gas produced, but no fetid odor.

Deep agar: Colonies with opaque center; gas formed.

Glucose broth: Rapid and marked turbidity.

Gelatin: Liquefied in 5 to 7 days.

Milk: Clotted, then digested in 2 to 3 days.

Coagulated serum: Slowly digested.

Pathogenicity, natural: Infantile diarrhea.

Pathogenicity, experimental: Guinea pig killed in 48 hours by subcutaneous injection which gives rise to putrid edema, peritoneal infiltration and acute nephritis.

7. *Eubacterium ethylicum* (Achalme and Rosenthal) P. 1938.

Synonym: B. gracilis ethylicum A. and R. 1906.

Habitat: Human stomach. Uncommon.

Morphology: Straight or slightly-curved rods, slender, occurring singly, in pairs or in short chains. Non-motile. No endospores. Gram-positive.

Physiology: Strict anaerobe. Opt. T. $= 37°C$. Survives a long period of time. Slight reducing powers.

Cultural characters: Gas produced, but not fetid.

Deep agar: Irregular colonies, at first punctiform, eventually measuring 2 mm. in diameter. Some strains show lenticular colonies.

Glucose broth: Flaky growth which sediments, leaving a clear fluid; NH_3 produced; indole not formed.

Peptone water: Same as glucose broth.

Gelatin: No liquefaction.

Milk: Clotted in 5 days; retraction of the clot; gas produced

Coagulated proteins: Not attacked.

Carbohydrates: Gas and acid from glucose, fructose, sucrose, lactose, mannitol, starch and glycerol.

Biochemistry: Nitrites not formed from nitrates; produces NH$_3$, acetic acid as the main fermentation product, sometimes butyric acid and traces of acetic acid, large quantities of ethanol.

Pathogenicity, natural: Isolated from a case of gastritis with nervous disorders.

Pathogenicity, experimental: In the guinea pig: local abscess followed by death after subcutaneous injection. In the rabbit: the same, followed by cachexia and intoxication.

8. *Eubacterium cadaveris* (Buday) P. 1938.

Synonym: Bacillus cadaveris butyricus Buday 1898.

Habitat: Corpses; pond mud. Quite uncommon.

Morphology: Straight rods, 0.6 to 0.7 μ $\times$ 3 to 6 μ; may occasionally produce filaments. Non-motile. No endospores. Gram-positive.

Physiology: Strict anaerobe. Opt. T. = 22-37°C. Neutral and safranin reduced.

Cultural characters: Abundant gas produced.

Deep agar: Snow-flake colonies; abundant gas, breaking up the agar; marked butyric odor.

Glucose broth: Abundant flakes in a clear fluid; gas; acid; H$_2$ and CO$_2$; butyric odor.

Gelatin: Partially and slowly liquefied.

Milk: Abundant growth; gas and rancid odor; coagulated with retraction of the clot.

Coagulated proteins: Not attacked.

Carbohydrates: Glucose and lactose fermented with formation of butyric acid, CO$_2$ and H$_3$. Fructose and maltose and galactose are sometimes fermented also.

Pathogenicity, natural: Non-pathogenic.

Pathogenicity, experimental: One hemolytic strain killed the mouse and guinea pig.

Biochemistry: Nitrites not formed from nitrates in the presence of lactose and galactose; produces NH$_3$, H$_2$S, volatile amines; aldehydes, ketones, alcohols, acetic, butyric and lactic acids.

9. *Eubacterium tortuosum* (Debono) P. 1938.

Synonym: Bacillus tortuosus Debono; *Bacteroides tortuosus* Bergey *et al.*

Habitat: Intestinal tract of man; river mud; canned cheese. Quite frequent.

Morphology: Straight rods of variable size, with rounded ends; winding chains. Non-motile. No endospores. Gram-positive.

Physiology: Strict anaerobe. Growth difficult. Low vitality. Neutral red reduced.

Cultural characters: Little gas produced.

Deep agar: Small, lenticular or irregular colonies, greyish. Small amounts of gas produced.

Glucose broth: Uniform turbidity, coherent, viscid sediment; gas.

Gelatin: Granular growth; no liquefaction.

Milk: Acidified, but not coagulated.

Carbohydrates: Acid and gas from glucose, lactose, sucrose, galactose, fructose, maltose, mannitol and starch.

Biochemistry: Nitrites not formed from nitrates; H_2S not formed; indole not formed; produces NH_3, acetylmethylcarbinol, formic, propionic and lactic acids.

Pathogenicity, natural: Usually non-pathogenic; one strain isolated from a subphrenic abscess.

Pathogenicity, experimental: Generally non-pathogenic; one strain produced a fatal hemorrhagic peritonitis in the guinea pig.

10. *Eubacterium pseudo-tortuosum* Prévot 1946.

Habitat: Intestinal tract of man. Uncommon.

Morphology: Straight or slightly-curved rods, 0.4 to 0.5 $\mu \times$ 3 to 4 μ; occurring as winding chains or undulating filaments. Non-motile. No endospores. Gram-positive, but easily decolorized.

Physiology: Strict anaerobe. Opt. T. $= 37°C$. Not thermoresistant. Opt. pH $= 7.4$. Survives several years. Neutral red and safranin reduced.

Cultural characters: Gas, but no fetid odor produced.

Deep agar: Lenticular colonies; gas produced.

Glucose VF broth: Abundant turbidity; large amounts of gas formed.

Peptone water: Turbid growth.

Gelatin: Liquefaction in 3 days.

Milk: Unchanged.

Coagulated proteins: Not attacked.

Carbohydrates: Glucose, fructose, maltose, sucrose, galactose, sorbitol and starch fermented.

Biochemistry: Nitrites formed from nitrates; produces NH_3, H_2S, formic, butyric and lactic acids, volatile amines, ethanol, aldehyde, acetone and acetylmethylcarbinol.

Pathogenicity, natural: Isolated from a case of acute purulent appendicitis.

Pathogenicity, experimental: Non-pathogenic for mouse and guinea pig.

11. *Eubacterium aerofaciens* (Eggerth) P. 1938.

Synonym: Bacteroides aerofaciens Eggerth 1935.

Habitat: Intestinal tract of man. Quite uncommon.

Morphology: Oval rods, 0.4 to 0.6 $\mu \times$ 2 to 3 μ, with rounded or pointed ends, occurring in chains of 2-10 elements. Non-motile. No endospores. Gram-positive.

Physiology: Strict anaerobe. Opt. T. = 37°C.

Cultural characters: Gas produced.

Deep agar: Coherent colonies 1 to 2 mm. in diameter.

Glucose broth: Slight turbidity.

Gelatin: No liquefaction.

Milk: Acidified, but not coagulated.

Coagulated proteins: Not attacked.

Carbohydrates: Acid and gas from glucose, maltose, fructose, sucrose, and lactose.

Biochemistry: Nitrites not formed from nitrates; H_2S not formed; indole not formed.

Pathogenicity, natural: Non-pathogenic.

Pathogenicity, experimental: In the mouse: Subcutaneous abscess healing spontaneously.

12. *Eubacterium biforme* (Eggerth) P. 1938.

Synonym: Bacteroides biforme Eggerth 1935.

Habitat: Intestinal tract of man. Uncommon.

Morphology: Short oval rods, 0.7 μ × 1.5 μ; occurring singly, in pairs or in short chains. Non-motile. No endospores. Gram-positive.

Physiology: Strict anaerobe. Opt. T. = 37°C. Vitality average.

Cultural characters: Large amounts of odorless gas produced.

Deep agar: Lenticular colonies 2 to 3 mm. in diameter.

Glucose broth: Turbid; acidified.

Gelatin: No liquefaction.

Milk: Acidified and coagulated.

Coagulated proteins: Not attacked.

Carbohydrates: Acid and abundant gas from glucose, fructose, maltose, galactose, mannose, lactose and dextrin.

Biochemistry: Nitrites not formed from nitrates; H_2S not formed; indole not formed; produces NH_3 volatile amines, aldehydes, ketones, acetic, butyric and lactic acids.

Pathogenicity, natural: Non-pathogenic.

Pathogenicity, experimental: Non-pathogenic for the mouse. Subcutaneous injection into the rabbit produces small abscesses.

13. *Eubacterium limosum* (Eggerth) P. 1938.

Synonym: Bacteroides limosus Eggerth 1935.

Habitat: Intestinal tract of man. Very uncommon.

Morphology: Short, oval rods, 0.5 to 1.5 μ × 1 to 5 μ; highly pleomorphic; sometimes undulating. Non-motile. No endospores. Gram-positive.

Physiology: Strict anaerobe. Opt. T. = 37°C.

Cultural characters: Gas produced.

Deep agar: Colonies, 2 to 4 mm. in diameter.

Blood-agar: No hemolysis.

Glucose broth: Mucoid turbidity; final pH 4.8.

Gelatin: Slow liquefaction.

Milk: Unchanged.

Coagulated proteins: Not attacked.

Carbohydrates: Acid and gas from glucose, fructose, manitol and dextrin.

Biochemistry: Nitrites not formed from nitrates; H_2S not formed; indole not formed.

Pathogenicity: Non-pathogenic.

14. *Eubacterium nitritogenes* Prévot 1940.

Habitat: Soil from Adelieland (French Antartica), intestinal tract of the carp, canned cheese.

Morphology: Straight, thick rods, 1.0 μ $\times$ 2.5 to 4.0 μ, with rounded ends; numerous coccid corpuscules. Non-motile. No endospores. Gram-positive.

Physiology: Strict anaerobe. Opt. T. $= 37°$C. Not thermoresistant. Opt. pH 6.5-7.8; acid-tolerant but not acidophilic. Survives more than 7 years. Neutral red reduced.

Cultural characters: Large amounts of odorless gas produced.

Deep agar: Lenticular colonies; gas.

Glucose VF broth: Abundant turbidity; gas.

Peptone water: Turbid growth; gas.

Gelatin: No liquefaction.

Milk: Unchanged.

Carbohydrates: Glucose and fructose actively fermented; sucrose and lactose weakly fermented.

Biochemistry: Nitrites formed from nitrates; H_2S not formed; indole not formed; produces volatile amines, propionic, butyric and lactic acids; acetylmethylcarbinol not formed.

Pathogenicity, natural: One strain isolated from a pleural fluid was slightly hemolytic and pathogenic.

Pathogenicity, experimental: Non-pathogenic for the mouse and the guinea pig. No toxin nor hemolysin.

15. *Eubacterium disciformans* (Massini) P. 1938.

Synonym: Bacillus disciformans Massini 1913.

Habitat: Respiratory tract, liver, skin. Frequent.

Morphology: Small, oval, rods, with rounded ends; 0.3 to 0.4 μ $\times$ 0.5 to 0.7 μ, occurring singly, in pairs or in small clumps. Non-motile. No endospores. Gram-positive (easily decolorized).

Physiology: Strict anaerobe. Opt. T. $= 37°$C. Killed at 56°C. Survives 10 to 30, days. Neutral red not reduced.

Cultural characters: No gas produced.

Lactose-deep agar: Punctiform colonies, becoming lenticular, growing as a thin disc in the upper portion of the agar; no gas.

Glucose broth: Fine, flaky growth which sediments, leaving a clear fluid. Indole not formed.

Gelatin: No growth.

Milk: Slowly coagulated.

Brain medium: No blackening.

Ereptone broth: Acidified.

Glucose agar broth: Acidified.

Carbohydrates: Glucose, fructose, maltose, lactose, sucrose, galactose, arabinose, manitol and starch are fermented.

Biochemistry: Nitrites not formed from nitrates; produces NH_3, formic, acetic and propionic acids.

16. *Eubacterium peociloides* (Roger and Garnier) P. 1938.

Synonym: Bacillus poeciloides Roger and Garnier; *Bacteroides poeciloides* (R. and G.) Hauduroy *et al.*

Habitat: Intestinal tract of man. Uncommon.

Morphology: Straight or slightly-curved rods, 0.8 μ $\times$ 3.0 μ, with rounded ends (sometimes pointed); occurring singly, in pairs or in small masses (V and L shapes)., Non-motile. No endospores. Gram-positive.

Physiology: Strict anaerobe. Opt. T. $=$ 37-38°C.

Cultural characters: No gas produced.

Deep agar: Small punctiform colonies, becoming confluent.

Glucose broth: Turbidity, which sediments.

Gelatin: No liquefaction.

Milk: No growth.

Potato: No growth.

Pathogencity, natural: Isolated from a case of intestinal occlusion.

Pathogenicity, experimental: Low virulence, but toxigenic; a sterile filtrate kills the guinea pig by progressive cachexia. The rabbit is killed in 5 days by the intravenous injection of 1 ml., without any apparent lesion (intoxication).

Note.—This species clearly differs from *R. ramosum* which produces gas, coagulates milk and has distinct morphological features.

17. *Eubacterium typhi-exanthematici* (Plotz) P. 1938.

Synonym: Bacillus typhi exanthematici Plotz 1914; *Corynebacterium typhi exanthematici* (Plotz) Hewlett.

Habitat: Intestinal tract of man. Quite uncommon.

Morphology: Straight or slightly-curved rods, 0.2 to 0.6 μ $\times$ 1 to 2 μ; pleomorphic (coccoid and involution forms). Non-motile. No endospores. Gram-positive.

Physiology: Strict anaerobe: Killed at 55°C. Filters through Berkefeld N. Obligate serophile.

Cultural characters: No gas produced.

Deep agar: Fluffy colonies.

Glucose broth: Flaky growth, leaving a clear fluid.

Gelatin: No growth.

Milk: Slightly acid.

Carbohydrates: Glucose, maltose, galactose and inulin are fermented.

Pathogenicity, natural: Isolated in cases of exanthematic typhus (secondary invader).

Pathogenicity, experimental: In the guinea pig: High temperature followed by death. Virulence rapidly lost.

Serology: The patient's serum contains agglutinins and precipitins.

18. *Eubacterium ventriosum* (Tissier) P. 1938.

Synonym: Bacillus ventriosus Tissier.

Habitat: Intestinal tract of the child and dog; buccal cavity of man. Quite frequent.

Morphology: Small, slender rigid rods, with square ends; occurring singly or in pairs, sometimes in long chains. Show a central swelling. Non-motile. No endospores. Gram-positive.

Physiology: Strict anaerobe. Opt. T. $= 37$°C. Survives 4 days only. Reducing powers variable.

Cultural characters: No gas produced; some strains are serophilic.

Deep agar: Small, lenticular colonies 2 to 3 mm. in diameter.

Broth: Slight, powdery turbidity.

Gelatin: No liquefaction.

Milk: Unchanged generally, but precipitated by some strains.

Carbohydrates: Glucose, fructose, galactose, maltose and sucrose are fermented.

Biochemistry: Nitrites not formed from nitrates; H_2S not formed; indole not formed; produces acetic acid alone or along with butyric and lactic acids; NH_3, volatile amines, aldehydes, ketones.

Pathogenicity, natural: Isolated from pulmonary abscess, purulent pleurisy, cervicitis, buccal abscess.

Pathogenicity, experimental: Non-pathogenic for laboratory animals.

Note.—Identical with *E. oviforme* (Tissier) P. 1938.

19. *Eubacterium minutum* (Tissier) P. 1938.

Synonym: Bacillus anaerobicus minutus Tissier; *Bacteroides minutus* (T.) Hauduroy *et al.*

Habitat: Intestinal tract of breast-fed infants. Uncommon.

Morphology: Very slender, straight rods, with rounded ends; 2 to 4 μ; occurring singly or in pairs. Non-motile. No endospores. Gram-positive.

Physiology: Strict anaerobe. Opt. T. = 37°C. Survives more than 2 weeks.

Cultural characters: No gas produced.

Deep agar: Delicate, irregular, oval colonies.

Glucose broth: Poor growth; slight turbidity.

Pathogenicity, natural: Isolated from a severe case of infantile diarrhea.

Pathogenicity, experimental: In the mouse: death in 12 days by intoxication.

20. *Eubacterium parvum* (Choukévitch) P. 1938.

Synonym: Coccobacillus anaerobicus parvus Choukévitch 1911.

Habitat: Intestinal tract of foal and man. Quite uncommon.

Morphology: Small, oval rods, 0.5 μ $\times$ 1.0 to 1.5 μ; occurring singly or in pairs; may produce filamentous forms. Non-motile. No endospores. Gram-positive.

Physiology: Strict anaerobe. Opt. T. = 37°C. Survives several years. Neutral red and phenosafanin reduced.

Cultural characters: No gas produced.

Deep agar: Small, lenticular colonies.

Glucose broth: Abundant turbidity; heavy sediment.

Gelatin: No liquefaction.

Milk: Coagulated in 20 to 25 days. Some strains coagulate more rapidly. No retraction of the clot.

Coagulated proteins: Not attacked.

Carbohydrates: Glucose, fructose, maltose, galactose and lactose are fermented.

Biochemistry: Nitrites not formed from nitrates; produces NH_3, aldehydes, alcohols, ketones, acetylmethylcarbinol, formic, butyric and lactic acids.

Pathogenicity, natural: Insolated in acute appendicitis, purulent pleurisy.

Pathogenicity, experimental: Non-pathogenic.

21. *Eubacterium lentum* (Eggerth) P. 1938.

Synonym: Bacteroides lentus Eggerth 1935.

Habitat: Normal human feces. Quite frequent.

Morphology: Short, oval rods, 0.5 to 1.0 μ $\times$ 2 to 3 μ; pleomorphic: coccoids forms and spindles measuring 6 μ; occurring in chains. Non-motile. No endospores. Gram-positive.

Physiology: Strict anaerobe. Opt. T. = 37°C.

Cultural characters: No gas produced.

Blood-deep agar: Small, non-hemolytic colonies 0.25 to 0.75 mm.

Gelatin: No liquefaction.

Milk: Unchanged.

Coagulated proteins: Not attacked.
Carbohydrates: Not attacked.
Biochemistry: Indole not formed; traces of H_2S produced.
Pathogenicity: Non-pathogenic.

22. *Eubacterium crispatum* Brygoo and Aladame 1953.

Habitat: Buccal cavity.
Morphology: Straight or slightly-curved rods, 1.0 μ $\times$ 3.0 μ; occurring singly or in winding and looped chains measuring 20 to 40 μ. Non-motile. No endospores. Gram-positive.
Physiology: Strict anaerobe. Not thermoresistant. Survives 1 month. Neutral red reduced. Serophilic on isolation.
Cultural characters: No gas, or odor produced.
Deep agar: Punctiform colonies.
Glucose VF broth: Abundant, uniform turbidity.
Peptone water: Discrete turbidity.
Gelatin: No liquefaction.
Milk: Slowly coagulated, partially digested.
Coagulated proteins: Not attacked.
Carbohydrates: Glucose, fructose, maltose, sucrose, lactose, galactose and starch are fermented.
Biochemistry: Nitrites not formed from nitrates; sulfides not reduced; produces NH_3, acetic and lactic acids. Urease-negative.
Pathogenicity, natural: Isolated in a phlegmon of dental origin.
Pathogenicity, experimental: Non-pathogenic. No toxin, or hemolysin.

23. *Eubacterium sarcosinogenum* Szulmajster and Kaiser 1960.

Habitat: Mud of the Louisiana bayou.
Isolation: On selective media containing creatinin.
Morphology: Rods 0.3 to 0.4 μ $\times$ 0.8 to 1.2 μ; occurring singly, in pairs or in short chains, sometimes in clumps. Non-motile. No endospores. Gram-positive (in 24-hour old cultures).
Physiology: Very strict anaerobe. Opt. T. $=30°C$. Killed at $56°C$ after 5 minutes. Opt. T. $=7.0$. Terminal pH in VF broth $+$ creatinin $=$ 8.5-9.0. Neutral red temporarily reduced. Catalase feebly positive.
Cultural characters: No gas, or fetid odor produced. Good growth is obtained only in media containing creatinin.
Creatinin-deep agar: Small, circular. whitish colonies; formation of crystals of sarcosin.
Creatinin-VF broth: Turbid; sediment; crystals of sarcosin.
Peptone water: No growth.
Gelatin: No liquefaction.
Milk: Unchanged. Milk added with creatinin is slowly digested (1 month).

Coagulated proteins: Not attacked.

Carbohydrates: Not attacked. In semi-synthetic media, glucose and sucrose are utilized.

Biochemistry: Nitrites not formed from nitrates; sulfites not reduced; in creatinin broth, produces 1.76g of volatile acids (20 parts acetic, 1 part formic and 1 part valeric), 1.53g. NH_3 and some acetone. Dissimilates and decarboxyaltes creatinin to produce sarcosin, NH_3 and CO_2.

Pathogenicity: Non-pathogenic for mice and guinea pigs.

Sub-genus *Butyribacterium* Barker and Haas 1944.

Definition.—Straight or slightly-curved rods; non-motile; Gram-positive; anaerobic to microaerophilic; ferments carbohydrates and lactic acid to produce CO_2, acetic and butyric acids; generally catalase-negative, but sometimes weakly positive. Habitat: intestinal tract of vertebrates.

Type species: *Butyribacterium rettgeri.*

1. *Butyribacterium rettgeri* Barker and Haas.

Synonym: Eubacterium rettgeri (B. and H) Prévot 1948.

Habitat: Intestinal tract of man and rat. Quite uncommon.

Morphology: Straight or slightly-curved rods, $0.7 \mu \times 2$ to 3μ; occurring singly, in pairs or in short chains. No branching, but sometimes swellings. Non-motile. No endospores. Gram-positive.

Physiology: Strict anaerobe. Opt. $T. = 37°C$; grows at 15-45°C. Resists at 60°C for 30 minutes at 70°C for 10 minutes. Neutral red and safranin reduced. Catalase-negative.

Cultural characters: Slightly fetid odor and gas produced.

Deep agar: Lenticular colonies; gas produced.

Glucose cystein agar: Circular, convex, smooth, finely granular colonies with delicately irregular border and opaque center; greyish-white with yellowish tinge.

Glucose broth: Abundant turbidity; sediment.

Peptone water: Turbid.

Glucose gelatin: No liquefaction.

Milk: Unchanged.

Coagulated proteins: Not attacked.

Carbohydrates: Acid and gas from glucose, maltose, fructose, glycerol and lactates.

Biochemistry: Nitrites not formed from nitrates; sulfites not reduced; produces NH_3, traces of H_2S, traces of indole, volatile amines, CO_2, acetic and butyric acids. Synthetisizes acetic acid from CO_2.

Pathogenicity: Non-pathogenic.

Sub-genus *Zymobacterium* Wachsman and Barker 1954.

Definition.—Straight rods, occurring singly or in short chains; non-motile; Gram-positive; anaerobic to microaerophilic; catalase-negative;

ferment carbohydrates. CO_2 and ethanol are produced from glucose with small quantities of acetic, formic and lactic acids.

Type species: Zymobacterium oroticum Wachsman and Baker 1954.

Zymobacterium oroticum nov. comb.

Synonym: Eubacterium oroticum Wachsman and Barker 1954.

Habitat: Isolated from bay mud.

Morphology: Rods, with pointed ends; 0.3 to 0.6 μ $\times$ 1.2 to 2.0 μ; occurring in intertwined chains. Non-motile. Gram-positive.

Physiology: Anaerobic to microaerophilic.

Cultural characters: Gas produced.

Yeast extract-glucose-tryptone broth: Rods with pointed ends, becoming ovoid.

Yeast extract-glucose-tryptone agar: Small, circular, convex colonies.

Gelatin: No liquefaction.

Milk: No growth.

Media containing orotic acid: Circular, convex colonies.

Carbohydrates: Acid and gas from glucose, fructose, sucrose, lactose, maltose, arabinose, galactose and mannitol.

Biochemistry: Nitrites not formed from nitrates; indole not formed; produces NH_3, CO_2, ethanol and acetic acid. Ferments orotic acid. Catalase-negative.

GENUS II: *CATENABACTERIUM* Prévot 1938.

Definition.—Straight or slightly-curved rods, non-motile, un-encapsulated, non-sporeforming, Gram-positive, showing no pseudo-branching, occurring usually in long chains or as filaments.

This genus actually comprises eleven species:

A) Species producing gas:
1. Large-sized arborescent colonies; non-proteolytic; saccharolytic; rancid odor; pyogenic.
   1. *Catenabacterium helminthoides,* page 168
2. Lenticular colonies; gelatin not liquefied; milk unchanged;
   2. *Catenabacterium contortum,* page 169
3. Gelatin not liquefied; milk coagulated.
   3. *Catenabacterium ruminantium,* page 169
4. White lenticular colonies; peptolytic; saccharolytic; non-pathogenic.
   4. *Catenabacterium filamentosum,* page 169
5. Lenticular colonies; putrid odor; non-saccharolytic; gelatin liquefied; milk coagulated; surface colonies exhibit giratory movement.
   5. *Catenabacterium rotans,* page 170

6. Swollen rods; obligate serophile; gelatin not liquefied; carbohydrates fermented.

   6. *Catenabacterium saburreum,* page 171

b) Species not producing gas:

7. White lenticular colonies; peptolytic; gelatinolytic; milk coagulated; saccharolytic; indole formed; pathogenic.

   7. *Catenabacterium lottii,* page 171

8. Lenticular or irregular colonies; viscous growth in fluid media; non-proteolytic; saccharolytic; non-pathogenic.

   8. *Catenabacterium catenaforme,* page 172

9. Black lenticular colonies; fetid odor; peptolytic; saccharolytic; pathogenic.

   9. *Catenabacterium nigrum,* page 172

10. Arborescent colonies; hemoglobinophilic; saccharolytic; non-pathogenic.

   10. *Catenabacterium leptotrichoides,* page 173

11. Swollen pleomorphic rods; ferment hemicellulose.

   11. *Catenabacterium hemicellulolyticum,* page 173

1. *Catenabacterium helminthoides* (Lewkowicz) P. 1938.

Synonym: Bacillus helminthoides Lewkowicz.

Habitat: Buccal cavity of the nursling; pond mud. Quite uncommon.

Morphology: Straight rods with rounded ends, or S-shaped forms, occurring as long filaments, 0.7 to 1.0 μ $\times$ 3 to 20 μ; fusiform or spherical swellings. Non-motile. No endospores. Gram-positive.

Physiology: Strict anaerobe. Opt. T. $= 37°$C. Killed at $60°$C. Survives 6-7 days, sometimes 3 months. Neutral red and phenosafranin reduced.

Cultural characters: Gas produced.

Deep agar: Fluffy, arborescent colonies, 3 to 5 mm. in diameter. Agar broken up by gas; rancid odor; acidified.

Glucose broth: Turbid; flaky sediment; abundant gas; rancid odor; acidified.

Gelatin: Liquefaction.

Milk: Acidified, but not clotted; gas; rancid odor.

Coagulated proteins: Not attacked.

Carbohydrates: Glucose, maltose, sucrose, sorbitol, mannitol and glycerol are fermented.

Biochemistry: Nitrites not formed from nitrates; produces NH_3, H_2S, alcohols, acetylmethylcarbinol, formic, butyric and lactic acids.

Pathogenicity, natural: Feebly pathogenic, or non-pathogenic.

Pathogenicity, experimental: In the rabbit: small abscesses.

2. *Catenabacterium contortum* Prévot 1947.

Habitat: Intestinal tract of man. Uncommon.

Morphology: Rods, 0.5 to 7 μ $\times$ 3 to 4 μ; occurring in long twisted chains of 30-50 or more elements. Non-motile. No endospores. Gram-positive.

Physiology: Strict anaerobe. Opt. T. = 37°C. Not thermoresistant. Survives for a long period of time. Neutral red reduced.

Cultural characters: Gas, but no fetid odor produced.

Deep agar: Lenticular colonies; gas produced.

Glucose broth: Slow, clotty growth; gas.

Gelatin: No liquefaction.

Milk: Unchanged.

Coagulated proteins: Not attacked.

Carbohydrates: Acid and gas from glucose, fructose, maltose, galactose, sucrose, xylose and arabinose.

Biochemistry: Nitrites not formed from nitrates; produces NH_3, indole, volatile amines, aldehydes, alcohols, acetylmethylcarbinol, formic, propionic and lactic acids.

Pathogenicity, natural: Isolated in two cases of putrid gangrenous appendicitis.

Pathogenicity, experimental: The intramuscular injection of 1 ml. of one of the strains killed a guinea pig by a toxic gelatinous edema. No toxin, or hemolysin.

3. *Catenabacterium ruminantium* Stellmach-Helwig 1960.

Habitat: Rumen of sheep.

Morphology: Rods; non-motile; Gram-positive. Very long filaments on agar media.

Physiology: Strict anaerobe. Opt. T. = 37° C. Not thermoresistant. Does not require CO_2 ,but growth enhanced by it.

Cultural characters: Pure cultures very difficult to obtain; gas produced.

Gelatin: No liquefaction.

Milk: Coagulated; no digestion.

Carbohydrates: Acid and gas from glucose, lactose, galactose, maltose, mannose, fructose, sucrose and starch.

Biochemistry: Nitrites formed from nitrates; indole not formed; acetoin not formed; produces H_2S. Citrates not utilized.

Systematic position: Related to *Catenabacterium contortum*.

4. *Catenabacterium filamentosum* (Jungano) P. 1938.

Habitat: Intestinal tract of the rat; natural cavities of man. Quite frequent.

Morphology: Large rods, with rounded ends; pleomorphic: short and swollen forms, long and undulating forms; bifurcations. Non-motile. No endospores. Gram-positive.

Physiology: Strict anaerobe. Opt. T $= 37°$ C. Survives several years. Neutral red reduced.

Cultural characters: Small quantities of gas formed (appear only when tube is shaken).

Deep agar: Quite large, lenticular colonies; small quantities of gas.

Glucose broth: Turbid; small quantities of gas; indole not formed.

Gelatin: No liquefaction.

Milk: Clotted.

Peptone water: Slight turbidity.

Coagulated proteins: Not attacked.

Carbohydrates: Glucose, fructose, maltose, galactose, lactose and sucrose are fermented.

Biochemistry: Nitrites not formed from nitrates; produces NH_3, volatile amines; ethanol, acetylmethylcarbinol, acetic and lactic acids (with traces of formic and propionic).

Pathogenicity, natural: Isolated in acute appendicitis, lung abscess, putrid pleurisy, uterine suppurative process.

Pathogenicity, experimental: Non-pathogenic for mouse or guinea pig.

5. *Catenabacterium rotans* Patocka and Sebek 1951.

Habitat: Genital tract of the woman.

Morphology: Short rods, 2 to 3.5 μ, occurring in long chains, sometimes winding, sometimes double, or as unsegmented filaments measuring 30 to 60 μ. Filaments may show piriform swellings containing large amounts of deoxyribonucleic acid. In old cultures, may be seen granules, spheroidal or elliposoidal bodies (yeast-like) made up of lipid material. Non-motile. No endospores. Gram-positive.

Physiology: Strict anaerobe. Opt. T. $= 35°$ C. Resists at $70°$ C for 30 minutes, but is killed at $80°C$.

Cultural characters: Abundant gas formed; highly putrid odor.

Deep agar: Lenticular colonies, sometimes budding, 3 mm. in diameter.

Blood agar (Fortner's method using *S. marcescens* as reducing agent): Motile colonies forming rings, double rings or 8-figures; young colonies measuring about 150 μ in diameter make a complete circle in 1½ to 2 minutes.

VF broth: Diffuse turbidity which sediments rapidly to leave a clear fluid; acidified to pH 6.0-6.2.

Gelatin: Liquefaction in 14 days.

Milk: Slowly and incompletely coagulated.

Coagulated proteins: Not attacked.

Carbohydrates: Slight acid formation from glucose, fructose, maltose and arabinose.

Biochemistry: Nitrites formed from nitrates; traces of NH_3, H_2S and indole formed.

Pathogenicity, natural: Unknown.

Pathogenicity, experimental: In recently isolated culture, will produce abscess formation and purulent meningitis; older cultures are non-pathogenic.

6. *Catenabacterium saburreum* Theilade and Gilmour 1961.

Habitat: Bucco-dental saburra.

Morphology: Short straight rods or slightly-curved filaments, with rounded ends, 1.0 to 1.2 μ $\times$ 15 to 35 μ; or long rods, 8 to 10 μ, occurring in chains of 2 to 6 cells. Some filaments may measure 100 to 200 μ, sometimes undulating or spirally-wound. Non-motile. No pseudo-branching. No endospores. Oval swellings, centrally or sub-terminally located. Gram-positive (becoming Gram-negative from the fifth day).

Physiology: Strict anaerobe. Obligate serophile. Catalase-positive. Terminal pH 4.7-5.5.

Cultural characters: Require an atmosphere containing 5% CO_2 and 95% N_2.

Blood agar (Douglas) in vacuo: Circular or oval colonies, 1 to 4 mm. in diameter, humid, translucent, with rhizoid border and granular, slightly raised center. The hairy filaments are made up of parallel intertwined filaments or of chains.

Brain-heart agar + 8.2% yeast extract + 5% serum: Denser, more granular colonies.

Liquid media: Long, light, hairy growth adhering to the walls of the tube.

Gelatin: No liquefaction.

Carbohydrates: Acid and CO_2 from glucose, fructose, galactose, mannose, lactose, raffinose, xylose and a-methylglucoside. Starch not hydrolyzed.

Biochemistry: Nitrites not formed from nitrates; acetoin not formed; H_2S not formed; produces indole.

7. *Catenabacterium lottii* (Lotti) P. 1938.

Habitat: Intestinal tract of man, especially appendix.

Morphology: Long, thin, straight rods, 3 to 4 μ, occurring in short chains or as very long filaments. Non-motile. No endospores. Gram-positive.

Physiology: Strict anaerobe. Opt. T. $=37°C$. Killed at 70° C. Survives 45 days.

Cultural characters: No gas produced.

Deep agar: Lenticular colonies.

Glucose broth: Turbid, with viscid sediment; no odor produced; acidified; traces of indole formed.

Gelatin: Liquefaction.

Milk: Coagulation.

Coagulated proteins: Not attacked.

Carbohydrates: Glucose only is fermented.

Pathogenicity, natural: Isolated in appendicitis.

Pathogenicity, experimental: In the guinea pig: multiple abscesses, cachexia and death.

8. *Catenabacterium catenaforme* (Eggerth) P. 1938.

Synonym: Bacteroides catenaformis Eggerth 1935.

Habitat: Intestinal tract of man, buccal cavity, and lung. Quite frequent.

Morphology: Slender rods, 0.3 to 0.5 μ, $\times$ 2 to 3.5 μ, occurring in long chains of 20-100 elements having an aspect of unsegmented filaments; globular swellings, 2 to 3 μ. Non-motile. No endospores. Gram-positive.

Physiology: Strict anaerobe. Opt. T. $= 37°$C. Neutral red and phenosafranin not reduced.

Cultural characters: No gas produced.

Deep agar: Irregular or lenticular colonies 2 to 3 mm. in diameter.

Glucose broth: Viscous zoogloea at the bottom of the tube, leaving a clear supernatant; acidified; indole not formed; H_2S not formed.

Gelatin: No liquefaction.

Milk: Unchanged. Some strains may precipitate or coagulate partially.

Coagulated proteins: Not attacked.

Carbohydrates: Glucose, maltose, fructose, lactose, galactose, dextrin, sucrose, glycerol and starch are fermented.

Biochemistry: Nitrites not formed from nitrates; produces NH_3, traces of H_2S, volatile amines, aldehydes, ethanol, formic, butyric and lactic acids.

Pathogenicity, natural: Isolated in putrid or purulent pleurisy, lung abscess, dental infections, post-appendicular phlegmon, purulent adenitis.

Pathogenicity, experimental: Non-pathogenic for mouse and guinea pig.

9. *Catenabacterium nigrum* (Repaci) P. 1938.

Synonym: *Streptobacillus niger gangrenae pulmonaris* Repaci.

Habitat: Lung.

Morphology: Pleomorphic rods: sometimes short rods, 0.6 μ $\times$ 1 to 2 μ, occurring in chains of 10-14 elements, sometimes very long and flexuous chains. Non-motile. No endospores. Gram-positive.

Physiology: Strict anaerobe. Opt. T. $= 37°$ C. Survives 1 month.

Cultural characters: No gas produced.

Deep agar: Delicate, lenticular colonies, which become black.

Glucose broth: Slight diffuse turbidity, with whitish mass of agglutinated filaments. Highly fetid odor.

Gelatin: No liquefaction.

Coagulated proteins: Not attacked.

Carbohydrates: Glucose feebly fermented.

Biochemistry: Indole not formed.

Pathogenicity, natural: Isolated from a gangrenous abscess of the lung.

Pathogenicity, experimental: In the guinea pig: massive infiltration of the skin with a woody consistency, followed by necrosis, fetid pus and death. Intraperitoneal injection causes death by intoxication.

10.   *Catenabacterium leptotrichoides* (Jay) P. 1938.

Synonym: Leptothrix sp. Jay.

Habitat: Carious teeth. Quite frequent.

Morphology: Long rods 0.3 μ $\times$ 8 μ, occurring often in chains or very long filaments; rounded, pointed or swollen ends. Non-motile. No endospores. Gram-positive.

Physiology: Strict anaerobe. Opt. T. $=$ 37-40°C. Not thermoresistant.

Cultural characters: Obligate hemophile (blood may be replaced by hydrocele fluid). No gas produced.

Blood agar: Arborescent colonies; no hemolysis.

Carbohydrates: Glucose, fructose, mannose, lactose, sucrose, arabinose, xylose, mannitol, dulcitol, sorbitol and inositol are fermented.

Pathogenicity: Non-pathogenic.

Note.—Although related by Jay to the genus *Leptothrix,* this species has no single character of this group; we therefore place it with the *Catenabacterium,* giving the specific name of *leptotrichoides.*

11.   *Catenabacterium hemicellulolyticum* (Walker) nov. comb.

Habitat: Rumen of the sheep.

Morphology: Rods, 0.2 μ $\times$ 2.5 μ, straight or slightly-curved, occurring in short chains, filaments or spirals; sometimes pointed ends. Non-motile. No endospores. Gram-positive in young cultures, Gram-negative in old cultures (Gram-positive cells still visible). Marked pleomorphism in old cultures: central swellings stained by Albert's reagent but not by iodine.

Physiology: Strict anaerobe. Requires CO_2. Catalase-negative.

Cultural characters: No gas nor fetid odor produced.

Hemicellulose media: Abundant growth; hemicellulose is broken down to xylose, glucose, arabinose and glucuronic acid. Terminal fermentation products are acetic and lactic acids.

Carbohydrates: L-rhamnose, D-glucose, maltose, cellobiose, starch and sodium glucuronate are fermented.

Biochemistry: Nitrites not formed from nitrates; H_2S not formed; resting cells produce acetic and propionic acids from hemicellulose as well as from lactic acid.

GENUS III: *RAMIBACTERIUM* Prévot 1938.

Definition.—Straight or slightly-curved rods, non-motile, unencapsulated, showing pseudo-branching, Gram-positive. This genus comprises six species and their varieties:

A) Species producing no indole:
1. Lenticular colonies; gas produced; milk clotted; saccharolytic; non-hemolytic; pathogenic.
   1. *Ramibacterium ramosum,* page 174
   1. bis. No gas produced; milk unchanged; pathogenic. Variety β of Lotti, page 175
   1. ter. No gas produced; milk unchanged; pathogenic; irregular colonies. Variety γ of Lotti, page 175
2. Milk unchanged; acetylmethylcarbinol not formed.
   2. *Ramibacterium pleuriticum,* page 175

B) Species producing indole:
3. Highly pleomorphic; lenticular colonies; gas produced; viscid zoogloea in fluid media; milk clotted; saccharolytic; hemolytic; fetid; pathogenic.
   3. *Ramibacterium ramosoides,* page 176
4. Small-sized slender, flexuous rods with pointed ends; circular colonies; milk slowly clotted; saccharolytic; H_2S produced; non-pathogenic.
   4. *Ramibacterium pseudo-ramosum,* page 177
5. Rods of average size; lenticular colonies; milk unchanged; lactose not fermented; saccharolytic; non-pathogenic.
   5. *Ramibacterium alactolyticum,* page 177
6. Milk unchanged; acetylmethylcarbinol formed; butyric and valerianic acids produced.
   6. *Ramibacterium dentium,* page 178

1. **Ramibacterium ramosum** (Veillon and Zuber) P. 1938.

Synonym: Bacillus ramosus Veillon and Zuber 1898; *Bacteroides ramosus* (V. and Z.) Hauduroy; *Fusiformis ramosus* Topley and Wilson.

Habitat: Natural cavities of man and animals; sea water. Very frequent.

Morphology: Straight, slender rods, sometimes undulating, sometimes filamentous; 0.3 to 0.4 $\mu \times$ 2 to 3 μ; form acute angles as in the letters V and Y; may show pseudo-branching and spherical swellings. Non-motile No endospores. Gram-positive.

Physiology: Strict anaerobe. Opt. T. $= 22$-$37°C$. Killed at $56°C$. Opt. pH $= 7$-8. Survives one month. Neutral red temporarily reduced.

Cultural characters: Moderate amounts of gas produced.

Deep agar: Lenticular colonies; some gas bubbles.

Glucose broth: Turbid; gas; rancid odor; acidified; indole not formed.

Peptone water: Very meager growth. Indole not formed.

Gelatin: No liquefaction.

Milk: Massive clot, which does not retract.

Coagulated proteins: Not attacked.

Carbohydrates: Acid and gas from glucose, maltose, galactose, sucrose, mannitol and lactose.

Blood media: No hemolysis.

Biochemistry: Nitrites not formed from nitrates; produces NH_3, acetyl-methylcarbinol, formic and acetic acids.

Pathogenicity, natural: Isolated in pure or mixed culture from cases of mastoiditis, otitis, pulmonary gangrene, putrid pleurisy, tubercular caverns, appendicitis, intestinal infections, balanitis, liver abscess, osteomyelitis, septicemia, pyemia, septicopyemia, urinary infections.

Pathogenicity, experimental: In the guinea pig: subcutaneous abscess, cachexia and death. Intramuscular injection produces a painful edema, and death by intoxication. In the rabbit: intravenous injection produces death through progressive wasting. The association of *F. biacutus* and the *enterococcus* increases its virulence. Filtrates contain a toxic substance which produces painful muscular contractions, sometimes fatal shock. No hemolysin.

Serology: Specific agglutination up to 1-5,000.

Varieties of *R. ramosum*

1. Variety β of Lotti.
   Appendicitis, intestinal infections. All characters similar to those of the normal species, except:
   a) *Peptone water:* No growth.
   b) *Glucose broth:* No gas produced.
   c) *Gelatin:* No growth.
   d) *Milk:* Unchanged.

2. Variety γ of Lotti.
   Appendicitis; intestinal tract. All characters similar to those of the normal species, except:
   a) *Cultural characters:* No gas produces, but fetid odor present.
   b) *Deep agar:* Irregular colonies.
   c) *Glucose broth:* Viscous zoogloea.
   d) *Milk:* Unchanged.

2.   *Ramibacterium pleuriticum* Prévot, Raynaud and Digeon 1946.

Habitat: Natural cavities of man, especially respiratory tract. Quite uncommon.

Morphology: Entirely similar to that of *R. ramosum;* Y-forms are frequently seen. Non-motile. No endospores. Gram-positive.

Physiology: Strict anaerobe. Opt. T. = 37°C. Not thermoresistant. Opt. pH = 7.8. Survives 10 to 15 days. Obligate serophile on isolation. Neutral red and safranin reduced.

Cultural characters: Slow growth, gas produced, but no odor.

Deep agar: Lenticular colonies; gas produced.

Glucose VF broth: Abundant turbidity; gas; quite coherent viscid sediment.

Peptone water: Slight turbidity; gas.

Gelatin: No liquefaction.

Milk: Unchanged.

Coagulated proteins: Not attacked.

Carbohydrates: Glucose and galactose actively fermented; sucrose and maltose fermented by a single strain.

Biochemistry: Nitrites not formed from nitrates; sulfites not reduced; produces NH_3, H_2S (traces), alcohol, ketones, volatile amines, acetic, valerianic and lactic acids. Indole not formed; acetylmethylcarbinol not produced.

Pathogenicity, natural: Isolated from cases of fetid purulent pleurisy, gangrenous phlegmon, rectocolitis, lung abscess.

Pathogenicity, experimental: Generally non-pathogenic for mouse and guinea pig. Some strains kill by general intoxication following local infection.

3.   *Ramibacterium ramosoides* (Runeberg) P. 1938.

Synonym: Bacillus ramosoides Runeberg 1908.

Habitat: Appendix, lacrymal gland, lung. Quite frequent.

Morphology: Pleomorphic rods: either ovoid forms occurring in short chains, or long, pseudo-branched forms; sometimes spheroids may be seen. In culture, similar to *R. ramosum.* Non-motile. No endospores. Gram-positive.

Physiology: Strict anaerobe. Opt. T. = 37°C. Survives 6 to 8 weeks.

Cultural characters: Moderate amounts of gas produced.

Deep agar: Lenticular colonies; small amounts of gas.

Glucose broth: Turbid; viscid, glairy sediment; gas; acid; indole and NH_3 formed.

Peptone water: Meager growth; indole formed.

Gelatin: No liquefaction.

Milk: Coagulated in 8 days.

Coagulated proteins: Not attacked.

Brain medium: Fetid odor.

Blood media: Hemolysis; fetid odor.

Carbohydrates: Glucose, maltose and lactose are fermented. Terminal products are 1 part acetic acid and 2 parts propionic acid.

Biochemistry: Nitrites not formed from nitrates (except by 1 strain); sulfites not reduced; produces NH_3 volatile amines, aldehydes, indole, acetic, propionic and sometimes lactic acids. Acetic acid may be the lone product sometimes.

Pathogenicity, natural: Isolated from cases of appendicitis, various suppurative processes (dacryocystitis, tubercular caverns), jugal abscess, post-abortive septicemia.

Pathogenicity, experimental: In the mouse: convulsions and instant death. In the guinea pig and rabbit: severe intoxication.

4. *Ramibacterium pseudoramosum* (Distaso) P. 1938.

Synonym: Bacillus pseudoramosus Distaso 1912; *Bacteroides pseudoramosus* (D.) Bergey 1923.

Habitat: Intestinal tract of man, buccal cavity. Very frequent.

Morphology: Similar to that of R. ramosum, but slightly smaller and flexuous; occurs in short and chains and angles. Non-motile. No endospores. Gram-positive.

Physiology: Strict anaerobe. Opt. T. $= 37°$ C. Neutral red temporarily reduced.

Cultural characters: Small amounts of gas produced.

Deep agar: Lenticular colonies; gas.

Glucose broth: Turbid; White sediment; indole and traces of H_2S formed.

Gelatin: No liquefaction.

Milk: Slowly coagulated.

Coagulated proteins: Not attacked.

Carbohydrates: Acid and gas from glucose, fructose, galactose, lactose and trehalose.

Biochemistry: Nitrites not formed from nitrates; produces NH_3, H_2S (traces), aldehyde, acetone, indole, formic, valerianic and lactic (traces) acids.

Pathogenicity, natural: Isolated from buccal, pulmonary appendicular abscesses.

Pathogenicity, experimental: Non-pathogenic for mouse and guinea pig.

5. *Ramibacterium alactolyticum* Prévot and Taffanel 1942.

Habitat: Buccal cavity. Quite frequent.

Morphology: Straight rods, occurring in zig-zag or undulating chains; pseudo-branching (Y-forms). Non-motile. No endospores. Gram-positive.

Physiology: Very strict anaerobe. Opt. T. $= 33$-$37°$C. Opt. pH $= 6$-8. Survives 3 months. Neutral red not reduced, but phenosafranine temporarily reduced.

Cultural characters: Small amounts of gas, but no fetid odor produced.

Deep agar: Lenticular colonies; little gas.

Glucose VF broth: Abundant turbidity; gas; acid.

Peptone water: Very meager growth; traces of indole formed.

Gelatin: No liquefaction.

Milk: Unchanged.

Coagulated proteins: Not attacked.

Carbohydrates: Glucose, fructose, galactose, arabinose and xylose are fermented.

Biochemistry: Nitrites not formed from nitrates; sulfites not reduced; produces NH_3, H_2S, indole, volatile amines, aldehydes, acetylmethylcarbinol, acetic, butyric and lactic acids.

Pathogenicity, natural: Isolated from bucco-dental suppurative processes, purulent pleurisy, brain abscess and jugal cellulitis.

Pathogenicity, experimental: Non-pathogenic for mouse and guinea pig.

Serology: Antiserum agglutinates homologous strain at 1-1,000 and heterologous strains at 1-100 and 1-500.

6.   *Ramibacterium dentium* Vinzent and Reynes 1947.

Habitat: Buccal cavity. Uncommon.

Morphology: Straight, slender rods, resembling *R. ramosum;* same size; short chains, clumps, pseudo-branching (Y-forms). Non-motile. No endospores. Gram-positive.

Physiology: Strict anaerobe. Opt. T. $= 37°$ C (grows already at 26° C). Killed at 65°C. Opt. pH $= 7$-8. Survives 1 month. Neutral red definitely reduced; safranin reduced temporarily

Cultural characters: Small amounts of gas, but no odor produced.

Deep agar: Punctiform colonies, appearing slowly, becoming fluffy.

Glucose VF broth: Clotty growth, sedimenting rapidly; gas.

Peptone water: Meager, clotty growth.

Gelatin: Abundant growth; no liquefaction.

Milk: Unchanged.

Coagulated proteins: Not attacked.

Carbohydrates: Glucose, fructose and mannitol are fermented.

Biochemistry: Nitrites not formed from nitrates; produces NH_3, indole, acetylmethylcarbinol, butyric and valerianic acids.

Pathogenicity, natural: Isolated from dental tartar, dental infections and purulent pleurisy.

Pathogenicity, experimental: Non-pathogenic for mouse and guinea pig. No toxin, nor hemolysin.

GENUS IV. *CILLOBACTERIUM* Prévot 1938.

Definition.—Straight or slightly-curved rods, motile, no endospores, unencapsulated Gram-positive. This genus actually groups ten species:

A) Non-proteolytic species:

1. Lenticular colonies; gas and viscid zoogloea in fluid media; gelatin not liquefied; milk unchanged; saccharolytic; indole not formed; pathogenic.

   1. *Cillobacterium moniliforme,* page 180

2. Irregular or arborescent colonies; broth turbid; gelatin not liquefied; milk unchanged; gas and fetid odor; non-pathogenic.

   2. *Cillobacterium guinaeensis,* page 180

3. Lenticular colonies; gas produced; gelatin not liquefied; milk slowly coagulated; saccharolytic; non-pathogenic.

   3. *Cillobacterium silvestris,* page 181

4. Obligate thermophile (55°C).

   4. *Cillobacterium thermophilum,* page 181

5. Aods containing an iodophilic substance; tan-colored colonies; cellulose and cellobiose fermented.

   5. *Cillobacterium cellulosolvens,* page 182

B) Gelatinolytic species:

6. Lenticular colonies, gas produced; gelatin liquefied; milk unchanged; saccharolytic; pathogenic.

   6. *Cillobacterium endocarditis,* page 182

7. Mulberry-shaped colonies, with satellite formations; gas produced; gelatin liquefied; milk unchanged; saccharolytic; indole and H_2S formed; pathogenic.

   7. *Cillobacterium meningitis,* page 183

C) Proteolytic species:

8. Spatula-shaped rods; circular colonies; gas produced; gelatin liquefied; milk clotted and digested; saccharolytic; indole formed.

   8. *Cillobacterium spatuliforme,* page 183

9. Thick, squat rods; lenticular colonies; gas produced; gelatin liquefied; milk clotted and digested; egg-white digested; saccharolytic; indole formed.

   9. *Cillobacterium multiforme,* page 184

10. Rods with square ends; fluffy colonies; gas and fetid odor; gelatin liquefied; milk digested; not saccharolytic; indole not formed.

   10. *Cillabacterium combesi,* page 185

1. *Cillobacterium moniliforme* (Repaci) P. 1938.

Synonym: Bacillus moniliformis Repaci 1910.

Habitat: Respiratory tract of man; soil of equatorial Africa. Quite uncommon.

Morphology: Straight rods, 0.7 μ $\times$ 3 to 4 μ; occurring singly or in pairs; metachromatic granules; spindle-shaped swellings. Motile. No endospores. Gram-positive.

Physiology: Strict anaerobe. Opt. T. = 37-41°C. Survives 30 days. Neutral red reduced.

Cultural characters: Gas produced.

Deep agar: Lenticular colonies 2 to 3 mm. in diameter. Abundant gas and agreable odor produced.

Glucose broth: Flaky growth, sedimenting rapidly to form a viscid mass; gas produced, but indole not formed.

Gelatin: No liquefaction.

Milk: Unchanged.

Coagulated proteins: Not attacked.

Carbohydrates: Acid and gas form glucose, fructose, galactose and lactose.

Biochemistry: Nitrites not formed from nitrates; produces NH_3, indole (traces), alcohol, acetone, acetylmethylcarbinol, formic, butyric and lactic acids.

Pathogenicity, natural: Isolated from a case of pulmonary gangrene.

Pathogenicity, experimental: In the guinea pig: subcutaneous abscess, sphacela of the skin, followed by death in 8 days.

2. *Cillobacterium guinaeensis* Digeon 1948.

Habitat: Savana of Mount Nimba in Guinea.

Morphology: Rods with practically square ends, 0.7 μ $\times$ 2.5 to 3.0 μ; occurring singly or in short chains. Motile. No endospores. Gram-positive.

Physiology: Strict anaerobe. Opt. T. = 37°C. Not thermoresistant. Survives at least 3 months. Neutral red and safranin reduced.

Cultural characters: Gas and fetid odor produced.

Deep agar: Irregular and arborescent colonies; gas.

Glucose VF broth: Uniform turbidity; gas and fetid odor.

Peptone water: Turbid; gas.

Gelatin: No liquefaction.

Milk: Unchanged.

Coagulated proteins: Not attacked.

Carbohydrates: Galactose only is fermented.

Biochemistry: Nitrites not formed from nitrates; sulfites not reduced; produces NH_3, H_2S, alcohol, acetylmethylcarbinol, acetic, valerianic and lactic acids.

Pathogenicity: Non-pathogenic.

Systematics: Very closely related to *C. moniliforme,* from which it differs by its irregular colonies, fetid odor, very weak saccharolytic powers and nonpathogenicity.

3. *Cillobacterium silvestris*. Lanthiez 1948.

Habitat: Primary forest on the Ivory Coast, and in Adelieland (French Antartica).

Morphology: Short, slender rods, 0.5 μ $\times$ 1.8 μ; some filamentous forms. Motile. Encapsulated. No endospores. Gram-positive.

Physiology: Strict anaerobe. Opt. T. $= 37°$C. Not thermoresistant. Survives more than 3 months. Neutral red and safranin reduced.

Cultural characters: Gas and fetid odor produced.

Deep agar: Lenticular colonies; large amounts of gas.

Glucose VF broth: Abundant diffuse turbidity; gas (H_2 and CO_2).

Peptone water: Very slight turbidity.

Gelatin: No liquefaction.

Milk: Very slowly clotted (1 month).

Coagulated proteins: Not attacked.

Carbohydrates: Glucose, fructose, maltose, galactose, sucrose, lactose, sorbitol, mannitol, starch and glycerol are actively fermented.

Biochemistry: Nitrites not formed from nitrates; sulfites not reduced; produces NH_3, H_2S (abundant), volatile amines, alcohols, acetylmethylcarbinol, acetic, propionic and lactic acids.

Pathogenicity: Non-pathogenic for mouse and guinea pig. No toxin nor hemolysin.

Systematics: Differs from *C. moniliforme* and *C. guinaeensis* by coagulation of milk, its well-extended fermentative properties and its fermentation type.

4. *Cillobacterium thermophilum* Prévot *et al.* 1954.

Habitat: Contaminated canned and country-made liver paste.

Morphology: Straight rods, 0.4 μ $\times$ 4 to 5 μ; occurring singly or in short chains; may show Y-forms. Slowly motile (1 single polar flagellum, which breaks easily and is not stained by the usual methods). Unencapsulated. No endospores. Gram-positive.

Physiology: Strict anaerobe. Opt. T. $= 55°$C; may become adapted to 37°C with difficulty. Killed at 70°C after 10 minutes. Survives more than 20 days. Neutral red definitely and safranin temporarily reduced.

Cultural characters: Gas, but no fetid odor produced.

Deep agar: Lenticular colonies.

Glucose broth: Abundant turbidity; gas.

Peptone water: No growth.

Gelatin: No liquefaction.

Milk: Clotted in 48 hours; retraction of the clot.

Coagulated proteins: Not attacked.

Carbohydrates: Glucose, fructose, maltose, lactose, galactose and starch are fermented.

Biochemistry: Nitrites not formed from nitrates; sulfites and sulfates not reduced; produces NH_3, H_2S (traces), alcohols, and at 55°C: 5 parts of acetic and 1 part of butyric acid, at 37°C: pure acetic acid.

Pathogenicity: Non-pathogenic for mouse and guinea pig.

5. *Cillobacterium cellulosolvens* Bryant *et al.* 1958.

Habitat: Rumen of cattle.

Morphology: Rods with pointed ends, 0.5 to 0.7 μ × 1 to 2 μ; occurring in chains of 8-10 elements; coccoid forms; motile by means of monotrichous or peritrichous (3-4) flagella. Cells contain material stainable by iodine. Gram-positive, with numerous Gram-variable forms; the Gram-variable forms have Gram-positive poles.

Physiology: Strict anaerobe. Opt. T. = 30-37°C. Terminal pH 4.8. Catalase-negative.

Cultural characters: No gas, nor fetid odor produced.

Cellulose-deep agar: Lenticular colonies.

Agar slant in vacuo: Flat or slightly convex, translucent colonies, tan-colored, 3 to 5 mm. in diameter.

Fluid media cellobiose: Abundant turbidity. Trypticase or yeast extract may replace rumen.

Gelatin: No liquefaction.

Carbohydrates: Glucose, cellobiose, maltose, sucrose, fructose, inulin, salicin, aesculin and cellulose are fermented. Reducing sugars are liberated from cellulose.

Biochemistry: Nitrites not formed from nitrates; indole and H_2S not formed; acetoin not produced. Produces lactic, acetic and formic acids (no CO_2).

Pathogenicity: Non-pathogenic.

6. *Cillobacterium endocarditis* (Routier and Braunberger) P. 1938.

Habitat: Probably natural cavities of man, mud, soil of Africa, Adelieland (French Antartica). Quite frequent.

Morphology: Pleomorphic rods; actively motile; no endospores. Gram-positive.

Physiology: Strict anaerobe. Opt. T. = 37°C. Neutral red reduced.

Cultural characters: Gas produced.

Deep agar: Lenticular colonies; gas.

Glucose broth: Turbid; sediment; gas.

Peptone water: Very meager growth.

Gelatin: Liquefaction in 2 to 5 days.

Milk: Unchanged.

Coagulated proteins: Not attacked.

Carbohydrates: Acid and gas from glucose, fructose, maltose, sucrose and arabinose.

Biochemistry: Nitrites not formed from nitrates; sulfites not reduced;

produces NH_3 H_2S, volatile amines, sometimes aldehydes and ketones, butyric acid with a second acid which may be; acetic, formic or propionic. Some strains equally produce lactic acid.

Pathogenicity, natural: Isolated by hemoculture from a subacute case of endocarditis with septicemia.

Pathogenicity, experimental: In the guinea pig: intramuscular injection of 2 to 5 ml. produces death in 2 to 6 days with extensive hemorrhagic edema, peritoneal hemorrhagic exsudate and visceral congestion. Hemoculture is positive. The sterile filterate kills mice (intravenous injection) at 1 to 20 ml.

Serology: Specific agglutination at 1-2,000.

6. *Cillobacterium meningitis* (Ghon, Mucha and Muller) P. 1938.

Synonym: Strain "SV" of Ghon, Mucha and Muller 1906.

Habitat: Unknown. Uncommon.

Morphology: Highly pleomorphic rods: ovoid with rounded ends, 1.5 μ $\times$ 3.5 μ, filaments with spindle-shaped swellings; actively motile; no endospores; Gram-positive, staining more intensely on the ends.

Physiology: Strict anaerobe. Opt. T. $= 22$-$37°C$. Opt. pH $= 7.8$-8.5. Survives several months. Neutral red reduced.

Cultural characters: Gas produced.

Deep agar: Mulberry-shaped colonies surrounded by smaller satellite colonies; gas.

Glucose broth: Turbid flaky sediment; gas.

Peptone water: Meager growth; flaky sediment.

Gelatin: Cloudy turbidity; slow liquefaction; gas.

Milk: Unchanged; gas.

Coagulated proteins: Not attacked.

Carbohydrates: Unknown.

Biochemistry: Produces H_2S, indole, ethanol, butyric, acetic and lactic acids.

Pathogenicity, natural: Isolated from fatal case of purulent meningitis of otitic origin.

Pathogenicity, experimental: In the guinea pig: subcutaneous injection produces a local abscess which is followed by death. In the rabbit: Gross infiltration.

8. *Cillobacterium spatuliforme* (Distaso) P. 1938.

Synonym: Bacillus tenuis spatuliformis Distaso 1932.

Habitat: Intestinal tract of the dog, intestinal tract of human corpses. Uncommon.

Morphology: Straigth or slightly-curved rods, with square ends, one of which is often in the shape of spatula, 1.0 to 1.2 μ $\times$ 2 to 4 μ; occurring singly, in pairs or in very short chains. Easily stainable capsule. Motile by means of 3-4 undulating, flagella usually attached 2 to each end. Motile coccoid forms. No endospores. Gram-positive.

Physiology: Strict anaerobe. Opt. T. $= 37°$C. Not thermoresistant. Survives for a long period of time. Neutral red and safranin irreversibly decolorized.

Cultural characters: Gas, indole and a slightly fetid odor produced.

Deep agar: Circular colonies; small quantities of gas.

Glucose broth: Abundant turbidity; abundant gas.

Gelatin: Liquefaction in 24 hours.

Milk: Coagulated, then digested.

Coagulated egg-white: Broken up by some strains.

Carbohydrates: Acid and gas from glucose and maltose.

Biochemistry: Nitrites not formed from nitrates; sulfites not reduced; produces NH_3, H_2S, indole, cresol, ethanol, volatile amines, aldehydes, acetic and lactic acids.

Pathogenicity, natural: Unknown.

Pathogenicity, experimental: Non-pathogenic for laboratory animals. Slightly active hemolysin.

9. *Cillobacterium multiforme* (Distaso) P. 1938.

Synonym: Bacillus multiformis Distaso 1912).

Habitat: Intestinal tract of the dog, soil of Equatorial Africa. Quite uncommon.

Morphology: Short thick rods, straight or slightly-curved, 3 μ in length; highly pleomorphic; motile; no endospores; Gram-positive.

Physiology: Strict anaerobe. Opt. T. $= 37°$C. Survives 12 days. Neutral red reduced.

Cultural characters: Gas and fetid odor produced.

Deep agar: Lenticular colonies; large quantities of gas.

Glucose broth: Turbid; gas and putrid odor.

Gelatin: Liquefaction.

Milk: Coagulated, then digested.

Coagulated egg-white: Digested.

Coagulated Fibrin: Digested.

Coagulated serum: Digested.

Carbohydrates: Acid and gas from glucose, lactose, fructose, maltose, galactose, sorbitol, mannitol and glycerol.

Biochemistry: Nitrites not formed from nitrates; produces NH_3, H_2S, indole (traces), formic, butyric and lactic acids.

Pathogenicity: Non-pathogenic. No toxin nor hemolysin.

10. *Cillobacterium combesi* Prévot and Laplanche 1947.

Habitat: Forest soil from French Guinea. Quite uncommon.

Morphology: Straight rods with square ends, 0.7 $\mu \times$ 3 to 4 μ; occurring singly or in pairs, more often in chains of 3-10 elements; motile with slow undulating movement; no endospores; Gram-positive.

Physiology: Strict anaerobe. Opt. T. = 37°C. Not thermoresistant. Survives more than 3 months. Neutral red and safranin reduced.

Cultural characters: Gas and fetid odor produced.

Deep agar: Irregular, fluffy or arborescent colonies; gas.

Glucose VF broth: Abundant turbidity; viscid zoogloea; gas.

Peptone water: Slight turbidity.

Gelatin: Liquefaction in 5 days.

Milk: Coagulated in 8 days, then digested.

Coagulated proteins: Not attacked.

Carbohydrates: Not fermented.

Biochemistry: Nitrites not formed from nitrates; produces NH_3, H_2S, ethanol, formic, butyric and valerianic acids; traces of acetylmethylca rbinol. Sulfites not reduced.

Pathogenicity, natural: Isolated from a swelling in the neck.

Pathogenicity, experimental: Non-pathogenic for mouse and guinea pig. No toxin. Sterile filtrate will hemolgze sheep red blood cells *in vitro.*

The taxonomical position of the germ described below is quite difficult to determine precisely at this time. Provisionally and with all reserves, we place it next to the *Bacteriaceae,* near the *Cillobacterium.*

GENUS: *Lachnospira* Bryant and Small 1956.

Definition.—Slightly-curved rods; motile by means of a single polar flagellum; no endospores; Gram-positive (easily decolorized).

Type species: Lachnospira multiparus Bryant and Small 1956.

Habitat: Rumen of catlle.

Morphology: Slightly-curved rods, 0.4 to 0.6 $\mu \times$ 2 to 4 μ, with pointed ends; occurring singly, in pairs, sometimes in short chains. Motile by means of a single polar flagellum. Gram-positive in cultures, rapidly becoming Gram-negative.

Physiology: Strict anaerobe. Opt. T. = 30-45°C. Catalase-negative.

Cultural characters: Grows in rumen added with glucose, or in media containing yeast extract and trypticase, without CO_2.

Agar slant in vacuo: Large, flat, white colonies.

Deep agar: Fluffy colonies.

Gelatin broth: Dense flakes which sediment rapidly.

Gelatin: No liquefaction.

Carbohydrates: Glucose, fructose, cellobiose, sucrose, salicin, aesculin and pectin are fermented; d-xylose weakly so; starch not hydrolyzed.

Biochemistry: Nitrites not formed from nitrates; acetoin usually produced; indole not formed nor H_2S; growth in glucose broth produces CO_2, H_2, ethanol, acetic, formic and lactic acids.

Chapter 5

ORDER III: *Spirillales* P. 1940.

Non-sporeforming Eubacteriales, comma-shaped or spirally-twisted; motile; strict or facultative anaerobes; Gram-negative.

We have already seen that this order comprises anaerobic species which are all Gram-negative; they therefore fall into the family of the *Vibrionaceae*.

FAMILY I: *VIBRIONACEAE*

Definition.—Gram-negative *Spirillales,* comma-shaped; motile. All the anaerobic species in this family may be grouped under the genus *Vibrio.*

GENUS *Vibrio* Muller.

Definition.—Short, rigid bacteria, comma-shaped; occurring singly or in spirals. Motile by means of peritrichous or polar flagella. No endospores. Gram-negative.

Besides numerous aerobic and facultatively anaerobic species, this genus comprises 12 anaerobic species and their varieties. Here is the key to their determination:

A) Species producing no gas:
   1. Vibrios of small size; actively motile; flat discoid colonies; clotty growth in broth; no odor; indole not formed; gelatin hot liquefied; milk unchanged; non-proteolytic; sacharolytic; pathogenic.
      1. *Vibrio stomatitis,* page 188
   2. Vibrios of average size; fluffy colonies; no turbidity in broth; no odor; indole not formed; gelatin not liquefied; milk unchanged; non-proteolytic; sacharolytic; non-pathogenic.
      2. *Vibrio buccalis,* page 188

3. Vibrios of large size; lenticular colonies; no turbidity in broth; putrid odor; indole not formed; gelatin not liquefied; milk unchanged; non-proteolytic; saccharolytic; non-pathogenic.

  3. *Vibrio putridus,* page 189

4. Vibrios occurring in long spirally-wound chains; peritrichous flagella; dew-drop colonies; gelatin not liquefied; milk unchanged; non-proteolytic; lactose only fermented; non-pathogenic.

  4. *Vibrio pseudo-spirochaeta,* page 189

5. Pleomorphic vibrios, occurring in long spirally-wound chains; two polar flagella; discoid colonies; flaky growth in broth; putrid odor; pathogenic.

  5. *Vibrio polymorphus,* page 189

5 bis. variety of the preceeding species; 5-6 peritrichous flagella; non-pathogenic.

  5 bis. *Vibrio polymorphus* var. *peritriche,* page 190

6. Very short vibrios; one single polar flagellum; fluffy colonies with opague center; flaky growth in broth; fetid odor; gelatin not liquefied; milk unchanged; saccharolytic; weakly pathogenic.

  6. *Vibrio tenuis,* page 190

7. Vibrios of average size; punctiform colonies; serophilic; disagreeable odor; gelatin not liquefied; milk unchanged; non-pathogenic.

  7. *Vibrio mulieris,* page 190

8. Vibrios of average size; one single polar flagellum; serophilic; punctiform colonies; no odor; gelatin not liquefied; milk unchanged.

  8. *Vibrio sputorum,* page 191

9. Vibrios of average size; 1-3 peritrichous flagella; cloudy colonies; no growth on the usual media.

  9. *Vibrio sputigenus,* page 191

9 bis. Variety of the preceeding species; very small size.

  9 bis.*Vibrio sputigenus* var. *minutissimus,* page 191

10. Vibrios of very small size; single polar flagellum; not serophilic; grows well on ordinary media; gelatin not liquefied; milk unchanged.

  10. *Vibrio bubulus,* page 191

B) Species producing gas:

11. Thick vibrios; fluffy spherical colonies; both turbid; fetid odor; feebly pathogenic.

  11. *Vibrio crassus,* page 192

11   bis. Variety of the preceding species; no turbidity in broth; reddish colonies.

11   bis. *Vibrio crassus* var. *D,* page 193

12. Very thin vibrios, showing one black granule; black lenticular colonies; broth turbid; gas and fetid odor; facultatively serophilic; gelatin not liquefied; milk coagulated, then digested; H₂S formed; indole not formed; pathogenic.

12.   *Vibrio niger,* page 193

1. *Vibrio stomatitis* (Repaci) P. 1940.

Synonym: Vibrion A Repaci 1909.
Habitat: Buccal cavity. Uncommon.
Morphology: Vibrios measuring 0.5 μ $\times$ 2 to 3 μ; actively motile: translation and rotation movements. No endospores. Gram-negative.
Physiology: Strict anaerobe. Opt. T. $= 37\,^\circ$C. Killed at 55°C. Survives 10 to 12 days.
Cultural characters: No gas produced.
Deep agar: Flat, discoid colonies.
Glucose broth: Clotty growth.
Gelatin: No liquefaction.
Milk: Slightly acidified; not coagulated.
Carbohydrates: Glucose and lactose are fermented.
Pathogenicity, natural: Isolated from a case of catarrhal stomatitis.
Pathogenicity, experimental: In the guinea pig: fatal peritonitis with turbid effusion in which the vibrios are found as pure culture. In the rabbit (Intravenous injection): death.

2. *Vibrio buccalis* (Repaci) P. 1940.

Synonym: Vibrion B Repaci 1909.
Habitat: Buccal cavity. Uncommon.
Morphology: Vibrios measuring 4 to 5 μ; spirals barely sketched; actively motile. No endospores. Gram-negative.
Physiology: Strict anaerobe. Opt. T. $= 37\,^\circ$C. Killed at 55°C. Survives 15 days.
Cultural characters: No gas produced.
Deep agar: Fluffy colonies.
Glucose broth: Abundant turbidity which leaves a clear supernatant. No odor, or indole formed.
Gelatin: No liquefaction.
Milk: Slightly acidified; not clotted.
Carbohydrates: Glucose, lactose and sucrose are feremented.
Pathogenicity, natural: Isolated in a case of stomatitis.
Pathogenicity, experimental: Non-pathogenic.

3. *Vibrio putridus* (Repaci) P. 1940.

Synonym: Vibrion C Repaci 1909.
Habitat: Buccal cavity. Uncommon.
Morphology: Vibrios of large size, 1 μ $\times$ 8 μ; motility unknown; no endospores. Gram-negative.
Physiology: Strict anaerobe. Opt. T. $=37°C$. Killed at 55°C. Survives for a long period of time.
Cultural characters: No gas produced.
Deep agar: Lenticular colonies, 2 to 3 mm in diameter, salmon-colored center.
Glucose broth: Auto-agglutinating growth; putrid odor; indole not formed.
Gelatin: No liquefaction.
Milk: Slightly acidified, not clotted.
Coagulated egg-white: Not attacked.
Carbohydrates: Glucose and lactose are fermented.
Pathogenicity: Non-pathogenic.

4. *Vibrio pseudo-spirochaeta* (Repaci) W.N.P. 1937.

Synonym: Spirochete A Repaci 1911-12 (related to the Vibrios by Veillon, A. Pettit, and Weinberg, Nativelle and Prévot).
Habitat: Buccal cavity. Uncommon.
Morphology: Short forms measuring 1 to 2 μ, long forms, 1 μ $\times$ 4 to 40 μ; the short forms have 1-2 polar or peritrichous flagella, while the longer forms have numerous peritrichous flagella (which sets them apart from the Spirochetes). The latter forms show spirals. No endospores. Gram-negative.
Physiology: Strict anaerobe. Opt. T. $=37°C$. Killed at 55° C. Survives 20 days.
Cultural characters: No gas produced; growth on the usual media.
Deep agar: Dew-drop like translucent colonies which then become discoid.
Milk: Slightly acidified, not clotted.
Coagulated egg-white: Not attacked.
Carbohydrates: Lactose fermented.
Pathogenicity: Non-pathogenic.

5. *Vibrio polymorphus* (Repaci) P. 1940.

Synonym: Spirochète B Repaci 1912; *V. pseudospirochaeta* B.W.N.P. (We prefer to call this species *V. polymorphus* for reasons of homonymy.)
Habitat: Buccal cavity. Uncommon.
Morphology: Pleomorphic vibrios: short and long forms; actively motile by means of two polar flagella. No endospores. Gram-negative.

Physiology: Strict anaerobe. Opt. T. = 37°C. Killed at 55°C. Survives 5 to 6 days.

Cultural characters: No gas produced; grows on ordinary media.

Deep agar: Discoid colonies, 1 mm in diameter.

Serum-agar: Cloudy colonies.

Glucose broth: Flaky growth; putrid odor.

Pathogenicity, experimental: In the guinea pig: Superficial necrosis of the skin, followed by abscess formation which eventually heals. In the rabbit: Abscess which heals spontaneously.

5bis. *Vibrio polymorphus* var. *peritriche* (Repaci) P. 1940.

Synonym: Spirochète C Repaci 1912; *Vibrio pseudo-spirochaeta* C (W.N.P.).

Differs from the normal species only by the presence of 5-6 peritrichous flagella.

6. *Vibrio tenuis* Veillon and Repaci 1912.

Habitat: Tubercular lung. Quite frequent.

Morphology: Very short, slender vibrios, 0.8 μ × 1.0 to 1.5 μ, with one pointed end; comma-shapes, S-shapes; very actively motile by means of a single polar flagellum. No endospores. Gram-negative.

Physiology: Strict anaerobe. Opt. T. = 37°C. Killed at 55°C. Survives 10 days.

Cultural characters: No gas produced, but putrid odor present.

Deep agar: Puntiform colonies surrounded by a cloudy halo.

Blood agar: Viscous, circular colonies.

Glucose broth: Meager growth in the form of a very light turbidity which sediments; fetid odor.

Gelatin: No liquefaction.

Milk: Unchanged.

Carbohydrates: Glucose, maltose, lactose, sucrose and mannitol are fermented.

Pathogenicity, natural: Secondary infection of tubercular caverns, infected wound of the mouth, dental caries, dental abscess, and all infections of a putrid nature.

Pathogenicity, experimental: Feebly pathogenic for laboratory animals.

7. *Vibrio mulieris* (Curtiss) P. 1940.

Synonym: Vibrio of Curtiss 1913.

Habitat: Genital tract of the woman (frequent in Czechoslovakia); Quite uncommon.

Morphology: Vibrios with rounded or pointed ends, 0.6 to 0.8 μ × 1.5 to 3.0 μ; occurring singly, in pairs or in S-forms; actively motile by means of 2-6 peritrichous flagella. No endospores. Gram-negative.

Physiology: Strict anaerobe. Opt. T. = 22-37°C. Killed at 55°C. Survives 4 weeks.

Cultural characters: No gas produced; obligate serophile.

Blood-deep agar: Non-hemolytic colonies, 2 mm. in diameter. Disagreeable odor.

Gelatin: No growth.

Milk: No growth.

Pathogenicity, natural: Isolated in leukorrhea from septic abortion and puerperal infection.

Pathogenicity, experimental: Non-pathogenic.

8. *Vibrio sputorum* (Tunicliff) P. 1940.

Habitat: Bronchi. Uncommon.

Morphology: Vibrios with pointed ends, occurring singly or in short undulating chains; actively motile; by means of a single polar flagellum; no endospores; Gram-negative.

Physiology: Strict anaerobe. Opt. T. = 35°C. Killed at 55°C.

Cultural characters: Obligate serophile; no gas produced.

Blood-agar: Clear, punctiform colonies.

Coagulated serum: Napiform growth; no odor.

Pathogenicity, natural: Isolated from cases of bronchitis.

Pathogenicity, experimental: Non-pathogenic.

9. *Vibrio sputigenus* (Miller) P. 1940

Synonym: Spirillum sputigenum Miller 1892 emend Muhlens 1909.

Habitat: Buccal cavity. Uncommon.

Morphology: Vibrios of average size, with pointed ends; occurring in pairs or in S-forms; actively motile by means of 1-2 flagella implanted in the concave side of the cell; no endospores; Gram-negative.

Physiology: Strict anaerobe. Opt. T. = 37°C. Killed at 55° C. Short-lived.

Cultural characters: No growth on the usual media; no gas produced.

Serum-deep agar: Delicate, fluffy, cloudy colonies, with opaque center.

Placenta-agar: Abundant growth.

Pathogenicity: Unknown.

Note.—According to a few authors, this species resembles *Selenomonas palpitans.*

9bis. *Vibrio sputigenus* var. *minutissimus* Muhlens.

Differs from the normal species only by its much smaller size.

10. *Vibrio bubulus* Florent 1953.

Synonym: Campylobacter bubulus Sébald and Véron.

Habitat: Most probably smegma of the bull; from there it can be found in the sperm and finally in the cow's vagina. Quite frequent.

Morphology: Small, slightly-curved, comma-shaped rods, 0.3 to 0.4 μ $\times$ 1.5 μ; occurring singly, sometimes in pairs, rarely in chains; in the latter case, it appears spirally-wound. Actively motile with back-and-forth movement; one single polar flagellum. No endospores. Gram-negative.

Physiology: Strict anaerobe of type I, slowly becoming type II. May give rise to mutants (irreversible) of type VI, while strains of type II may be kept indefinitely. Phenosafranin partly decolorized.

Cultural characters: No gas produced, but a distinct odor of H_2S.

Deep agar: Fluffy colonies, 1 to 2 mm in diameter, translucent, with opaque center.

Glucose VF broth: More abundant turbidity; odor of H_2S.

Peptone water: Meager growth.

Milk: Unchanged.

Brain-medium: Abundant growth.

Coagulated proteins: Not attacked.

Carbohydrates: Not fermented.

Biochemistry: Nitrites not formed from nitrates; produces NH_3, H_2S, acetic and lactic (traces) acids.

Pathogenicity: Non-pathogenic. No toxin, or hemolysin.

11. *Vibrio crassus* (Veillon and Repaci) P. 1940.

Synonym: Spirillum crassum Veillon and Repaci 1912.

Habitat: Buccal cavity and lung. Quite frequent.

Morphology: Thick vibrios, with pointed ends, 0.6 to 0.8μ $\times$ 2 to 3 μ occurring as S-forms; motile by means of long, slender, peritrichous flagella; no endospores; Gram-negative.

Physiology: Strict anaerobe. Opt. T. $=$ 37°C. Killed at 55°C. Survives 5 days to 3 weeks; transfers will allow several months' survival. Neutral red and safranin reduced.

Cultural characters: Small amounts of gas and fetid odor produced.

Deep agar: Circular, cloudy, fluffy colonies, with maximum growth in the critical zone; no gas formed.

Glucose broth: Slight turbidity; sediment; fetid odor; little gas formed.

Peptone water: Slight turbidity.

Gelatin: No liquefaction.

Milk: Unchanged.

Coagulated proteins: Not attacked.

Carbohydrates: Not fermented.

Biochemistry: Nitrites not formed from nitrates; produces NH_3 H_2S (large amounts), volatile amines, acetone, indole (traces), aldehydes, and acetic acid.

Pathogenicity, natural: Isolated in putrid secondary infections of tubercular caverns and of the mouth, and from a brain abscess.

Pathogenicity, experimental: In the guinea pig: gangrenous abscess. In the rabbit: feebly pathogenic.

Note.—May grow in association with *Fusiformis.*

11bis.   **Vibrio crassus** var. D (Repaci).

Synonym: Spirille D Repaci 1912.

Differs from the normal species only by the reddish color of its colonies and its pathogenicity for laboratory animals.

12.   **Vibrio niger** (Rist) P. 1940.

Synonym: *Spirillum nigrum* Rist 1898.

Habitat: Natural cavities of man. Quite frequent.

Morphology: Long, slender vibrios, with rounded ends, 0.3 μ $\times$ 1 to 2 μ; comma-forms, S-shapes; black granule which swells the cell; actively motile; no endospores; Gram-negative.

Physiology: Strict anaerobe. Opt. T. = 21-37°C. Killed at 55° C. Survives 14 months in the ice-box. Neutral red reduced.

Cultural characters: Facultative serophile. Gas produced.

Deep agar: Lenticular, black, cloudy colonies; gas produced.

Blood-deep agar: Small, delicate, non-hemolytic colonies.

Peptone water: Meager growth; gas, putrid odor; H_2S.

Gelatin: No liquefaction; putrid odor; H_2S.

Milk: Slowly coagulated, then digested; H_2S.

Coagulated ascitic fluid: No liquefaction; H_2S.

Biochemistry: Indole not formed; produces ethanol, butyric and lactic acids.

Pathogenicity, natural: Isolated in purulent otitis, mastoiditis, pulmonary gangrene, meningitis, appendicitis.

Pathogenicity, experimental: In the guinea pig: death after 15 days without any apparent lesion.

Species *incertae* sedis:

Vibrio succinogenes Wollin *et al.* 1960.

Habitat: Rumen of cattle.

Morphology: Slightly-curved rods; motile by means of a single polar flagellum; no endospores; Gram-negative.

Physiology: Strict anaerobe. Catalase-negative. Presence of cytochrome.

Cultural characters: Its growth depends upon the presence of paired substances, one which acts as electron donor, the other as electron receiver. Donors may be malate, fumarate and nitrate. Fatty acids with C_2-C_5 chains, lactate, serine, methionine, aliphatic alcohols from C_1 to C_5 cannot support growth in the presence of fumarate. Sulfates, CO_2, O_2 crotonate and pyruvate do not support growth in the presence of formate. Reduction of fumarate by washed cells in the presence of H_2 produces succinate. Although

4 moles of H_2 are taken up for every molecute of nitrate by washed cells, no nitrites are formed; but in the presence of formate and nitrate, nitrites are formed. Four amino acids are essential for growth; glutamate, aspartate, alanine and cysteine. No vitamins are required.

Carbohydrates: Not fermented.

Biochemistry: Urea is not hydrolyzed; sulfates are not reduced; not photosynthetic; choline not utilized; produces H_2S from cysteine and thioglyocollate.

APPENDIX

We place here, with all the necessary reserve, the sub-genus *Selenomonas* (Prowazek) Boskamp 1922, and its type species *Selenomonas palpitans* (Simons) Boskamp 1922.

Sub-genus *Selenomonas* (Prowazek) Boskamp 1922.

Vibrios, motile by means of a tuft of flagella inserted in the middle of the concave surface of the cell.

Selenomonas palpitans (Simons) Boskamp 1922.

Habitat: Cecum of the guinea pig, intestinal tract of rodents and of certain herbivorous animals (gazelle, giraffe, antelope, deer).

Morphology: Vibrios, 1.8 to 2.3 μ $\times$ 6 to 9 μ, occurring in spiral chains; motile by means of a tuft of flagella (more than 12) inserted in the middle of the concave side; zones stainable by iodine (glycogen); cell-wall difficult to see; nuclear apparatus visible in the concave side without any special staining procedure; direct division, each daughter-cell bearing half of the nucleus and of the flagella; Gram-negative. Special motility: jerking rotary movement with rapid oscillations.

Physiology: Strict anaerobe.

Cultural characters: Slow growth on ordinary media.

Thioglycollate-blood agar: More rapid and more abundant growth.

Note.—According to Lessel and Breed, this species could be identical with *Spirillum sputigenum,* but slightly different from *Selenomonas ruminantium* (Certes 1889) Wenyon 1926 which was isolated from rumen of herbivorous animals. We should equally note here that certain authors consider this species to be a Protozoon.

2. *Selenomonas ruminantium* (Certes) Wenyon 1926

Synonym: Ancyromonas ruminantium Certes 1889; *Selenomastix ruminantium* Woodcock and Lapage 1913.

Habitat: Rumen of cattle, sheep, deer and goats. Frequent.

Morphology: Rigid, crescent-shaped cells, 2 to 3 μ $\times$ 9 to 11 μ; motile by means of a tuft of flagella, 8 to 9 μ long, implanted on the concave side; homogeneous cytoplasm with condensation of chromatin at the base of the flagella; reproduction by transverse binary fission beginning at the base of the flagella, each daughter-cell receiving one-half of these; Gram-negative.

Physiology: Strict anaerobe. Opt. pH = 4.3-4.4.

Cultural characters: The basal medium for the growth of the ovine strain consists of casein hydrolyzate added with yeast extract, ammonium salts and 1% glycerol. Growth stimulated by sodium salts of volatile fatty acids, especially acetate.

Carbohydrates: Xylose, arabinose, glucose, fructose, galactose, lactose, cellobiose, aesculin, salicin are fermented. Some strains ferment in addition: sucrose, mannitol, trehalose, glycerol, dextrin, inulin, starch and lactate.

Biochemistry: Nitrites formed from nitrates; produces H_2S from cysteine; acetoin produced by some strains; CO_2 produced by all strains; fermentation products are either acetic and propionic acids, or formic and butyric acids, in addition to lactic acid and sometimes succinic acid.

2bis. **Selenomonas ruminantium** var. *lactilyticus* Bryant 1956.

Bovine strain fermenting lactate to produce acetic and propionic acids; ferments also xylane.

Next to the *Selenomonas,* we place the physiologic sub-genera recently described by Bryant and Small.

Sub-genus **Butyrivibrio** Bryant and Small 1956.

Definition.—Monotrichous, Gram-negative vibrios; anaerobic; no endospores; ferment glucose to produce large amounts of butyric acid.

Type species: Butyrivibrio fibrisolvens Bryant and Small 1956.

Habitat: Rumen of cattle.

Morphology: Slightly-curved rods, 0.4 to 0.6 μ $\times$ 3 to 5 μ; with slightly pointed ends; motile by means of a single polar flagellum; no endospores; Gram-negative.

Physiology: Strict anaerobe. Opt. T. = 30-37°C. Opt. pH = 4.6-5.6. Catalase-negative.

Cultural characters: Gas produced, but no fetid odor.

Glucose broth (in an atmosphere of N_2). Turbid.

Agar slant (in an atmosphere of N_2): Slightly-convex colonies, 2-4 mm in diameter.

Gelatin: Liquefaction by some strains.

Coagulated proteins: Attacked by some strains.

Carbohydrates: Variable fermentation of hexoses, pentoses, di- and poly-saccharides, glycerides, xylane and starch. Some strains ferment cellulose.

Biochemistry: Nitrites not formed from nitrates; indole not formed; produces H_2S (traces), acetoin, large quantities of butyric acid, small amounts of acetic acid, CO_2 and H_2.

Sub-genus II: *Succinovibrio* Bryant and Small 1956.

Definition.—Vibrios producing succinic acid as the main fermentation product.

Type species: *Succinovibrio dextrinosolvens* B. and S. 1956.

Habitat: Rumen of cattle.

Morphology: Similar to the preceding, but smaller: 0.3 to 5 μ $\times$ 1 to 5 μ.

Physiology: Strict anaerobe. Opt. T. $= 30$-$37°$ C.

Cultural characters: Growth stimulated by CO_2.

Glucose-rumen media: Abundant growth.

Gelatin: No liquefaction.

Coagulated proteins: Not attacked.

Carbohydrates: Glucose, d-xylose, l-arabinose, maltose, galactose, fructose, sucrose, mannitol, dextrin and pectin fermented; starch not hydrolyzed.

Biochemistry: Nitrites not formed from nitrates; produces acetic, formic, and succinic acids from glucose.

Recent research work concerning the sulfate-reducing bacteria has not confirmed the existence of spore material in the group *desulfuricans:* we therefore place this species in a temporary listing, while the sporeforming species *orientis* and *ferroxydans* will be dealt with in the genus *Sporovibrio* Starkey.

Genus *Desulfovibrio* Kluyver and van Niel 1936.

Definition.—Vibrios occurring singly or in short spiral-like chains; swollen forms; actively motile by means of a single polar flagellum; strict anaerobes reducing sulfates to H_2S.

Type species: *Desulfovibrio desulfuricans* (Beijerinck) Kluyver and
van Niel 1936.

1. Short vibrios, showing a black granule; single polar flagellum; black colonies in iron-sulfate agar; grows well at $25°C$; H_2S formed from sulfates; large amounts of gas formed; requires organic hydrogen donor; aliphatic fatty acids not used as hydrogen source; do not completely dehydrogenate the culture media; non-pathogenic.
    1. *Desulfovibrio desulfuricans* page 197
    1bis. Halophilic variety of the preceding species; requires high NaCl content in the culture media.
    1 bis *Desulfovibrio desulfuricans* var. *aestuarii* page 197

1 ter. Thermophilic variety; requires temperatures between 45°-70°C.

1 ter. *Desulfovibrio desulfuricans* var. *thermodesulfuricans*, page 198

2. Short vibrios with a black granule; black colonies; reduces sulfates to H_2S; aliphatic fatty acids used as hydrogen source as well as numerous other organic substances; saccharolytic; completely reduces the culture media; non-pathogenic.

2. *Desulfovibrio rubentschicki,* page 198

2bis. Variety incapable of utilizing acetates as hydrogen source.

2bis. *Desulfovibrio rubentschicki* var. *anomalus,* page 198

3. Thick vibrias, containing cytochrome, utilize lactate or pyrievate.

3. Desulfovibrio gigas, page 198

1. **Desulfovibrio desulfuricans** (Beijerinck) Kluyver and
van Niel 1936.

Synonym: Spirillum desulfuricans Beijerinck 1895; *Microspora desulfuricans* Migula 1900; *Vibrio desulfuricans* Baars 1931; *Sporovibrio desulfuricans* (B) Starkey 1938.

Habitat: Soft waters (especially Holland canals); silt, soil, mineral waters. Quite frequent.

Morphology: Short vibrios, 0.5 to 1.0 μ × 3 to 4 μ; pleomorphic: spiral-like chains of 10-12 vibrios; black polar granule; actively motile by means of a single polar flagellum; Gram-negative.

Physiology: Strict anaerobe. Opt. T. $=$ 30-55°C. Survives for a long period of time.

Cultural characters: Gas produced; requires mineral medium, containing sulfate.

Van Delden medium (agar-gelatin $+$ sulfate $+$ Na lactate): Black fluffy colonies; H_2S formed.

Beijerinck's medium (iron sulfate-asparagin-Na lactate gelatin): Black punctiform colonies; H_2S.

Nutrition: Chemotrophie; may utilize a large number of organic compounds as hydrogen source, except secondary and tertiary alcohols, and aliphatic fatty acids. Does not completely reduce the media. The best source of hydrogen is either Na lactate, K malate or salts of aliphatic fatty acids with side-chains.

Carbohydrates: Not utilized.

Lipids: Attacked.

Sulfates: Reduces to H_2S; agents of sulfide formation and deposits.

Pathogenicity: Non-pathogenic.

1bis. **Desulfovibrio desulfuricans** var. **aestuarii** (van Delden-Baars)
P. 1948.

Synonym: Microspora aesturaii van Delden 1904.

Habitat: Estuaries of the Netherlands, oil wells of California.

Morphology: Similar to that of the normal species.

Physiology: Similar to that of the normal species, except that it requires a high salt content (30% of NaCl); this is the halophilic variety, which may be trained slowly but progressively to grow in the absence of salt.

Nutrition: Similar to that of the normal species.

1ter. *Desulfovibrio desulfuricans* var. *thermodesulfuricans* (Elion) P. 1948.

Synonym: Vibrio thermodesulfuricans Elion 1925.

Habitat: Oil wells of California; soft waters of Holland.

Morphology: Similar to that of the normal species.

Physiology: Similar to that of the normal species, except that it grows well at 30-65°C, but reduction of sulfates is maximum at 55°C. This is the thermophilic variety, which can be trained easily through the use of young cultures; readaptation is equally easy.

2. *Desulfovibrio rubentschicki* (Baars) P. 1948.

Synonym: Vibrio rubentschicki Baars 1931.

Habitat: Soft waters, soil. Quite frequent.

Morphology: Similar to that of *D. desulfuricans.*

Physiology: Similar to that of *D. desulfuricans,* except its nutrition.

Nutrition: May utilize as hydrogen source any secondary and tertiary alcohol, carbohydrates and aliphatic acids. They are omnivorous. Finally, they completely reduce the culture media.

Pathogenicity: Non-pathogenic.

2bis. *Desulfovibrio rubentschicki* var. *anomalus* (Baars) P. 1948.

Synonym: Vibrio rubentschicki var. *anomalus* Baars 1931.

Habitat, Morphology and Physiology: Similar to that of the normal species.

Nutrition: Cannot utilize acetates (main difference with the normal species).

3. *Desulfovibrio gigas* Legall 1936.

Habitat: Pond in Berre.

Morphology: Thick, slightly-curved rods, $1 \mu \times 5$ to 6μ, occurring sometimes in pairs or in short chains; motile by means of a tuft of polar flagella; Gram-negative.

Physiology: Strict anaerobe. Opt. T. $= 30\text{-}35°C$. Contains cytochrome, desulfoviridin and hydrogenase.

Cultural characters: Grows only on special media containing lactate and sulfate.

Biochemistry: Reduce sulfates to sulfides; may utilize pyruvates instead of lactate, but not glucose nor acetate.

The genus *Spirillum* contains one functional anaerobic species:

Spirillum itersoni Giesberg 1936.

Habitat: Water.

Morphology: Very small spirals, 0.5 μ $\times$ 3 to 3.5 μ; spiral width 1.0 to 1.5 μ; motile by means of bipolar tufts of flagella; Gram-negative.

Physiology: Anaerobic, growth in the presence of nitrate and organic nitrogen or NH_3. Opt. T $=$ 30° C. Catalase-positive.

Peptone agar: White colonies, becoming riddled and dark-brown.

Gelatin: No liquefaction.

Potato: Orange-brown growth.

Peptone broth: Good growth.

Carbohydrates: Acid but no gas from glucose, fructose, ethanol, n-propanol, n-butanol and glycerol.

Biochemistry: Utilizes acetic, propionic, n-butyric, tartaric, fumaric, lactic, citric and succinic acids as well as ammonium salts.

Chapter 6

Class B: **SPORULALES**

Definition.—Sporeforming *Eubacteriales.*
We would like to call attention to the fact that the anaerobic *Sporulales* are distributed among three orders: *Clostridiales, Plectridiales* and *Sporovibrionales.*

ORDER I: CLOSTRIDIALES P. 1938.

Definition.—*Sporulales* with a central or subterminal spore which swells the rod to produce clostridial forms. This order is subdivided into two families: *Endosporaceae* and *Clostridiaceae.*

FAMILY I: *ENDOSPORACEAE* P. 1938.

Definition.—Gram-negative *Clostridiales.*
This family presently groups two genera:
1. Straight or slightly-curved rods, with central or subterminal spore; motile; Gram-negative.
   Genus I: *Endosporus,* page 200
2. Straight or slightly-curved rods, and central or subterminal spore; non-motile; Grom-negative.
   Genus II: *Paraplectrum,* page 208

GENUS I: *ENDOSPORUS* Prévot 1938.

Motile *Endosporaceae.*
This genus groups presently 16 species:

A) Non-pigmented species:
1. Rods of large size, with winding swellings; motile; double-sporeforming; arborescent colonies; microaerophilic; fetid gas produced; gelatin liquefied; milk coagulated; pathogenic.
   1. *Endosporus utriculus,* page 202
2. Filamentous rods; oval, central spore; motile; strict anaerobe; circular colonies; gas formed; gelatin liquefied; milk coagulated; non-pathogenic.
   2. *Endosporus mucosus,* page 202

3. Rods of average size; occurring in short chains; motile; club-shaped, subterminal spore; strict anaerobe; lenticular colonies; gas and fetid odor produced; gelatin partly liquefied; milk coagulated; non-pathogenic.
   3. *Endosporus foetidus,* page 202

4. Fusiform rods; ferment alanin.
   4. *Endosporus propionicus,* page 203

5. Straight rods; ferment uric acid.
   5. *Endosporus acidi-urici,* page 203

6. Straight rods, with cylindrical spore; ferment uric acid.
   6. *Endosporus cylindrosporus,* page 204

7. Gas produced; viscid growth; gelatin not liquefied; milk unchanged.
   7. *Endosporus viscifaciens,* page 204

8. Require a special medium containing apple-leaves, and adjusted to pH 8.5-10 by KOH or NaOH.
   8. *Endosporus brevifaciens,* page 204

B) Chromogenic species:

a) purple:

9. Short, thick rods; motile by means of peritrichous flagella; racket-shaped, central or subterminal spore; arborescent colonies; strict anaerobe; indole formed; gelatin not liquefied; milk clotted; saccharolytic; gas produced, but no H_2S formed.
   9. *Endosporus belfantii,* page 205

10. Short, thick rods; motile by means of peritrichous flagella; double-sporeforming; gas produced; indole not formed.
    10. *Endosporus maggiorai,* page 206

b) green:

11. Rods with oval spore; motile by means of peritrichous flagella; arborescent colonies; gas produced; indole not formed; gelatin not liquefied; milk clotted; saccharolytic; non-pathogenic.
    11. *Endosporus lustigii,* page 206

12. Related to the preceeding species; indole formed; greenish pigment becoming pink.
    12. *Endosporus ottlenghii,* page 206

13. Related to the preceeding species; indole formed; greenish pigment becoming purple or orange.
    13. *Endosporus rossii,* page 207

14. Related to the preceeding species; slender and slightly curved; spore invisible but thermoresistant; greenish pigment becoming brown; indole not formed.
    14. *Endosporus sclavoei,* page 207

15. Related to the preceeding species; short rods; 1-2 subterminal spores; indole formed; greenish pigment becoming brown.
15. *Endosporus paglianii,* page 207

c) pink:

16. Pleomorphic rods; encapsulated; central spore; motile; granulose- and glycogen-positive; lenticular colonies; gas (amylic odor); gelatin not liquefied; milk clotted; saccharolytic; non-pathogenic.
16. *Endosporus venturellii,* page 207

1. Endosporus utriculus (Nacciarone) nov. comb.

Synonym: Bacillo otricolare Nacciarone 1917.
Habitat: Isolated from gangrenous war wounds. Uncommon.
Morphology: Long, thick, straight rods, with winding swellings and rounded ends, in the form of an utricule, 1.5 $\mu \times$ 4 to 6 μ; motile; may be double-spored; Gram-negative.
Physiology: Microaerophilic. Opt. T. $= 36°C$ (20-40°C).
Cultural characters: Gas produced.
Deep agar: Circular colonies.
Glucose broth: Turbid; flaky sediment; gas.
Gelatin: Slow liquefaction.
Milk: Acidified and coagulated.
Pathogenicity, natural: Gas phlegmon.

2. Endosporus mucosus (Klein) P. 1938.

Synonym: Bacillus mucosus Klein 191; *Clostridium mucosum* (Klein) Bergey *et al.*
Habitat: Isolated from blood pudding. Uncommon.
Morphology: Long, slender, filamentous rods, 1.5 $\mu \times$ 2.5 μ; actively motile; central, oval spores, 1.5 $\mu \times$ 2.5 μ; Gram-negative (Gram-positive according to Buchanan and Hammer).
Physiology: Strict anaerobe. Opt. T. $= 37°C$. Resists at 80°C for 15 minutes.
Cultural characters: Gas produced.
Deep agar: Circular colonies; gas.
Gelatin: Slow liquefaction.
Milk: Coagulated.
Pathogenicity: Non-pathogenic.

3. Endosporus foetidus (Weigmann) P. 1938.

Synonym: Bacillus anaerobius foetidus Weigmann; *Paraplectrum foetidum* Weigmann.
Habitat: Isolated from fermented cheese. Uncommon.
Morphology: Straight rods, 0.6 $\mu \times$ 2.6 μ; occurring in chains of 3-6

cells; motile; subterminal spore, swelling the rod to a club; Gram-negative.

Physiology: Strict anaerobe. Opt. T. $= 37°C$.

Cultural characters: Gas produced.

Deep agar: Lenticular colonies.

Glucose broth: Turbid; gas.

Gelatin: Partial liquefaction.

Milk: Coagulated, then peptonized; gas; cheesy odor.

Pathogenicity: Non-pathogenic.

4. *Endosporus propionicus* (Cardon and Barker) P. 1948.

Synonym: Clostridum propionicum Cardon and Barker 1946.

Morphology: Spindle-shaped rods, 0.8 $\mu \times 3$ μ, quite swollen; occurring singly or in pairs; motile by means of 3-5 peritrichous flagella; oval, subterminal spore appearing late but rapidly freed; Gram-negative.

Physiology: Strict anaerobe. Opt. T. $= 28$-$37°C$. Catalase-negative.

Cultural characters: No gas produced; requires alanine.

Deep agar: Lenticular colonies.

Yeast autolysate broth alanine: Diffuse turbidity.

Carbohydrates: Not fermented.

Biochemistry: Acetic and propionic acids produced from alanine; serine, lactates, acrylates and pyruvates may also be attacked; propionic and butyric acids produced from threonine.

Pathogenicity: Non-pathogenic.

5. *Endosporus acidi-urici* (Liebert, emend. Barker and Back) P. 1948.

Synonym: Bacillus acidi-urici Liebert 1909; *Clostridium acidi-urici* (Liebert) Barker and Beck.

Habitat: Soil (garden earth, forest, mud from San Francisco bay, sand from Provo, Utah), fecal matter from *Colaptes auratus.* Quite frequent.

Morphology: Straight rods, 0.5 to 0.7 $\mu \times 2.5$ to 4 μ; actively motile by means of 10 peritrichous flagella; subterminal, oval spore, 0.9 $\mu \times$ 1.2 μ, which swells the rod; Gram-negative.

Physiology: Strict anaerobe. Opt. T. $= 31$-$37°C$. Opt. pH $= 7.6$-8.1.

Cultural characters: Small amounts of gas formed; no growth on ordinary media; requires a synthetic medium containing uric acid or purines, added with 0.01 to 0.02% thioglycollic acid or Na sulfite.

Deep agar: Whitish colonies, 1 to 2 mm. in diameter, either compact or roughly spherical with an irregular surface.

Proteins: Not attacked.

Carbohydrates: Not fermented.

Syntheic media: Yeast autolyzate-agar + uric acid + Na thioglycollate + phosphate + sulfate + NaOH. Uric acid may be replaced by xanthine, hypoxanthine or other purines.

Biochemistry: Uric acid, purines and glycine fermented to CO_2, NH_3 and acetic acid.

Pathogenicity: Non-pathogenic.

6. *Endosporus cylindrosporus* (Barker and Beck) P. 1948.

Synonym: Clostridium cylindrosporum Barker and Beck 1941.

Habitat: Same habitat as *E. acidi-urici.*

Morphology: Rods, 1 μ $\times$ 4 to 7 μ; motile by means of peritrichous flagella; cylindrical, subterminal or central spore; generally Gram-negative. Under unfavorable conditions of temperature and pH, produces slightly curved filaments; 30 to 40 μ long.

Physiology: Strict anaerobe. Opt. T. = 31-37°C. Opt. pH = 7.6-8.1.

Cultural characters: Small amounts of gas produced.

Deep agar: Small, white, circular, colonies, 1 to 2 mm. in diameter, with dull edge and gummy consistency. Other colonies may be thin, transparent, soft and invasive, irregular, arborescent.

Synthetic media: Yeast autolyzate-agar + uric acid + Na thioglycollate + phosphate + sulfate + Na hydroxyde.

Biochemistry: NH_3, CO_2, acetic acid and glycine produced from uric acid, xanthine, hypoxanthine and other pureines.

Pathogenicity: Non-pathogenic.

7. *Endosporus viscifaciens* (Sherman and Erb) P. 1947.

Synonym: Clostridium viscifaciens Sherman and Erb 1935.

Habitat: Fertile soil; grain, plants.

Morphology: Rods, 3 to 10 μ in length; motile; oval, central or subterminal spore, 1 to 2 μ, swelling the rod; granulose positive; Gram-negative.

Physiology: Strict anaerobe. Opt. T. = 32-36°C (growth at 15-42.5°C). Opt. pH = 4-8.

Cultural characters: Gas produced.

Deep agar: Unknown.

Broth: Tendency towards flocculation and formation of a viscid sediment.

Gelatin: No liquefaction.

Milk: Acidified, then coagulated, but not digested.

Carbohydrates: Glucose, maltose, sucrose, lactose, dextrin, starch, glycerol, mannitol and salicin are fermented; heavy viscid sediment.

Biochemistry: Nitrites formed from nitrates; indole not formed; produces NH_3 from peptones; Ca lactate not fermented; terminal products: 66% butanol, 31% iso-propanol and 3% acetone.

8. *Endosporus brevifaciens* (Bucher) nov. comb.

Synonym: Clostridium brevifaciens Bucher 1961.

Habitat: Intestinal tract of the caterpillar *Malacosoma pluviale* suffering from brachytosis.

Morphology: 1. In the intestinal tract of the host: Rods with rounded ends, 1 μ $\times$ 6 to 7 μ, occurring singly or in pairs; dimensions variable; motile (as a fish swims), but the distribution of the flagella is unknown; oval, centrally or subterminally-located spore not swelling the rod; spore 1.6 μ $\times$ 3 to 3.5 μ, stainable by fuchsin, acid-fast, freed by autolysis of the mature bacillus; Gram-negative.

2. In broth: shorter forms, occurring more often in pairs, seldom by three; no spore formation.

Physiology: Strict anaerobe. Opt. pH $=$ 8.5-10.2; Requires a high concentration of K or Na and a growth factor from apple-leaves. Special culture medium: Apple-leaves 50g, ascorbic acid 0.4g, distilled water 250 ml., KOH q.s. to adjust pH at 9.0. Basal medium (Phosphate-trypsinized broth Difco): Turbid; optimum growth occurs as a disk in the higher levels of the medium. Solid medium: (glucose-thioglycollate-basal medium-agar): Meager growth; microscopic colonies, 50 to 150 μ in diameter, with irregular border.

Pathogenicity: Brachytosis in the larvae of *M. pluviale*.

9. **Endosporus belfantii** (Carbone and Venturelli) P. 1938.

Synonym: Bacillus belfantii Carbone and Venturelli 1925; *Clostridium belfantii* (C. and V.) Bergey *et al.*

Habitat: Mud from Italian streams. Uncommon.

Morphology: Straight rods, 0.4 to 0.6 μ $\times$ 1.5 to 2.0 μ; filaments up to 7 μ; motile by means of peritrichous flagella; oval, central or subterminal spore, swelling the rod to a racket; Gram-negative.

Physiology: Strict anaerobe. Opt. T. $=$ 35-37°C. (growth at 28-40°C). Resists at 100°C for 15 minutes.

Cultural characters: Gas produced.

Deep agar: Arborescent colonies; gas.

Glucose broth: Turbid; indole formed.

Gelatin: No liquefaction.

Milk: Coagulated ;gas

Potato broth: Abundant growth; gas produced; formation of a purple pigment appearing only in the presence of starch.

Coagulated proteins: Not attacked.

Carbohydrates: Acid and gas from glucose, fructose, maltose, sucrose, lactose, mannitol and starch.

Biochemistry: No H_2S formed; produces ethanol, iso-propanol, propanol and butanol, butyric and propionic acids.

Pathogenicity: Non-pathogenic.

10. *Endosporus maggiorai* (Carbone and Veurelli) P. 1938.

Synonym: Bacillus maggiorai C. and V.; *Clostridium maggiorai* (C. and V.) Bergey.

Habitat: Mud from Italian streams. Uncommon.

Morphology: Short, thick, straight rods, 0.3 to 0.6 μ $\times$ 2.5 to 4 μ; motile by means of peritrichous flagella; subterminal spore, single or double; Gram-negative.

Physiology: Similar to that of the preceding species.

Cultural characters: Similar to those of the preceding species, in particular purple pigment in the presence of starch. Difference with *E. belfantii:* Tart odor (not ethylic) on fresh potato medium.

Peptone broth: Indole not formed.

Milk agar: Purple colonies.

Biochemistry: Ethanol not formed; propionic and butyric acids.

Serology: No cross-reaction with *E. belfantii.*

11. *Endosporus lustigii* (Carbone and Venturelli) P. 1938.

Synonym: Bacillus lustigii C. and V. 1925; *Clostridium lustigii* (C. and V.) Bergey.

Habitat: Mud from Lucca (Italy). Uncommon.

Morphology: Straight rods, similar to the preceding; 0.2 to 0.4 μ $\times$ 2 to 5 μ; motile by means of peritrichous flagella; one single oval spore, 0.1 to 0.2 μ $\times$ 0.3 to 0.5 μ; Gram-negative.

Physiology: Strict anaerobe. Opt. T. $=$ 35-37°C (28-40°C). Resists at 100°C for 2 to 4 minutes. Survives indefinitely.

Cultural characters: Gas produced.

Deep agar: Lenticular colonies.

Glucose broth: Turbid; gas; indole not formed.

Potato-broth: Abundant growth; gas; colorless foam; medium clarified in 8 to 10 days; butyric odor; greenish pigment becoming organe.

Gelatin: No liquefaction.

Milk: Coagulated; gas.

Coagulated proteins: Not attacked.

Carbohydrates: Glucose, fructose, sucrose, mannose and mannitol are fermented.

Biochemistry: Produces ethanol, propanol and butanol, butyric and acetic acids.

Pathogenicity: Non-pathogenic.

Serology: Specific agglutination.

12. *Endosporus ottolenghii* (Carbone and Venturelli) P. 1938.

Synonym: Bacillus ottolenghii C. and V.; *Clostridium ottolenghii* (C. and V.) Bergey.

Habitat: Mud from Italian streams. Uncommon.

Morphology: Similar to that of *E. lustigii.*

Physiology: Similar to that of *E. lustigii;* green pigment. Difference with *E. lustigii:* indole formed in peptone water, green pigment becoming pink and no cross-reaction.

13. *Endosporus rossii* (Carbone and Venturellii) P. 1938.

Synonym: Bacillus rossii C. and V. 1925; *Clostridium rossii* (C. and V.) Bergey.

Habitat: Mud from Lucca (Italy). Uncommon.

Morphology: Similar to that of *E. ottolenghii,* but thicker: 0.4 to 0.6 μ.

Physiology: Similar to that of *E. ottolenghii:* indole formed, green pigment becoming purple or orange, no cross- reaction, produces acetic and butyric acids.

14. *Endosporus sclavoei* (Carbone and Venturelli) P. 1938.

Synonym: Bacillus sclavoei C. and V. 1925.

Habitat: Retting flax in Umbria (Italy). Uncommon.

Morphology: Quite similar to the preceding species, but thinner and slightly-curved, 0.1 to 0.3 μ $\times$ 1.8 to 2.5 μ; spores have not been seen, but their existence is proven by the thermoresistance of the rod.

Physiology: Similar to that of the preceding species. Resists at 100°C for 1 minute. Green pigment, becoming brown.

Peptone broth: Indole not formed.

Serology: Highly specific agglutination.

15. *Endosporus paglianii* (Carbone and Venturelli) P. 1938.

Synonym: Bacillus paglianii C. and V. 1925; *Clostridium paglianii* (C. and V.) Bergey.

Habitat: Soil of Milan. Uncommon.

Morphology: Similar to that of the preceding species, but shorter, 0.3 to 0.4 μ $\times$ 0.6 to 1.0 μ. One or two subterminal spores.

Physiology: Quite similar to that of the preceding species; greenish pigment, becoming brown.

Peptone broth: Indole formed.

Biochemistry: Butyric and propionic acids produced.

Serology: Highly specific agglutination.

16. *Endosporus venturellii* (de Tomasi) P. 1938.

Synonym: Bacillus venturellii de Tomasi 1925, *Clostridium venturellii* (T) Bergey.

Habitat: Potato skin. Uncommon.

Morphology: Pleomorphic rods, 0.5 to 0.8 μ $\times$ 2.5 to 8 μ, sometimes fusiform, sometimes clostridial; very long forms measuring 18 to 20μ;

motile; encapsulated; central, clostridial spore, $1 \mu \times 2 \mu$; iodine positive: glycogen and granulose; Gram-negative.

Physiology: Strict anaerobe. Opt. T. $= 18\text{-}25°C$. Resist at $100°C$ for 5 minutes. Survives indefinitely.

Cultural characters: Gas produced.

Maltose-deep agar: Yellowish, lenticular colonies, becoming pink; gas; odor of acetone.

Potato mash: Abundant, foamy growth; pink foam with red spots; gas; amylic odor.

Glucose broth: Turbid; amylic odor.

Gelatin: No growth.

Milk with CaCO$_3$: Coagulated, becoming pink.

Coagulated proteins: Not attacked.

Carbohydrates: Glucose, maltose, fructose and starch (pink pigment) are fermented with the production of acetone and amyl alcohol.

Biochemistry: Produces acetic acid, propanol, iso-butanol and n-butanol.

Pathogenicity: Non-pathogenic.

Serology: Highly specific agglutination.

GENUS II: *PARAPLECTRUM* Fischer 1895.

Nonmotile *Endosporaceae.*

This genus contains only three species, of which here is the key to their determination:

1. Short rods with subterminal spore; non-motile; encapsulated in exsudates; circular colonies; non-proteolytic; gelatin not liquefied; milk unchanged; non-saccharolytic; indole not formed; no gas produced; pathogenic.
   1. *Paraplectrum malenominatum,* page 208
2. Long, thick rods, with oval, subterminal spore; non-motile; fluffy colonies ;gas produced; gelatin liquefied; milk clotted; saccharolytic; indole formed; non-pathogenic.
   2. *Paraplectrum pappulum,* page 209
3. Requires a growth factor from apple-leaves and a highly alcaline pH.
   3. *Paraplectrum malacosomae,* page 210

1. *Paraplectrum malenominatum* (Jungano) P. 1938.

Synonym: Pseudo-coli anaerobie Jungano 1908; *Bacillus malenominatus* (Jungano) W.N.P. 1937.

Habitat: Large intestine of man. Uncommon.

Morphology: Short rods, $1 \mu \times 2$ to 3μ, with rounded ends; non-motile; encapsulated in pathological material; filamentous forms in old cultures; subterminal spore; Gram-negative.

Physiology: Strict anaerobe. Opt. T. = 22-37°C. Resists at 80°C. Survives several months.

Cultural characters: No gas produced, but fetid odor present.

Deep agar: Small, circular colonies, regular, sometimes lenticular.

Glucose broth: Diffuse turbidity; sediment; indole formed.

Gelatin: No liquefaction.

Milk: Unchanged.

Coagulated proteins: Not attacked.

Carbohydrates: Not fermented. Some strains ferment hexoses and hexobioses.

Biochemistry: Nitrites not formed from nitrates; sulfites not reduced; produces NH_3, H_2S, volatile amines, aldehydes, indole, cresols, acetic, butyric and lactic acids.

Pathogenicity, natural: Isolated in infantile diarrhea and in a case of bronchiectasis.

Pathogenicity, experimental: In the guinea pig: Intraperitoneal injection produces a fatal septicemia in 24 hours. In the rabbit: Intraperitoneal injection: idem. No toxin, nor hemolysin.

2. *Paraplectrum pappulum* (de Gaspari) P. 1938.

Synonym: Bacillus pappulus de Gaspari 1911.

Habitat: Rancid saugage. Uncommon.

Morphology: Straight or slightly-curved rods, 0.8 μ × 4 to 6 μ; occurring in pairs or in short chains of 3-5 elements; filamentous forms in old cultures; oval, subterminal spore, 1.5 μ × 3 μ; Gram-negative. non-motile;

Physiology: Strict anaerobe. Opt. T. = 30-37°C. Resists at 100°C for 2 to 15 finutes. Neutral red and safranin temporarily reduced.

Cultural characters: Gas and fetid odor produced.

Deep agar: Irregular, fluffy colonies; large amounts of gas; rancid odor.

Glucose broth: Turbid; large amounts of gas; sediment; indole.

Gelatin: Liquefaction.

Milk: Clotted.

Coagulated egg-white: Slowly attacked.

Carbohydrates: Acid and gas from glucose, sucrose, lactose, maltose, inulin.

Biochemistry: Nitrites not formed from nitrates; produces NH_3, H_2S, volatile amines, ketones, acetic, propionic, butyric and lactic acids.

Pathogenicity, natural: Isolated from a fecaloid abscess.

Pathogencity, experimental: Non-pathogenic for laboratory animals.

3. *Paraplectrum malacosomae* (Bucher) P. 1961.

Synonym: Clostridium malacosomae Bucher 1961.

Habitat: Intestinal tract and fecal matter from *Malacosoma pluviale* suffering brom brachytosis.

Morphology: 1. In its normal habitat: Rods of variable dimensions, $1 \mu \times 4$ to 7μ, with rounded ends; occurring singly or in pairs; non-motile; oval, subterminal spore, $1.5 \mu \times 2$ to 3μ, stainable by carbol-fuchsin; Gram-negative.

2. In broth: occurs rarely in short chains; spores not formed.

Physiology: Strict anaerobe. Opt. pH is high. Requires high concentration of K or Na, and a growth factor found in an alcaline extract of apple-leaves. Fluid media (Same special medium described for *E. brevifaciens*): Formation of a coalescent mass, leaving a clear fluid. Special agar: Very small colonies, 0.5 mm. in diameter, circular, slightly elevated, translucent, with irregular border; surface is either rough or brilliant and undulating.

Pathogenicity: Brachytosis of the caterpillar *M. pluviale*.

FAMILY II: *CLOSTRIDIACEAE* (Fischer emend.).

Definition.—Gram-positive *Clostridiales*.
This family may be subdivided into three genera:

1. Rods with clostridial, central or subterminal spore; non-motile; unencapsulated; Gram-positive.
   1. *Inflabilis,* page 211
2. Rods with clostridial, central or subterminal spore; non-motile; encapsulated; Gram-positive.
   2. *Welchia,* page 222
3. Rods with clostridial, central or subterminal spore; motile by means of peritrichous flagella.
   3. *Clostridium,* page 227

GENUS I: *INFLABILIS* Prévot 1938.

Non-motile, unencapsulated *Clostridiaceae*.
This genus comprises actually 17 species of which here is the key to their determination:

A) Species producing gas:

a) Proteolytic:

1. Rods of average size; lenticular colonies; gas and putrid odor formed; gelatin liquefied; milk and egg-white digested; growth in the presence of bile; glucose fermented; highly pathogenic.
   1. *Inflabilis satellitis,* page 213
2. Lenticular colonies; gas and putrid odor formed; produces caproic and propionic acids; toxigenic.
   2. *Inflabilis talis,* page 213
3. Rods of large size; arborescent colonies; gelatin liquefied; milk and egg-white digested; lipidolytic; saccharolytic; indole formed; grey pigment; non-pathogenic.
   3. *Inflabilis indolicus,* page 214
4. Thick rods; fluffy or arborescent colonies; gelatin liquefied; milk digested; produces acetic, valerianic and lactic acids.
   4. *Inflabilis mangenoti,* page 214
5. Rods of large size; gas and fetid odor produced; proteolytic; saccharolytic; non-pathogenic.
   5. *Inflabilis litus-eburense,* page 215

b) Not proteolytic:

6. Lenticular colonies; gelatin liquefied; milk digested; glucose fermented; indole not formed; non-pathogenic.
   6. *Inflabilis plagarum,* page 215

7. Rods of very large size; punctiform colonies; gelatin not liquefied; milk unchanged; pathogenic; hemolytic.

   7. *Inflabilis teras,* page 216

8. Rods of large size; lenticular colonies; gelatin liquefied; saccharolytic; no fetid odor; feebly pathogenic; hemolytic.

   8. *Inflabilis sanguicole,* page 216

9. Lenticular colonies; gelatin not liquefied; milk clotted; peptolytic; lipidolytic; indole not formed; saccharolytic; not pathogenic.

   9. *Inflabilis barati,* page 217

10. Lenticular colonies; gelatin not liquefied; milk unchanged; saccharolytic; produces acetic, butyric and lactic acids; non-pathogenic.

    10. *Inflabilis setiensis,* page 218

11. Bright red colonies on potato medium; gelatin not liquefied; milk clotted; carbohydrates feebly fermented; indole not formed, or H_2S; non-pathogenic.

    11. *Inflabilis carbonei,* page 219

12. Grey, fluffy colonies; milk unchanged; gelatin not liquefied; saccharolytic; non-pathogenic.

    12. *Inflabilis filiformis,* page 219

13. Lenticular colonies; gelatin not liquefied; milk coagulated into a spongy mass; saccharolytic; highly active urease; pathogenic for laboratory animals; hemolytic.

    13. *Inflabilis lacustris,* page 220

B) Species producing no gas:

a) Proteolytic:

14. Rods of large size; flat colonies; gelatin liquefied; milk clotted, then digested; saccharolytic; non-pathogenic.

    14. *Inflabilis pseudo-perfringens,* page 220

b) Not proteolytic:

15. Rods of large size; fluffy colonies; gelatin not liquefied; milk unchanged; non-pathogenic.

    15. *Inflabilis magnus,* page 221

16. Rods of large size; arborescent colonies; gelatin not liquefied; milk unchanged; indole not formed; non-pathogenic.

    16. *Inflabilis rectus,* page 221

17. Thick rods; spore of very large size; lenticular colonies; gelatin not liquefied; milk unchanged; indole not formed; pathogenic.

    17. *Inflabilis megalosporus,* page 222

1. *Inflabilis satellitis* (Loris-Melikov) P. 1938.

Synonym: Bacillus satellitis Loris-Melikov 1911.

Habitat: Oysters, intestinal tract of typhoid patients. Quite frequent.

Morphology: Rods of average size, with rounded ends; filamentous forms in old cultures; non-motile; ovoid, elongated spores; Gram-positive.

Physiology: Strict anaerobe. Opt. T. $= 37°$C. Resists 3 minutes at 100°C.

Isolation: In bile broth; then agar heated 1 minute at 100°C.

Cultural characters: Gas produced.

Deep agar: Delicate, transparent, lenticular colonies; putrid gas.

Glucose broth: Slight turbidity; powdery sediment; putrid odor (H_2S); indole formed; neutral reaction.

Gelatin: Liquefaction.

Milk: Digested.

Coagulated egg-white: Digested in 1 month.

Pure bile: Good growth.

50% bile-broth: Abundant growth.

Carbohydrates: Glucose fermented (slightly acidified).

Biochemistry: Produces NH_3, H_2S, indole, phenol, butyric and acetic acids.

Pathogenicity, natural: Necrotizing action in typhoid fever.

Pathogenicity, experimental: In the guinea pig: Intraperitoneal injection of 1 ml. produces death in 24 hours, with peritonitis, elective action on the intestinal lymphoid tissue, enlargement of mesenteric glands and follicles, necrosis of the lymphoid plates. Hemoculture is positive. By ingestion, progressive wasting and death within 8 to 20 days; same lesions as per injection.

2. *Inflabilis talis* Prévot *et al.* 1947.

Habitat: Intestinal tract of man; canned fish. Uncommon.

Morphology: Straight rods, 0.7 to 0.8 $\mu \times$ 3 to 5 μ; non-motile; unencapsulated; clostridial spore; Gram-positive.

Physiology: Strict anaerobe. Opt. T. $= 37°$C. Opt. pH $= 7.4$. Resists 10 minutes at 70° C and 5 min. at 80°C. Survives indefinitely. Neutral red and safranin reduced.

Cultural characters: Gas and putrid odor produced.

Deep agar: Lenticular colonies, sometimes becoming irregular; gas.

Glucose VF broth: Abundant turbidity; gas and putrid odor.

Gelatin: Liquefaction.

Milk: Coagulated, then digested.

Coagulated proteins: Partly digested.

Carbohydrates: Glucose, fructose, galactose, sucrose, sorbitol and glycerol are fermented.

Biochemistry: Nitrites formed from nitrates in the presence of maltose; produces NH_3, indole (traces), amines, ethanol, aldehydes, ketones, propionic, caproic and lactic acids.

Pathogenicity, natural: Isolated from a case of appendicular gangrene.

Pathogenicity, experimental: Kills guinea pig in 6 days without any local lesion, but with hepatic degeneration and pulmonary congestion. Toxin is rapidly fatal by intravenous injection.

3. *Inflabilis indolicus* (Gratz and Vas) P. 1938.

Synonym: Bacillus indolicus G. and V. 1914.

Habitat: Liptauer cheese, river mud. Quite frequent.

Morphology: Slender rods, 0.8 to 1.0 μ $\times$ 5 to 8 μ; occurring in short chains and filaments; non-motile; unencapsulated; oval, subterminal spore, 1 to 2 μ; Gram-positive.

Physiology: Strict anaerobe. Resists 10 minutes at 100°C. Neutral red reduced.

Cultural characters: Gas produced.

Deep agar: Large-sized, arborescent or fluffy colonies.

Glucose broth: Diffuse turbidity; abundant, mucoid but not coherent sediment; gas and putrid, penetrating odor; indole and H_2S formed.

Gelatin: Liquefaction in 10 days.

Milk: Digested; alkaline reaction; strong odor; gas.

Egg-white: Digested.

Casein: Digested.

Coagulated serum and fibrin: Digested.

Lard: Digested.

Carbohydrates: Acid and gas from glucose, fructose, maltose, galactose, sorbitol, mannitol, glycerol, starch and lactose.

Biochemistry: Nitrites formed from nitrates by some strains; produces NH_3, H_2S, indole, grey pigment, scatole (traces), alcohols, aldehydes, ketones, volatile amines, acetic, butyric and lactic acids.

Pathogenicity: Non-pathogenic.

4. *Inflabilis mangenoti* Prévot, and Zimmès-Chaverou 1947.

Habitat: Swampy forest soil on the Ivory Coast.

Morphology: Short, thick rods with rounded ends, 1.6 to 1.8 μ $\times$ 3 to 4 μ; sometimes oval rods or very long filaments, 6 to 8 μ; occurring in long chains; non-motile; clostridial spore; Gram-positive.

Physiology: Strict anaerobe. Opt. T. $= 37$°C. Resists 3 minutes at 70°C. Survives more than 6 months. Neutral red reduced.

Cultural characters: Small amounts of gas and fetid odor produced.

Deep agar: Irregular, fluffy or arborescent colonies; small amounts of gas.

Glucose VF broth: Abundant, flaky turbidity, sedimenting rapidly into viscid masses; small amounts of gas; fetid odor.

Peptone water: Clotty growth.

Gelatin: Liquefaction in 24 hours.

Milk: Digested in 24 hours.

Coagulated proteins: Slowly digested.

Carbohydrates: Glucose and maltose are fermented.

Biochemistry: Nitrites not formed from nitrates; produces NH_3, H_2S, volatile amines, indole, scatole (small amounts), alcohols, acetic, valerianic and lactic acids.

Pathogenicity: Non-pathogenic. No toxin, or hemolysin.

5. *Inflabilis litus-eburense* Laplanche and Saissac 1948.

Habitat: Savana and humus on the Ivory Coast.

Morphology: Straight rods with rounded ends, 1 μ $\times$ 4 to 6 μ; occurring in short chains; non-motile; clostridial, subterminal and free spores; Gram-positive.

Physiology: Strict anaerobe. Opt. T. $= 37°C$. Resists 10 minutes at $100°C$. Survives more than 6 months. Neutral red and safranin reduced.

Cultural characters: Gas and fetid odor produced.

Deep agar: Fluffy colonies; gas.

Glucose VF broth: Abundant turbidity; gas; fetid odor; viscid sediment, but not coherent.

Peptone water: Slight turbidity; gas.

Gelatin: Liquefaction in 24 hours.

Milk: Coagulated, then digested.

Coagulated serum: Partly digested.

Fibrin: Digested.

Coagulated egg-white: Not attacked.

Carbohydrates: Glucose, fructose, maltose galactose and sorbitol are fermented.

Biochemistry: Nitrites not formed from nitrates; produces NH_3, H_2S, volatile amines, alcohols, acetone, acetylmethylcarbinol, formic, acetic, butyric and lactic acids.

Pathogenicity: Non-pathogenic for the guinea pig. No toxin, or hemolysin.

6. *Inflabilis plagarum* (Adamson) P. 1938.

Habitat: Isolated from war wounds, river mud, gorilla feces. Quite uncommon.

Morphology: Slender, slightly-curved rods, with rounded ends; occurring singly, in short chains or in filaments; non-motile; rare oval spore, subterminal, barely swelling the rod; Gram-positive.

Physiology: Strict anaerobe. Opt. T. = 37°C. Resists 1 minute at 100°C. Phenosafranin reduced.

Cultural characters: Gas, but no fetid odor produced.

Deep agar: Lenticular colonies; gas.

Glucose broth: Diffuse turbidity; gas; indole not formed.

Gelatin: Liquefaction in 3 to 4 days.

Milk: Partly coagulated; digested in 3 to 4 days.

Coagulated proteins: Not attacked.

Carbohydrates: Glucose, fructose, maltose, galactose, lactose, and mannitol are fermented.

Biochemistry: Nitrites not formed from nitrates; produces NH_3, H_2S, volatile amines, alcohols, ketones aldehydes, acetic, valerianic and lactic acids.

Pathogenicity: Non-pathogenic.

7. *Inflabilis teras* (Knorr) P. 1938.

Synonym: Bacillus teras Knorr 1919.

Habitat: Soil, respiratory tract, river mud, soil of Africa, potopoto. Quite frequent.

Morphology: Short, thick rods; coccoid involution forms and long filamentous forms; highly pleomorphic on Loeffler's medium; non-motile; subterminal spore, lemon-shaped; Gram-positive.

Physiology: Strict anaerobe. Opt. T. = 37°C. Resists 10 minutes at 80°C and sometimes 5 minutes at 100°C. Survives several months. Neutral red reduced.

Cultural characters: Gas and fetid odor produced.

Deep agar: Punctiform or irregular colonies; gas.

Glucose broth: Diffuse turbidity; gas; markedly acid.

Gelatin: No liquefaction.

Milk: Unchanged.

Coagulated proteins: Not attacked.

Carbohydrates: Glucose, fructose, maltose, galactose, sucrose and glycerol are fermented.

Biochemistry: Nitrites not formed from nitrates; produces NH_3, H_2S, indole (none or traces), alcohols, adehydes, ketones, acetylmethylcarbinol, acetic, butyric and lactic acids.

Pathogenicity, experimental: Young cultures produce in the rabbit and guinea pig local edema and suppuration, with hemorrhagic infiltration of the abdomen, and progressive wasting. The sterile filtrate kills the rat in 7 to 13 days; it will also hemolyze sheep red blood cells.

8. *Inflabilis sanguicole* (Vaucher *et al.*) P. 1938.

Synonym: Anaerobic bacillus of Vaucher *et al.*

Habitat: Human body, oysters. Quite frequent.

Morphology: Large rods, 5 μ in length, with rounded ends; non-motile; oval, central spore; Gram-positive.

Physiology: Strict anaerobe. Opt. T. $= 37°$C. Resists 20 minutes at 60°C, and 10 minutes at 70°C. Survives several months. Neutral red and safranin are reduced.

Cultural characters: Gas produced.

Deep agar: Lenticular colonies; gas.

Blood agar: Hemolysis.

Glucose broth: Abundant turbidity; large amounts of gas.

Gelatin: Liquefaction in 3 days.

Milk: Clotted in 40 hours.

Coagulated egg-white: Not attacked.

Coagulated serum and fibrin: Not attacked.

Carbohydrates: Glucose, maltose, fructose, galactose, lactose, sucrose, arabinose, xylose and starch are fermented.

Biochemistry: Nitrites not formed from nitrates; produces NH_3, H_2S, indole, volatile amines, aldehydes, propionic, valerianic, lactic and butyric (traces) acids.

Pathogenicity, natural: Isolated by hemoculture from a case of septicemia.

Pathogenicity, experimental: In the guinea pig: Subcutaneous injection gives rise to a slight local tumefaction which heals spontaneously in a few days. In the dog: septicemia.

9. *Inflabilis barati* (Tissier) P. 1938.

Synonym: Bacillus of Tissier and Barat 1918.

Habitat: Beer wort from the North, war wounds, intestinal tract of man. Quite frequent.

Morphology: Rods with swollen center and pointed ends; occurring singly or in short chains of 2 to 8 cells; young forms are short and ovoid; spherical, centrally-located spore swells the rod; Gram-positive; stains blue with iodine.

Physiology: Strict anaerobe. Opt. T. $= 18°$ —37°C. Resists 1 minute at 100°C. Survives indefinitely. Neutral red is reduced.

Cultural characters: Gas, but no fetid odor produced.

Deep agar: Lenticular colonies; gas.

Glucose broth: Clotty growth, which sediments; gas.

Gelatin: No liquefaction.

Milk: Spongy clot.

Peptones: Digested to amino acids; indole not formed.

Lipids: Digested.

Coagulated proteins: Not attacked.

Carbohydrates: Glucose, lactose, galactose, fructose, maltose, mannitol and starch are fermented as well as sucrose and inulin.

Biochemistry: Nitrites not formed from nitrates; sulfites reduced to sulfides; produces NH_3, H_2S, traces of acetylmethylcarbinol, formic, butyric and lactic acids.

Pathogenicity, natural: Isolated in acute appendicitis, feces from typhoid patients, pectoral myositis, furunculosis.

Pathogenicity, experimental: Non-pathogenic for laboratory animals.

10. *Inflabilis setiensis* Prévot and Raynaud 1944.

Habitat: River mud, oysters from Sète, soil of Africa, canned conger, intestinal tract of man. Quite frequent.

Morphology: Rods measuring 0.7 μ $\times$ 1.5 to 2 μ; non-motile; clostridial spores; Gram-positive.

Physiolgy: Strict anaerobe. Opt. T. $= 37°$C. Resists 1 minute at 100°C. Opt. pH $=$ 7 to 8. Survives 6 months. Neutral red and phenosafranin are reduced.

Cultural characters: Gas, but no fetid odor produced.

Deep agar: Lenticular colonies; gas.

Glucose VF broth: Diffuse turbidity; gas.

Gelatin: No liquefaction.

Milk: Unchanged.

Coagulated proteins: Not attacked.

Carbohydrates: Glucose, fructose, galactose, lactose, maltose, sucrose, xylose, arabinose and glycerol are fermented.

Biochemistry: Nitrites not formed from nitrates; sulfites not reduced; produces NH_3, volatile amines, acetone, ethanol, acetic, butyric and lactic acids.

Pathogenicity: Non-pathogenic. No toxin, or hemolysin.

11. *Inflabilis carbonei* (Arnaudi) P. 1940.

Synonym: Clostridium carbonei Arnaudi 1936.

Habitat: Potato. Uncommon.

Morphology: Rods with fusiform or rounded ends, 0.8 to 1.0 μ $\times$ 3.5 to 4.5 μ; non-motile; subterminal spore; Gram-positive; numerous polar granules; granulose-positive.

Physiology: Strict anaerobe. Opt. T. $= 37°$C. Resists 10 minutes at 95°C; killed after 10 minutes at 100°C. Opt. pH $=$ 6 to 8. rH decreases by the 4th to 5th day, then increases.

Cultural characters: Gas produced (maximum at 4th to 5th day).

Glucose-deep agar: No growth.

Agar slant (in vacuo): Flat, colorless, glistening colonies with irregular border.

Maltose-agar slant: Irregular colonies, slight pink color.

Glucose broth: Slight turbidity; no pigment.

Maltose broth: Abundant turbidity; heavy yellowish-pink sediment; gas, but no H_2S or indole formed.

Gelatin: No growth.

Milk: Coagulated with formation of pink-colored flakes; not digested.

Digested milk (ideal medium): Abundant turbidity; red, flaky sediment; indole, but no H_2S formed.

Roux' potato medium: Thin, punctiform, opaque, colonies; intense strawberry color.

Coagulated proteins: Not attacked.

Rice broth: Discrete strawberry-colored growth.

Cellulose and hemp: Not attacked.

Carbohydrates: Glucose, maltose, sucrose, galactose, fructose and raffinose are weakly fermented; lactose is actively fermented, particularly in acid media.

Biochemistry: Production of gas $(CO_2 + H_2 + CH_4)$, butyric acid and ethanol.

Red pigment: Soluble in alcohol and acetone; insoluble in ether, chloroform and water. Not influenced by light. Becomes yellow in the presence of 1% NaOH and becomes red again upon neutralisation by acetic acid.

Pathogenicity: Non-pathogenic.

Serology: Intravenous injection into the goat produces a serum which agglutinates the homologous strain up to 1-50,000 while not reacting with other chromogenic clostridia.

12. *Inflabilis filiformis* (Debono) P. 1950.

Synonym: Bacillus filiformis Debono (C. f. Bakt. 1912, *62,* 234); *Clostridium filiformis* Bergey *et al.* 1923.

Habitat: Intestinal tract of man; contaminated tomato preserves.

Morphology: Slender rods, 0.5 to 0.8 $\mu \times$ 3 to 5 μ; occurring singly, in pairs, short chains or filaments; non-motile; very small, spherical, subterminal spore; Gram-positive.

Physiology: Strict anaerobe. Opt. T. $= 37°C$. Resists 1 minute at 100°C. Neutral red irreversibly reduced, phenosafranin temporarily reduced.

Cultural characters: Gas, but no fetid odor produced.

Deep agar: Irregular, grey, translucent colonies, usually filamentous, sometimes fluffy.

Glucose broth: Very slight turbidity; sediment; gas.

Gelatin: No liquefaction.

Milk: Acidified, but not coagulated.

Coagulated proteins: Not attacked.

Potato: Filamentous, greyish growth.

Carbohydrates: Acid and gas from glucose, fructose, lactose, galactose, and maltose; sucrose, dulcitol, xylose, arabinose and starch are sometimes fermented.

Biochemistry: Nitrites not formed from nitrates; sulfites not reduced; produces NH_3, H_2S, volatile amines, ethanol, formic, propionic and lactic acids.

13.   *Inflabilis lacustris* Prévot, Thouvenot, Petrigalla and Sillioc 1956.

Habitat: Deposits from high mountain lakes on the Ruvenzori range (Congo). Quite frequent.

Morphology: Rods with rounded ends, 0.8 to 1.0 μ $\times$ 2 to 4 μ; non-motile; unencapsulated; clostridial spore (rare on ordinary media, more numerous and sometimes free in Ellner's medium); Gram-positive.

Physiology: Strict anaerobe. Resists 10 minutes at 80°C, 5 minutes at 90° and 1 minute at 100°C. Neutral red and phenosafranin definitely reduced, safranin temporarily reduced.

Cultural characters: Explosive gas and fetid odor produced.

Deep agar: Lenticular colonies; gas.

Glucose VF broth: Abundant turbidity; rapid, heavy sediment.

Peptone water: Slight turbidity.

Gelatin: No liquefaction or very slowly liquefied by some strains.

Milk: Rapidly coagulated with or without alveolar retraction.

Coagulated proteins: Not attacked.

Carbohydrates: Acid and abundant gas from glucose, fructose, maltose, sucrose, galactose, lactose, starch and glycerol.

Biochemistry: Nitrites formed from nitrates by some strains in the presence of glycerol; sulfites reduced to sulfides; produces NH_3 (abundant), H_2S (traces), volatile amines, ethanol, aldehydes, ketones, indole, phenol, scatole, acetic and butyric acids (sometimes a third higher acid).

Pathogenicity: Non-pathogenic or weakly so: In the guinea pig, local abscess or cutaneous necrosis. No toxin. Some strains produce a slightly active, soluble hemolysin.

14.   *Inflabilis pseudo-perfringens* (Adamson) P. 1938.

Habitat: War wounds, swamp mud. Quite uncommon.

Morphology: Short thick rods, with square ends; morphologically identical with *W. perfringens,* but has no capsule; occurs in short chains and filaments; non-motile; rare spore located subterminally, rapidly freed from the bacillary body; Gram-positive.

Physiology: Strict anaerobe. Opt. T. = 37°C. Resists 3 minutes at 80°C. and 20 minutes at 70° C. Survives several months. Neutral red and safranin reduced.

Cultures characters: No gas, nor fetid odor produced.

Deep agar: Flat, opaque, lenticular colonies with blurred edges; no gas formed.

Glucose broth: Turbid; no gas.

Gelatin: Liquefaction.

Milk: Coagulated in 3 to 4 days, then digested.

Coagulated proteins: Not attacked.

Carbohydrates: Acid but no gas from glucose, maltose, fructose, and galactose.

Biochemistry: Nitrites not formed from nitrates; produces NH_3, H_2S, indole not formed; volatile amines, aldehydes, acetylmethylcarbinol, acetic, butyric and lactic acids. Sulfites not reduced.

Pathogenicity: Generally non-pathogenic. Some strains may produce skin necrosis in the guinea pig.

15.   *Inflabilis magnus* (Choukévitch) P. 1938.

Synonym: Streptobacillus anaerobicus magnus Choukévitch 1911.

Habitat: Large intestine of the horse. Quite frequent.

Morphology: Straight, thick rods with rounded ends, 1.0 to 1.5 μ $\times$ 6 to 10 μ; occurring in short chains and filaments; non-motile; rare subterminal spore, seldom seen; Gram-positive.

Physiology: Strict anaerobe. Opt. T. $=$ 18-37°C. Resists 6 minutes at 100° C. Neutral red and safranin reduced.

Cultural characters: No gas produced.

Deep agar: Fluffy, translucent colonies.

Glucose broth: Meager, slimy growth.

Gelatin: No liquefaction.

Milk: Unchanged.

Pathogenicity: Non-pathogenic.

16.   *Inflabilis rectus* (Choukévitch) P. 1938

Synonym: Streptobacillus anaerobicus rectus Choukévitch 1911.

Habitat: Large intestine of the horse. Uncommon.

Morphology: Rods with square ends, 0.8 μ $\times$ 5 to 7 μ; occurring singly or in pairs; oval spore, located centrally or subterminally; Gram-positive.

Physiology: Strict anaerobe. Opt. T. $=$ 22-37° C. Resists 5 minutes at 100°C. Survives more than 1 year. Neutral red reduced.

Cultural characters: No gas formed, but fetid odor present.

Deep agar: Dense, circular, arborescent colonies; no gas produced.

Glucose broth: Diffuse turbidity; sediment; indole not formed.

Gelatin: No liquefaction.

Milk: Unchanged.

Coagulated proteins: Not attacked.

Carbohydrates: Glucose, fructose, maltose, sucrose, galactose, arabinose, xylose, mannitol, sorbitol, inulin and starch are fermented.

Biochemistry: Nitrites not formed from nitrates; indole not formed; produces NH_3, H_2S, volatile amines, aldehydes, acetylmethylcarbinol, acetic, valerianic and lactic acids.

Pathogenicity: Non-pathogenic.

16bis. *I. rectus* var. *conglobatum* (Zeetti).

We relate to the above species the new strain described by Zeetti in 1934 under the name *Bacterium conglobatum* which differs only by the absence of carbohydrate fermentation.

17. *Inflabilis megalosporus* (Choukévitch) P. 1938.

Synonym: Bacillus megalosporus Choukévitch 1911.

Habitat: Intestinal tract of the horse. Quite uncommon.

Morphology: Rods with rounded ends, 1 μ $\times$ 3 to 5 μ; non-motile; large spherical spore, either subterminal or occupying nearly the entire rod; Gram-positive.

Physiology: Strict anaerobe. Opt. T. $=$ 18-37° C. Resists 20 minutes at 100° C. Neutral red reduced permanently.

Cultural characters: No gas produced.

Deep agar: Delicate, lenticular colonies.

Glucose broth: Diffuse turbidity; indole not formed.

Gelatin: No liquefaction.

Milk: Unchanged.

Carbohydrates: Glucose, fructose, maltose, sucrose, lactose, glycerol, starch, and sometimes galactose are fermented.

Biochemistry: Nitrites not formed from nitrates; sulfites not reduced; indole not formed; produces NH_3, ketones, H_2S (traces), acetic, butyric and lactic acids.

Pathogenicity, natural: Isolated in a case of purulent pleurisy (Hanoi).

Pathogenicity, experimental: Intraperitoneal injection into the guinea pig produces purulent peritonitis.

GENUS II: *WELCHIA* Pribram 1929.

Non-motile, encapsulated *Clostridiaceae*.

This genus comprises actually 2 species and their varieties; here is the key to their determination:

1. Rods of large size; lenticular colonies; large amounts of gas produced; gelatin liquefied; spongy clotting of milk; saccharolytic (including glycerol and inulin); hemolytic; highly pathogenic (hypertoxic gaseous phlegmon); specific toxin; very active hemolysin; toxigenic formula: $\alpha\eta\theta\chi$; specific antitoxin; little or no indole formed; acrolein produced; lipolytic.

1. *Welchia perfringens,* page 223

1 bis.—Variety which does not clot milk or very slowly.

1 bis. *W. perfringens* var. *egens,* page 224

1 ter. Variety which does not liquefy gelatin; indole not formed; hemolysin appearing slowly; pathogenic (diarrhea in piglets and other young domestic animals).

1 ter. *W. perfringens* var. *zoodysenteriae,* page 225

1 quarto. Variety with toxigenic formula $\alpha\theta\tau\chi\gamma$; pathogenic for calves (enterotoxemia).

1 quarto. *W. perfringens* var. *vitulitoxicus,* page 225

2. Species closely related to the preceding, from which it differs only by the liquefaction of coagulated serum; coagulation of egg-yolk medium; glycerol and inulin irregularly fermented; highly pathogenic (lamb dysentery); specific toxin and hemolysin having some antigenic relationship with the preceding; its antitoxin will neutralize the toxins of *W. perfringens; W. perfringens* antitoxin will not neutralize its toxins; antigenic formula: $\alpha\beta\chi\delta\epsilon\theta\lambda$.

2. *Welchia agni,* page 225

2 bis. Variety liquefying coagulated serum; partial digestion of coagulated egg-white; glycerol fermented with the production of acrolein; highly pathogenic (enterotoxemia of sheep); toxin not neutralized by *W. perfringens* antitoxin, but neutralized by *W. agni* antitoxin; antigenic formula: $\alpha\beta\delta\theta\chi$.

2 bis. *W. agni* var. *paludis,* page 226

2 ter. Variety not attacking egg-white; glycerol fermented, but not inulin; enterotoxemia of sheep; very active toxin appearing slowly; active hemolysin; antigenic formula: $\alpha\epsilon\theta\chi\lambda$.

2 ter. *W. agni* var. *wilsdoni,* page 226

2 quarto. Highly thermoresistant variety; necrotic enteritis of man; antigenic formula: $\alpha\beta\gamma$.

2 quarto. *W. agni* var. *hominitoxicus,* page 227

1. *Welchia perfringens* (Veillon and Zuber) P. 1938.
Type A (human)

Synonym: Bacillus perfringens Veillon and Zuber 1898; *Bacillus aerogenes capsulatus* Welch and Nuttall 1892; *Bacillus phlegmonis emphysematosae* Fraenkel; *Bacillus welchii* Migula; *Clostridium welchii* Bergey *et al.; Clostridium perfringens* (V. and Z.) Hauduroy *et al.*

Habitat: Soil, water, air (dust), mud, marine sediments, intestinal tract of man and animals; universal geographic distribution: from the poles to the equator. Extremely frequent.

Morphology: Short, thick rods with practically square ends, 0.8 to 1.2 μ $\times$ 3 to 4 μ; non-motile; encapsulated; central or subterminal spore swelling the rod; Gram-positive.

Physiology: Strict anaerobe. Opt. T. $= 37°$ C (18-38°). Resists 2 to 10 minutes at 100°C (some strains more or less). Opt. pH $= 6$-8. Survives 6 months. Neutral red and safranin reduced.

Cultural characters: Large amounts of gas produced.

Deep agar: Lenticular colonies; agar broken up by gas.

Glucose broth: Abundant diffuse turbidity; explosive gas (H_2); butyric odor; H_2S; markedly acidified (pH 5.5).

Blood broth: Rapidly hemolyzed.

Peptone water: Meager growth; little or no indole formed.

Gelatin: Slowly liquefied.

Milk: Rapid coagulation; spongy clot; gas.

Coagulated egg-white: Partly attacked (becomes translucent).

Coagulated serum: Partly attacked.

Carbohydrates: Acid and gas from glucose, fructose, maltose, galactose, sucrose, lactose, raffinose, mannose, starch, dextrin, glycerol and glycogen; sometimes inulin and salicin (4 fermentation groups).

Biochemistry: Nitrites formed from nitrates in the presence of galactose and glycerol; N_2 formed from nitrates in the presence of glucose; indole not formed or traces; sulfites rapidly reduced to sulfides (endocellular reductase giving black colonies in sulfite-iron agar); produces NH_3, H_2S, CO_2 and H_2, amino acids (from casein), volatile amines, aldehydes, ketones, acetylmethylcarbinol, acrolein, butyric and acetic acids; procollagenase dissolving collagenase A of Nageotte; hyaluronidase depolymerizing hyaluronic acid.

Pathogenicity, natural: Gas gangrene, gaseous phlegmon, puerperal septicemia, appendicitis, enteritis, gas jaundice, etc.

Pathogenicity, experimental: Injection into the guinea pig of 0.1 ml. of a 24-hour old culture produces a gaseous phlegmon followed by myolysis and hemolysis. Injection into the rabbit of 0.5 ml. gives rise to gaseous edema, hemolysis and death. Mice and pigeons are also susceptible.

Toxin: In glucose broth, appears in 15 to 24 hours; 0.25 ml. will kill the guinea pig by intravenous injection, 0.5 ml., the mouse. Contains 3 main factors: a) lecithinase, which liberates phosphorylcholine and stearooleylglyceride from lecithin, and is also hemolytic and necrotizing; θ) non-necrotizing hemolysin; η) lethal. The toxin produces hematuria and epistaxis in animals (laked blood). Antigenic formula.

Serology: Specific agglutination up to 1-2,500.

Immunization: By means of toxoid and anaculture.

Toxoid: Obtained by adding 4 parts formaldehyde per 1,000 of toxin.

Antitoxin: Specific; neutralizes the toxins of *W. perfringens* in low concentration.

Varieties of *W. perfringens*.

1bis. *W. perfringens* var. *egens* (Stoddard) P. 1938.

Synonym: Bacillus egens Stoddard.

Habitat, Morphology, Physiology: Similar to that of *W. perfringens.*

Difference: Coagulation of milk is slower; egg-white is not attacked.

Toxins: Completely neutralized by *W. perfringens* antitoxin.

1 ter. *W. perfringens* var. *zoodysenteriae*
(Detre and Rohonyi) P. 1938.

Synonym: Bacillus zoodysenteriae hungaricus D. and R. 1927.

Habitat: Isolated in dysentery of young domestic animals and piglets.

Morphology, Physiology: Similar to those of *W. perfringens.*

Difference: Gelatin not liquefied; indole not formed.

Pathogenicity, natural: Fatal dysentery of piglets.

Pathogenicity, experimental: 24-hour old cultures are pathogenic for guinea pig, mouse, pigeon, rabbit, pregnant sows, ewes, cows and their offspring. Animals 1 week-old and older are not susceptible.

Toxin unknown.

1 quarto. *W. perfringens* var. *vitulitoxicus* (Bosworth) P. 1949.
Type E (bovine)

Habitat: Farm areas where calf enterotoxemia is prevalent.

Morphology, Physiology, Cultural characters: Identical with those of *W. perfringens.*

Pathogenicity, natural: Enterotoxemia of young calves.

Pathogenicity, experimental: Ingestion of fluid cultures will reproduce the natural disease.

Toxin: Complex; antigenic formula: $\alpha\theta\tau\chi\lambda$, where τ is a necrotizing and lethal factor different from η, and λ a gelatinase inhibited by normal serum.

2. *Welchia agni* (Dalling) P. 1938.
Type B (ovine)

Synonym: Bacillus agni Dalling; *Lamb dysentery bacillus* Dalling; *Bacillus* L. D.

Habitat: Intestinal tract of young-born sheep suffering from dysentery. Frequent.

Morphology: Identical with *W. perfringens.*

Physiology: Identical with *W. perfringens.*

Cultural characters: Similar to those of *W. perfringens,* except:

1. Coagulated serum is not digested.
2. Gelatin is more rapidly liquefied.
3. Alcaline egg-yolk medium is rapidly coagulated.
4. Glycerol is less frequently fermented.

Pathogenicity, natural: Fatal dysentery of young lambs.

Pathogenicity, experimental: Ingestion of pure cultures will reproduce the natural disease.

Toxin: Highly active exotoxin; mouse killed by intravenous injection of

0.001 ml.; pathogenic also for guinea pig, rabbit, pigeon, and sheep; produces necrotic lesions; no hematuria; thermolabile; antigenic formula: $\alpha\beta\gamma\delta\epsilon$, where β is thermolabile, necrotic and lethal, γ is lethal and necrotic, δ is hemolytic, ϵ is lethal and necrotic, α is a lecithinase.

Hemolysin: Acts upon red blood cells of rabbit, sheep and guinea pig.

Antitoxin: Will neutralize the toxins of *W. perfringens* and *W. agni.*

Biochemistry: Similar to that of the preceding species.

Varieties of *W. agni.*

2 bis. *W. agni* var. *paludis* (McEwen) P. 1938. Type C (ovine)

Synonym: Bacillus paludis McEwen 1930.

Habitat: Intestinal tract of sheep dying from enterotoxemia. Frequent.

Morphology: Similar to *W. agni.*

Physiology: Similar to *W. agni.*

Cultural characters: Similar to those of *W. agni,* except:

1. Rapid digestion of coagulated serum.
2. Egg-yolk medium more frequently coagulated.
3. Incomplete digestion of coagulated egg-white.
4. Disintegration of meat.
5. Blackening of brain medium.
6. Inulin and mannitol not fermented. Glycerol fermented with production of acrolein.

Pathogenicity, natural: Enterotoxemia of sheep.

Pathogenicity, experimental: Injection of 0.025 to 0.002 ml. of fluid culture into the guinea pig will produce fatal gas gangrene in 24 hours with myolysis and edema. Pigeon and sheep are also susceptible.

Hemolysin: Highly active: 0.001 ml. will hemolyze sheep red blood cells.

Toxin: Quite active: produces edema and necrosis; thermolabile; not neutralized by *W. perfringens* antitoxin; neutralized by *W. agni* antitoxin; *W. paludis* antitoxin will not neutralize completely the toxins of *W. perfringens;* antigenic formula: $\beta\gamma\delta\alpha\epsilon$.

Biochemistry: Similar to that of the preceding species.

2 ter. *W. agni* var. *wilsdoni* (Wilsdon) P. 1938.

Synonym: Bacillus perfringens D Wilsdon 1931.

Habitat: Intestinal tract of sheep suffering from enterotoxemia. Frequent.

Morphology and *Physiology:* Similar to that of *W. agni.*

Cultural characters: Similar to those of *W. agni.*

Difference:

1. Liquefaction of gelatin in 24 hours.
2. Brain medium blackened.

3. Egg-white not attacked. Egg-yolk medium not coagulated.

4. Coagulated serum not attacked.

5. Dulcitol, salicin and inulin not fermented.

Pathogenicity, natural: Fulminating enterotoxemia of the sheep.

Pathogenicity, experimental: Injection into or ingestion by the guinea pig, mouse, rabbit, pigeon and sheep will give rise to pink, gaseous edema, followed by myolysis and death.

Toxin: Highly active: mouse killed by 0.01ml.; produces necrosis of the skin, serous edema and nervous phenomena; no hematuria; thermolabile; antigenic formula: $\alpha\epsilon\theta\chi\lambda$, where ϵ is lethal and necrotizing, and λ hemolytic; neutralized by B and D antitoxins.

Hemolysin: Feebly active *in vivo;* highly active *in vitro:* 0.004 ml will hemolyze 0.1 ml. red cells.

Biochemistry: Similar to that of the preceding species.

Note.—*W. agni* var. *ovitoxicus* (Bennetts) P. 1938.

Synonym: Bacillus ovitoxicus Bennetts 1932.

Has been identified afterwards as *W. agni* var. *wilsdoni.*

2 quarto. **Welchia agni** var. **hominitoxicus** (Zeissler and Rassfeld). P. 1929. Type F (human)

Synonym: Bacillus enterotoxicus (Z. and R.) Dieckmann 1949.

Habitat: Probably soil of Russia and intestinal tract of man.

Morphology: Frequently fusiform, and occurring in chains of clostridia.

Physiology: Marked thermoresistance: 120 to 180 minutes at 100°C.

Cultural characters, Biochemistry: Identical with those of *W. agni.*

Pathogenicity, natural: Isolated from the small intestine in cases of necrotizing enterotoxemia, and in food responsible for this toxi-infection (semi-preserves).

Pathogenicity, experimental: The Hamburg disease has been reproduced experimentally by ingestion of fluid cultures.

Toxin: antigenic formula: $\alpha\beta\gamma$; neutralized by *W. agni* (type B) antitoxin.

Genus III. *CLOSTRIDIUM* Prazmowski 1880[1].

Motile *Clostridiaceae.*

The genus *Clostridium* comprises more than one hundred anaerobic species (4 of which are facultative). These species form several natural

---

[1] The origin of the word goes back to Trécul (1863) who used it to designate the swollen sporeforming rods of the butyric fermentation.

sub-groups to which we assign the rank of sub-genera, determined from the physiological, biochemical and, especially, pathogenic characters.

Here is the key to the determination of these sub-genera:

A) Non-pathogenic sub-genera, natural fermenters of ternary compounds:

    I. Carbohydrates fermented, in particular starch and lactate; pectin and cellulose not attacked; main fermentation product is butyric acid; non-pathogenic.
        Sub-genus of *Cl. butryicum*, page 228

    II. Cellulose fermented.
        Sub-genus of *Cl. naviculum*, page 239

    III. Pectin fermented.
        Sub-genus of *Cl. aurantibutyricum*, page 240

B) Sub-genera pathogenic either in pure culture or in mixed culture.

    IV. Produce either malignant edema (red) or blackleg in pure culture. pure culture.
        Sub-genus of *Cl. septicum*, page 253

    V. Produce white or pink gelatinous edema in pure culture.
        Sub-genus of *Cl. novyi*, page 258

    VI. Produce botulism either by preformed toxin or in pure culture.
        Sub-genus of *Cl. botulinum*, page 265

    VII. Produce putrid and toxic lesions and gangrene either in pure or in mixed culture; proteolytic and putrid.
        Sub-genus of *Cl. sporogenes*, page 269

    VIII. More or less pathogenic, producing lesions without any specific characters; non-proteolytic.
        Sub-genus of *Cl. fallax*, page 286

    IX. Species not included in the above sub-genera.
        Group IX; page 298

SUB-GENUS I: *CLOSTRIDIUM BUTYRICUM*
(agents of butyric fermentation).

Definition.—Clostridia with iodophil granules; motile by means of peritrichous flagella; generally non-proteolytic, but saccharolytic (except pectin and cellulose); lactates attacked; non-pathogenic; produce butyric and acetic acids, or acetone and butanol with liberation of CO_2 and H_2. The numerous species proposed by various authors are highly related and closely linked together by several intermediary varieties; here is the key to their determination, modified in accord with recent work:

    1. Type species: Lenticular or arborescent colonies; gas formed; broth turbid showing auto-agglutination; saccharolytic (amylolytic)

but not cellulolytic nor pectinolytic; non-proteolytic; gelatin not liquefied; milk clotted; Ca lactate fermented; butyric and acetic acids are the main fermentation products; non-pathogenic.

    1. *Clostridium butyricum,* page 230

Varieties:

    1 bis. Lactate not attacked; butyric acid and ethanol produced.
       1 bis. *Cl. amylozme,* page 231
    1 ter. Lactate not attacked; butyric and lactic acids produced.
       1 ter. *Cl. saccharobutyricum,* page 231
    1 quarto. Ca lactate attacked; milk unchanged; butyric acid produced only.
       1 quarto. *Cl. tyrobutyricum,* page 232
    1 quinto. Starch not fermented.
       1 quinto. *Cl. beijerincki,* page 232

  2. Irregular colonies; gelatin not liquefied; milk clotted; saccharolytic (lactose, mannitol and soluble starch mainly); lactates not attacked; atmospheric N_2 fixed; produces acetic and butyric acids, ethanol, iso-propanol, butanol, and acetone.

    2. *Cl. butylicum,* page 232

Varieties:

    2 bis. Produces butanol and iso-propanol.
       2 bis. *Cl. americanum,* page 233
    2 ter. Produces butanol and iso-propanol.
       2 ter. *Cl. orthobutylicum,* page 233
    2 quarto. Saccharolytic (lactose and soluble starch mainly); produces butanol mostly.
       2 quarto. *Cl. mulleri,* page 233
    2 quinto. Gelatin liquefied; milk clotted and partly digested; actively saccharolytic (lactose, glycerol, starch and dextrin mainly); butanol is the main fermentation product.
       2 quinto. *Cl. perbutylicum,* page 233
    2 sexto. Gelatin not liquefied; milk clotted and partly digested; saccharolytic (lactose and starch mainly); produces butanol and propanol.
       2 sexto. *Cl. butylpropylicum,* page 234
    2 septo. Gelatin not liquefied; milk clotted; saccharolytic (starch, dextrin and glycogen); produces butyric acid, acetone, ethanol, iso-propanol, butanol; nitrites formed from nitrates.
       2 septo. *Cl. toanum,* page 234

  3. Triangular sporal capsule; atmospheric N_2 fixed; saccharolytic (not lactose, starch nor lactate); produces butyric and acetic acids, ethanol, propanol and butanol.

    3. *Cl. pastorianum,* page 235

4. Elongated forms and micro-oidia; lenticular colonies; gelatin not liquefied; starch and lactate fermented; atmospheric N_2 fixed; produces ethanol, propanol, iso-propanol and iso-butanol.

    4. *Cl. amylobacter,* page 235

5. No growth on meat media; grows exclusively on starch media; gelatin not liquefied; milk clotted; produces acetic, butyric and lactic acids, acetone, ethanol and butanol.

    5. *Cl. amylolyticum,* page 236

6. Stained purple by iodine; motility disappears rapidly; arborescent colonies; gelatin not liquefied or slowly liquefied; milk clotted; saccharolytic; amylolytic.

    6. *Cl. iodophilum,* page 236

7. Elongated sporangia; numerous spores; gelatin not liquefied; milk clotted; saccharolytic (lactose, starch, dextrin, glycogen mainly); atmospheric N_2 fixed; produces acetic and butyric acids.

    7. *Cl. madisonii,* page 237

8. Milk unchanged; saccharolytic (lactose, dextrin, starch and glycerol mainly); lactates fermented in the presence of acetate; produces acetic and butyric acids.

    8. *Cl. lactoacetophilum,* page 237

9. Gelatin rapidly liquefied; milk clotted; saccharolytic (lactose, cellobiose); nitrites formed from nitrates; a-amino-butyrate attacked to form NH_3, acetate and butyrate.

    9. *Cl. aminobutyricum,* page 238

10. Arborescent colonies; gelatin not liquefied; milk clotted; indole not formed; saccharolytic; amylolytic; cellulose not attacked; utilizes acetate, propionate and butyrate.

    10. *Cl. polyfermenticum,* page 238

11. Similar to the preceding, but incapable of utilizing propionate.

    11. *Cl. saccharophilicum,* page 238

12. Similar to the preceding, but capable of peptonizing milk.

    12. *Cl. saccharopetum,* page 239

13. Similar to the preceding, but incapable of utilizing salts of straight-chain acids.

    13. *Cl. saccharopostulatum,* page 239

1. **Clostridium butyricum** (Pasteur) Prazmowski 1880.

Synonym: Vibrion butyrique Pasteur; *Bacilles butyriques* (Pasteur) Macé.

Habitat: Soil (especially, fertile), plants (particularly roots and tubercules); intestinal tract of animals; universally distributed. Extremely frequent.

Morphology: Rods measuring 0.8 to 1.0 μ $\times$ 3 to 12 μ; motile by means of peritrichous flagella; central or subterminal spore which swells the rod; coccoid forms may be seen; Gram-positive, easily decolorized; iodophilic granules.

Physiology: Not very strict anaerobe. Opt. T. $= 37°C$ (18-42°). Resists 10 minutes at 80°C. Neutral red and safranin reduced.

Cultural characters: Large amounts of gas are produced; rancid odor.

Deep agar: Lenticular or arborescent colonies; gas.

Glucose broth: Uniform turbidity or auto-agglutination.

Gelatin: No liquefaction.

Milk: Clotted.

Coagulated proteins: Not attacked.

Carbohydrates: Hexoses, hexobioses, pentoses, lactose and starch are fermented; Ca lactate fermented.

Biochemistry: Produces CO_2, H_2, butyric and acetic acids (sometimes propionic and valerianic in addition); in media saturate with $CaCO_3$, production of acetone and butanol.

Pathogenicity: Non-pathogenic. Some strains are hemolytic on account of the high acid content of their cultures, but not due to a true hemolysin.

1 bis. *Cl. butyricum* var. *amylozyme* (Perdrix) Prévot 1938.

Habitat: Soil, etc. Frequent.

Morphology, physiology: Identical with the preceding.

Cultural characters: Identical with the preceding.

Carbohydrates: Glucose, sucrose, lactose and starch are fermented; Ca lactate and cellulose not attacked.

Biochemistry: Produces butyric acid, ethanol and amyl alcohol.

1 ter. *Cl. butyricum* var. *saccharobutyricum* Schattenfroh and Grassberger 1900.

Synonym: Granulobacillus saccharobutyricus mobilis non liquefaciens S. and G.

Habitat: Soil, cow's milk. Frequent.

Morphology: Identical with the preceding species.

Physiology: Similar to that of the preceding species. Resists 3 minutes at 100°C.

Cultural characters: Gas produced.

Deep agar: Lenticular or arborescent colonies.

Glucose broth: Turbid; gas.

Peptone water: Slight turbidity.

Gelatin: No liquefaction.

Milk: Clotted.

Ca lactate: Not fermented.

Carbohydrates: Mono- and di-saccharides are fermented as well as starch and glycerol; cellulose not attacked.

Biochemistry: Produces CO_2, H_2, butanol (traces), acetylmethyl-carbinol, butyric, formic, acetic and lactic acids.

Pathogenicity: Non-pathogenic.

1 quarto. *Cl. tyrobutyricum* van Beynum and Pette 1935.

Habitat: Silage, cheese, decomposing organic material.

Morphology: Rods measuring 0.8 to 1.2 μ $\times$ 2 to 15 μ; motile; ovoid, subterminal spore swelling the rod; Gram-positive.

Physiology: Strict anaerobe.

Tomato-agar: Opaque, convex, yellowish-cream colonies.

Tomato-deep agar: Lenticular colonies.

Gelatin: No liquefaction.

Milk: Unchanged.

Carbohydrates: Glucose, fructose, arabinose and Ca lactate are fermented.

Biochemistry: Nitrites may be formed from nitrates; H_2S not formed; indole not produced; produces butyric acid mostly.

Systematics: Variety of *Cl. butyricum.*

1 quinto. *Cl. beijerincki* (Donker) Bergey *et al.*

Synonym: Clostridium beijerincki Donker 1926.

Habitat: Soil, and fermenting plant tissues.

Morphology, Physiology: Identical with those of *Cl. butyricum.*

Carbohydrates: Glucose, lactose, sucrose, galactose, fructose, inulin and mannitol are fermented; glycerol and starch are not attacked.

2. *Clostridium butylicum* (Beijerinck) Donker 1926.

Synonym: Granulobacter butylicum Beijerinck 1893.

Habitat: Soil, especially fertile. Frequent.

Morphology: Rods measuring 0.8 to 1.0 μ $\times$ 3 to 5 μ; motile by means of peritrichous flagella; ovoid, clostridial spore, often free; Gram-positive; granulose-positive.

Physiology: Strict anaerobe. Opt. T. $= 30°$ C. Resists 10 minutes at $80°$ C.

Cultural characters: Gas, but no fetid odor produced.

Agar slant (in vacuo): Circular or irregularly-round colonies, moist, raised, creamy.

Deep agar: Lenticular colonies.

Glucose broth: Turbid, sedimenting rapidly.

Gelatin: No liquefaction.

Milk: Clotted.

Coagulated proteins: Not attacked.

Carbohydrates: Glucose, sucrose, lactose, xylose, mannitol, salicin, inulin, soluble starch are fermented; Ca lactate not attacked.

Biochemistry: Nitrites not formed from nitrates; atmospheric N_2 fixed; produces ethanol, iso-propanol, butanol, acetone, acetic and butyric acids.

Pathogenicity: Non-pathogenic.

2 bis. *Cl. butylicum* var. *americanum* Pringsheim 1906.

Synonym: Clostridium americanum Pringsheim 1906. This variety differs from the preceding one only by the presence of n-butanol and iso-butanol in the fermentation products.

2 ter. *Cl. orthobutylicum* Grimbert.

Synonym: B. orthobutylicus Grimbert 1893.

Habitat: Soil.

Morphology: Rods with rounded ends, 1.5 μ $\times$ 3 to 6 μ; motile; clostridial spore giving an aspect of bell-clapper; Gram-positive; no blue stain with iodine.

Physiology: Strict anaerobe. Resists 10 minutes at 80° C. Grows on Grimbert's medium added with peptone and carbohydrate.

Carbohydrates: Ca lactate and cellulose not attacked; glucose, maltose, sucrose, lactose, galactose, arabinose, glycerol, starch, dextrin and inulin are fermented.

Boichemistry: Produces CO_2, H_2, n-butanol, iso-butanol, acetic and butyric acids with sometimes a trace of formic acid.

Pathogenicity: Non-pathogenic.

2 quarto. *Cl. mulleri* McClung and McCoy nov. comb.

Synonym: Cl. granulobacter acetobutylicum Muller 1940.

Morphology: Rods with rounded ends, 1.4 μ $\times$ 3 to 10 μ; occurring in short chains; fusiform sporangia; subterminal or terminal spore; motile; Gram-positive.

Physiology: Strict anaerobe. Opt. T. $=$ 28-33° C.

Agar slant: Circular, convex, granular colonies.

Broth: No growth.

Gelatin: No liquefaction.

Milk: Acid and gas, partial coagulation.

Potato: Gas; odor of butanol.

Carbohydrates: Acid and gas from glucose, sucrose, lactose, maltose, inulin, starch, salicin, dextrin, mannitol and galactose.

Biochemistry: Nitrites not formed from nitrates; indole not formed; produces H_2S (traces), and butanol mostly.

2 quinto. *Cl. perbutylicum* Beesch nov. comb.

Synonym: Cl. saccharoacetoperbutylicum Beech 1948.

Habitat: Soil, corn cobs. Uncommon.

Morphology: Rods measuring 0.7 to 2.0 μ $\times$ 3 to 12 μ; occurring singly, in pairs or in short chains; motile by means of peritrichous flagella; fusiform sporangia; cylindrical, subterminal spore; Gram-positive; granulose-positive.

Physiology: Strict anaerobe. Opt. T. $=$ 29-31°C. Opt. pH $=$ 5.5-5.3

Cultural characters: Gas, but no fetid odor produced.

Agar slant: Circular or irregularly-round, creamy-white, convex, translucent colonies.

Broth: No growth.

Gelatin: Liquefaction.

Milk: Coagulated, then partially peptonized.

Potato: Abundant, viscid growth with butylic odor.

Carbohydrates: Acid and gas from glucose, fructose, maltose, galactose, sucrose, lactose, raffinose, mannose, melibiose, xylose, arabinose, salicin, glycerol, starch, glycogen and dextrin.

Biochemistry: Nitrites not formed from nitrates; main fermentation product is butanol.

Pathogenicity: Non-pathogenic.

2 sexto. *Cl. butylpropylicum* Beesch and Legg.

Synonym: Cl. *amylosaccharobutylpropylicum* Beesch and Legg 1947.

Habitat: Soil.

Morphology: Rods measuring 0.6 to 1.5 μ $\times$ 2.8 to 12 μ; with rounded ends; motile by means of peritrichous flagella; fusiform sporangia; cylindrical or ovoid spore, 0.5 μ to 2.0 μ $\times$ 0.8 to 2.8 μ, located subterminally or terminally; Gram-positive; granulose-positive.

Physiololgy: Strict anaerobe. Opt. T. $=$ 29-32° C. Opt. pH $=$ 5.4-5.8.

Cultural characters: Gas, but no fetid odor produced.

Agar: Circular, extensive, convex, opalescent colonies.

Gelatin: No liquefaction.

Broth: Slight turbidity.

Milk: Coagulated in 10 days; partial digestion in 15 days.

Potato: Extensive, viscid growth; liquefaction.

Carbohydrates: Acid and gas from glucose, fructose, galactose, mannose, salicin, aesculin, trehalose, arabinose and xylose.

Biochemistry: Nitrites not formed from nitrates; indole not formed; produces H_2S (traces), butanol and propanol.

2 septo. *Cl. toanum* Baba 1943.

Habitat: Japan.

Morphology: Rods measuring 1 μ $\times$ 5 μ; occurring singly or in short chains; encapsulated; motile; clostridial forms; ovoid, central or subterminal spore; Gram-positive (easily decolorized); granulose-positive.

Physiology: Strict anaerobe. Opt. T. for growth $= 33\,°C$. Opt. T. for fermentation $= 35\text{-}37°$ C. Opt. pH for growth $= 6\text{-}7$. Opt. pH for fermentation $= 5.8\text{-}6.5$. Catalase-negative.

Cultural characters: Gas produced.

Deep agar: Gas.

Agar slant (in vacuo): Moist, irregular, white colonies.

Gelatin: No liquefaction.

Glucose broth: Abundant turbidity; gas; odor of butanol.

Milk: Coagulated.

Coagulated serum: Slight liquefaction.

Potato: Moist, white colonies.

Carbohydrates: Glucose, arabinose, fructose, mannose, galactose, sucrose, maltose, trehalose, dextrin, soluble starch and glycogen are fermented.

Biochemistry: Nitrites not formed from nitrates; produces acetone, ethanol, butanol, iso-propanol and butyric acid.

3. *Cl. pastorianum* Winogradsky 1893.

Habitat: Fertile soil of St. Petersburg.

Morphology: Similar to *Cl. butyricum,* with the exception that the spore envelope is triangular.

Physiology: Similar to *Cl. butyricum.*

Cultural characters: Differs from *Cl. butyricum* only by the fact that it will grow in broth.

Carbohydrates: Glucose, galactose, fructose, sucrose, inulin and dextrin are fermented. Glycerol, starch, lactose, mannitol and Ca lactate are not fermented.

Biochemistry: Produces CO_2, H_2, butyric and acetic acids, ethanol, propanol, n-butanol and iso-butanol. Atmospheric N_2 is fixed.

4. *Cl. amylobacter* A. and M. Bredemann.

Habitat: Soil, sand, plants. Frequent.

Morphology: Similar to *Cl. butyricum;* numerous micro-oidia and iodophilic granules.

Physiology: Microaerophilic. Opt. T. $= 37°$ C. Resists at $80°$ C, but is killed after 5 minutes at $100°$ C.

Cultural characters: Large amounts of gas produced.

Deep agar: Lenticular colonies; gas.

Gelatin: No liquefaction.

Milk: Coagulated.

Carbohydrates: All fermented, including starch and Ca lactate.

Biochemistry: NH_3 not formed; produces ethanol, butanol, iso-butanol, n-propanol and iso-propanol; will fix atmospheric nitrogen.

5. *Cl. amylolyticum* Prévot and Saissac 1950.

Habitat: Fertile soil (Ile-de-France).

Morphology: Rods measuring 0.8 to 1.0 μ $\times$ 4 to 5 μ; actively motile; very large (2μ) oval, subterminal spore; Gram-positive (bipolar staining); iodophilic granules; alternating stained and unstained zones in the non-sporeforming rods.

Physiology: Strict anaerobe. Opt. T. $=$ 33-37°C. Grows at 22° C. Resists 1 minutes at 100° C. No growth on autoclaved meat media. Neutral red and safranin reduced temporarily.

Isolation: Soil column added with starch; transfers from amylolytic zones unto potato mash supply an enriched culture which can be purified by seeding into bean-deep agar.

Cultural characters: Large amounts of gas, but no fetid odor produced; marked butyric odor. Grows exclusively on starch media. Bean-deep agar: Small, fluffy, opaque, irregular, white colonies; gas.

Potato-deep agar: Same type of colony as above; gas.

Potato mash: Rapid, abundant growth; large amounts of gas; markedly acid (pH 4.5); butyric odor; the mash is disintegrated, becomes liquid, viscid.

Glucose VF broth: No growth.

Autoclaved peptone water: No growth.

Filtered peptone water: Slight turbidity; gas.

Gelatin: No liquefaction.

Milk: Massive clot without retraction or digestion.

Coagulated proteins: Not attacked.

Carbohydrates: Starch and lactose very actively fermented; glucose, fructose, galactose, maltose, sucrose and mannitol feebly fermented; pectin not attacked.

Biochemistry: Nitrites formed from nitrates in the presence of starch; sulfites slowly and partly reduced in the presence of starch; produces NH_3 (traces), large amounts of acetone, butanol and ethanol; H_2S not formed, nor acetoin. Fermentation of potato mash produces 1 part each of acetic and butyric acids, traces of lactic acid.

Pathogenicity: Non-pathogenic. No toxin, nor hemolysin.

6. *Cl. iodophilum* Nanna Svartz 1927.

Synonym: Cl. butylicum iodophilum Nanna Svartz.

Habitat: Intestinal tract of man. Quite frequent.

Morphology: Similar to *Cl. butylicum,* with the exception that mature rods rapidly become non-motile; quite numerous iodophilic granules.

Physiology: Strict anaerobe. Killed after 2 to 4 minutes at 100° C.

Cultural characters: Gas produced.

Deep agar: Lenticular colonies.

Gelatin: No growth.

Milk: Rapid coagulation.

Carbohydrates: Glucose, fructose, galactose, mannose, sucrose, lactose, maltose, arabinose, salicin, starch and glycerol are fermented; cellulose is not attacked.

Pathogenicity: Non-pathogenic.

7. *Cl. madisonii* McCoy 1946.

Habitat: Fertile soil (Madison, Wisconsin).

Morphology: Rods with rounded ends, 0.5 to 1.2 μ $\times$ 3 to 5.8 μ; occurring singly or in short chains; numerous subterminal or terminal spores, cylindrical or ellipsoidal, 0.7 to 1.3μ $\times$ 1.3 to 2.4 μ; motile; elongated, fusiform sporangia; Gram-positive; granulose-positive.

Physiology: Strict anaerobe. Opt. T. = 92-33° C (28-42°C). Opt. pH = 5.0 -6.0 (4.3-7.6).

Cultural characters: Gas produced.

Blood agar: No hemolysis.

Gelatin: No liquefaction.

Milk: Coagulated; gas; no digestion.

Brain-medium: Not blackened.

Carbohydrates: Glucose, mannose, fructose, sucrose, maltose, lactose, trehalose, amnnitol, arabinose, xylose, galactose, melezitose, starch, dextrin, inulin, glycogen, aesculin, sorbitol, raffinose, amygdalin and inositol are fermented.

Biochemistry: Nitrites not formed from nitrates; indole not formed; H_2S produced; will fix atmospheric nitrogen; produces acetic and butyric acids.

8. *Cl. lactoacetophilum* Blat and Barker 1947.

Habitat: Soil.

Morphology: Rods measuring 0.8 μ $\times$ 4.6 μ; motile by means of more than 20 peritrichous flagella; oval spore, 1.0 μ $\times$ 1.5 μ; Gram-positive.

Physiology: Strict anaerobe. Opt. T. = 39° C. Opt. pH = 6.2-7.4.

Cultural characters: Gas produced.

Deep agar: Circular, fluffy or arborescent colonies.

Milk: Unchanged.

Carbohydrates: Glucose, fructose, galactose, mannose, xylose, arabinose, rhamnose, lactose, sucrose, maltose, trehalose, raffinose, dextrin, starch, xylane, glycerol, mannitol, inositol, sorbitol and dulcitol are fermented; lactate is fermented only in the presence of Na acetate.

Biochemistry: Nitrites not formed from nitrates; produces acetic and butyric acids, CO_2, H_2; lactate oxidized to acetate and CO_2, then acetate is converted to butyrate.

Pathogenicity: Non-pathogenic.

9. *Cl. aminobutyricum* Hardman and Stadtman 1960.

Habitat: Marine mud of North Carolina.

Morphology: Rods measuring 0.4 to 0.8 μ $\times$ 1.2 to 1.7 μ; occurring singly, in pairs and sometimes in short chains, seldom in long chains; actively motile; oval, subterminal spore swelling the rod to a clostridium; Gram-positive.

Physiology: Strict anaerobe. Opt. T. = 31-37°C.

Cultural characters: Gas, but no fetid odor produced.

Deep agar: Lenticular colonies, 2 to 4 mm. in diameter, yellowish-white, with translucent border, becoming viscous upon aging.

Broth: Abundant turbidity.

Gelatin: Rapid liquefaction.

Milk: Rapid coagulation, abundant gas.

Carbohydrates: Acid and gas from glucose, fructose, maltose, lactose, galactose, xylose, arabinose, cellubiose and mannitol; sucrose, starch, dextrin, dulcitol, glycerol and sorbitol feebly fermented; Inulin, adonitol and pectin are not fermented.

Biochemistry: Nitrites formed from nitrates; produces H_2S and indole; α-aminobutyrate may serve as sole source of carbon; effectively, the germ was first isolated on a medium containing this sole source of carbon; 2 moles of aminobutyrate are converted to 2 moles of NH_3.

Pathogenicity: Non-pathogenic. No toxin, or hemolysin.

Species *incertae sedis:*

10. *Cl. polyfermenticum* Partansky and Henry 1935.

Habitat: Mud, sulfite liquor. Quite frequent.

Morphology: Similar to *Cl. butylicum.*

Physiology: Similar to *Cl. butylicum.*

Deep agar: Arborescent colonies.

Peptone broth: Flaky growth; indole not formed.

Gelatin: No liquefaction.

Milk: Coagulated.

Coagulated serum: Not attacked.

Carbohydrates: Acid and gas from xylose, glucose, fructose, galactose, sucrose, lactose, maltose, raffinose, starch, inulin, salicin, ethanol, glycerol, mannitol and dulcitol.

Biochemistry: Nitrites not formed from nitrates; sulfite liquor is fermented; acetate, propionate and butyrate are utilized.

Blood: No hemolysis.

11. *Cl. saccharophilicum* Partansky and Henry 1935.

Habitat: Mud, water, polluted lakes.

Morphology, Physiology: Similar to that of the preceding species.

Deep agar: Arborescent colonies.

Other media: Similar to that of the preceding species.

Carbohydrates: Acid and gas from glucose, fructose, galactose, sucrose, lactose, maltose, raffinose, starch, salicin and glycerin.

Coagulated serum: Not attacked.

Blood: No hemolysis.

Biochemistry: Sulfite liquor is fermented with production of gas, butyric and acetic acids; nitrites not formed from nitrates; acetate and butyrate utilized, but not propionate.

12. *Cl. saccharopetum* Partansky and Henry 1935.

Quite similar to the preceding species, from which it differs by:
1. Fermentation of carbohydrates: xylose, glucose, fructose, galactose, sucrose, lactose, maltose, raffinose, starch and salicin are fermented.
2. Peptonization of milk, following coagulation.

13. *Cl. saccharopostulatum* Partansky and Henry 1935.

Analogous to the preceding species, from which it differs by:
1. Fermentation of carbohydrates: glucose, fructose, galactose, sucrose, lactose, maltose, raffinose, starch, inulin and glycerol are fermented.
2. Non-utilization of salts of acylic acids.

Sub-genus II: *CLOSTRIDIUM NAVICULUM.*
(Agents of cellulolysis)

This group comprises only one strictly anaerobic species and two facultative species:
1. Strict anaerobe; lenticular colonies; gas produced; gelatin not liquefied; saccharolytic; amylolytic; cellulolytic; atmospheric nitrogen utilized.
   1. *Clostridium naviculum,* page 239
2. Facultative anaerobe; saccharolytic; amylolytic; cellulolytic; non-proteolytic; mineral nitrogen utilized.
   2. *Clostridium myxogenes,* page 240
3. Species related to the preceding; mucoid growth; cellulolytic activity is less marked and disappears in mineral media.
   3. *Clostridium mucosum,* page 240

1. *Clostridium naviculum* (Wehmer) Prévot 1938.

Synonym: Amylobacter navicula Wehmer 1898.

Habitat: Soil, intestinal tract of man and animals; rumen. Frequent.

Morphology: Straight or fusiform rods, 1.7 μ $\times$ 4 to 7 μ; occurring singly or in short chains; motile; central or subterminal spore, 1 μ $\times$ 2 μ; iodophilic granules (red or blue); Gram-positive.

Physiology: Strict anaerobe. Opt. T. = 37° C. Resists 3 minutes at 90°C, but is killed after 5 minutes at 100° C.

Cultural characters: Gas produced in the presence of cellulose.

Cellulose-deep agar: Lenticular colonies.

Gelatin: No liquefaction.

Milk: Coagulated; casein is precipitated, but not digested.

Carbohydrates: Glucose, lactose, raffinose and salicin are fermented with the production of lactic acid as well as higher fatty acids; but no butyric acid; glycerol fermented with the production of propionic acid; starch is fermented with the production of propionic acid as well as higher fatty acids; cellulose is fermented to CO_2 and H_2, but no CH_4; atmospheric nitrogen is utilized.

Biochemistry: Produces ethanol, n-butanol, iso-butanol, n-propanol, iso-propanol, traces of amyl alcohol, volatile acids (propionic and higher homologs of butyric acid), lactic acid.

2. *Clostridium myxogenes* Simola 1931.

Differs from the preceding species by: its facultative anaerobiosis, utilization of pentoses, hexoses and polysaccharides as well as starch and cellulose which is converted to cellobiose and glucose; non-proteolytic; utilizes inorganic nitrogen.

3. *Clostridium mucosum* Simola 1931.

Species similar to the preceding, except that its cultures are mucoid, its cellulolytic activity is less marked and disappears in mineral media. (facultatively anaerobic).

Sub-genus III: *CLOSTRIDIUM AURANTIBUTYRICUM.*
(Agents of pectinolysis and retting).

Actually, 15 species of strictly anaerobic pectinolytic *Clostridia* are known along with 3 varieties and 2 facultatively anaerobic or microaerophilic species.

I. STRICT ANAEROBES.

They may be subdivided into pigmented species and colorless species; in each subdivision may be considered the stable pectinolytic species which maintain in artificial culture their pectinolytic enzymes (protopectinase, pectinesterase, polygalacturonidase, etc.) and the unstable pectinolytic species which may lose one or several pectinolytic enzymes in artificial culture; nonetheless, they still ferment more or less actively vegetable fibres.

A) Pigmented species:

a) Stable pectinolytic species:

1. Large-sized rods; granulose-positive; grow preferably in vegetable media (starchy); gelatin liquefied; milk clotted; orange-pink colonies; saccharolytic (amylolytic) and pectinolytic; produce acetic and butyric acids.

  1. *Clostridium aurantibutyricum,* page 242

2. Rods of average size; iodophilic granules and volutin present; grows only on vegetable media; orange, fluffy colonies; gas produced; gelatin liquefied; milk coagulated, then digested; saccharolytic and pectinolytic; produce acetic and lactic acids.

  2. *Clostridium felsineum,* page 243

  2 bis. Variety of the preceding species; produces propionic and butyric acids.

  2 bis. *Cl. felsineum* var. *maynonei,* page 244

  2 ter. Thermophilic variety of the preceding species.

  2 ter. *Cl. felsineum* var. *sikokianum,* page 244

  2 quarto. Canary-yellow-greenish variety of the preceding species.

  2 quarto. *Cl. felsineum* var. *flavum,* page 244

3. Rods of average size; granulose-positive; gelatin liquefied; coagulated egg-white attacked; pink colonies; milk coagulated, then digested; saccharolytic (amylolytic) and pectinolytic; gas produced; produce formic, butyric and lactic acids.

  3. *Clostridium roseum,* page 245

4. Large-sized rods; no iodophilic granules; yellow lenticular colonies; gas produced; gelatin not liquefied; saccharolytic and pectinolytic.

  4. *Clostridium haumanni,* page 246

5. Canary-yellow pigment on yeast-extract media; gelatin liquefied; milk coagulated; saccharolytic; produces butyric acid.

  5. *Clostridium flavum,* page 246

b) Unstable or uncertain pectinolytic species:

6. Large-sized rods; subterminal spore; bright-red or pink non-diffusible pigment on certain media; turbid broth; gas produced; gelatin not liquefied; milk unchanged; saccharolytic; feebly pectinolytic; galacturonic acid actively fermented.

  6. *Clostridium rubrum,* page 247

7. Large-sized rods; coral-red arborescent colonies; grows on ordinary media; gas produced; fecaloid odor; gelatin liquefied; saccharolytic; marked retting activity; produces acetone and butanol.

  7. *Clostridium corallinum,* page 247

8. Large-sized rods; saturn-red, fluffy colonies at 26° C; pigment-producing capacity lost at 37°C; gelatin not liquefied; milk unchanged; moderate retting activity; produces valerianic and propionic acids.

  8. *Clostridium saturni-rubrum,* page 248

B) Colorless species:

c) Stable pectinolytic species:

9. Rods of average size; non-pigmentforming; large amounts of gas produced; gelatin liquefied; milk coagulated, then digested; coagulated egg-white digested; saccharolytic; actively pectinolytic; produces tyramine and putrescin; large amounts of acetone and butanol produced.

> 9. *Clostridium acetobutylicum,* page 249

10. Rods of average size; non-pigmentforming; gas produced; gelatin liquefied; milk coagulated; coagulated egg-white not attacked; saccharolytic; moderate pectinolytic activity.

> 10. *Clostridium laniganii,* page 249

11. Rods of average size; gas produced; gelatin not liquefied; milk slowly coagulated; coagulated egg-white not attacked; saccharolytic; actively pectinolytic; produces tyramine, tryptamine, putrescin and β-phenylethylamine.

> 11. *Clostridium omnivorum,* page 250

12. Large-sized rods; gas produced; gelatin not liquefied; milk slowly coagulated; coagulated egg-white not attacked; saccharolytic; actively pectinolytic; produces tyramine.

> 12. *Clostridium pectinolyticum,* page 250

d) Unstable or uncertain pectinolytic species:

13. Large-sized rods; gas produced; gelatin liquefied; milk coagulated; saccharolytic; unstable pectinolytic activity, but active retting agent; cellulolytic.

> 13. *Clostridium gürfelii,* page 251

14. Rods of average size; gas produced; mucoid growth; milk coagulated; saccharolytic; moderate pectinolytic activity; produces numerous neutral solvents from sucrose.

> 14. *Clostridium kaneboi,* page 251

II. FACULTATIVELY ANAEROBIC OR MICROAEROPHILIC:

15. Growth at 42-45°C; produces crystals of dextrin from starch; acetoin not formed.

> 15. *Clostridium macerans,* page 252

16. Growth at 30°C; produces acetoin; crystals of dextrin not formed from starch.

> 16. *Clostridium polymyxa,* page 252

> 1. **Clostridium aurantibutyricum** Hellinger 1947.

Habitat: Hibiscus stumps (South Africa).

Morphology: Average-sized and long rods with rounded ends, 0.6 to 1.0 μ × 4 to 9 μ; occurring singly and in short or long chains; motile by means of peritrichous flagella; subterminal, clostridial spore, 1 μ × 2 μ; granulose-positive; Gram-positive.

Physiology: Strict anaerobe; Opt. T. = 30°C. Resists 2 minutes at 100°C.

Cultural characters: Gas produced.

Deep agar: Red colonies.

Yeast-glucose-agar: Orange-red colonies.

Gelatin: Liquefaction.

Milk: Rapid coagulation; spongy clot.

Potato: Not attacked.

Carrot: Disintegrated.

Glucose agar (*in vacuo*): Light pink or light orange colonies. Pigmentation is more intense in the center of the colony; it has a tendency to disappear upon transfer or in the presence of air.

Carbohydrates: Glucose, sucrose, maltose, galactose, fructose, lactose, arabinose, xylose, mannose, starch, dextrin, salicin and pectin are fermented.

Biochemistry: Nitrites not formed from nitrates; fermentation of glucose and corn produces: acetic and butyric acids, acetone, butanol, ethanol, isopropanol, lactic and formic acids, acetylmethylcarbinol.

2. *Clostridium felsineum* (Carbone and Tombolato) Bergey *et al.*

Synonym: Bacillus felsineus C. and T. 1917.

Habitat: Retting mud from Bologna, bakers' leaven, textile plants. Very frequent.

Morphology: Straight rods, 0.5 to 0.7 μ × 3 to 4 μ; occurring singly or in short chains; actively motile by means of numerous peritrichous flagella; light blue stain with iodine; volutin present; clostridial, subterminal spore; Gram-positive.

Physiology: Very strict anaerobe. Opt. T. = 20-37° C. Resists 1 minute at 100°C.

Cultural characters: No growth on meat media; requires media with a plant base; gas produced.

Isolation: On milk agar added with an extract of flax or hemp, followed by potato pap containing hemp.

Carrot agar: Orange, fluffy colonies, which turn brown, then black; gas produced.

Gelatin: Rapid liquefaction.

Potato pap: Viscid mass with ester odor; gas and orange foam.

Carrot juice: Mucoid fermentation.

Flax stalk: Gaseous fermentation.

Milk: Coagulated; orange clot.

Carbohydrates: Glucose, fructose, mannose, galactose, maltose, sucrose, lactose, arabinose and xylose are fermented; starch is not fermented.

Biochemistry: Produces ester, small quantities of acetic and lactic acids, never butyric acid. The orange pigment is a carotene.

Enzymes: Highly active pectinase; marked retting activity; presence of a protease (gelatinase and caseinase).

Pathogenicity: Non-pathogenic.

Serology: Strictly specific agglutination.

2 bis. *Cl. felsineum* var. *maynonei* (Carbone) 1917.

Habitat, Morphology, Physiology: Similar to that of *Cl. felsineum.*

Biochemistry: Neatly different from *Cl. felsineum:* acetone, nor aldehyde produced, but propanol, iso-propanol, iso-butanol, propionic and butyric acids.

2 ter. *Cl. felsineum* var. *sikokianum* (Kaji and Saito 1952) nov. comb.

Habitat: Bark of *Wikstroemia sikokiana* (Japan).

Morphology: Straight rods, 0.7 to 1.2 μ $\times$ 2.4 to 7.2 μ; motile by means of peritrichous flagella; oval, clostridial spore, 1.4 μ $\times$ 2.4 μ; sporangia measuring 1.2 μ to 6.7 μ; Gram-positive.

Physiology: Microaerophilic. Opt. T. = 37°C. Opt. pH = 6-7.

Cultural characters: Gas produced.

Wheat mash-agar: Thin, smooth, orange colonies, becoming yellow; gas.

Wheat mash: Turbid; large amounts of gas produced; orange-chrome pigment; orange viscid sediment becoming red, then brown.

Potato mash: Same as above.

Meat broth: Very meager growth.

Gelatin: No liquefaction. A cube of gelatin placed in yeast-potato mash is liquefied.

Milk: Coagulated; red clot; gas.

Coagulated egg-white in wheat mash: Partial digestion.

Carbohydrates: Acid and gas from arabinose, xylose, glucose, mannose, fructose, lactose, galactose, maltose, sucrose, raffinose, and rhamnose; acid, but no gas, from starch, dextrin, glycogen, inulin and pectin.

Biochemistry: Nitrites not formed from nitrates; sulfites and thiosulfates reduced to sulfides; produces acetone, butanol, acetic and butyric acids as well as CO_2 and H_2. Active retting of the bark of *W. sikokiana* for the production of paper.

2 quarto *Cl. felsineum* var. *flavum* Kaiser 1961.

Habitat: Mud from Dax.

Morphology: Straight rods. 0.7 μ $\times$ 4 to 6 μ; motile by means of peritrichous flagella; eccentric spore making the rod spear-shaped; free spores are cylindrical, with square ends, 1 μ $\times$ 2 μ; Gram-positive.

Physiology: Strict anaerobe. Opt. T. $=$ 30-37°C.

Deep agar: Green-canary yellow, lenticular colonies, becoming fluffy.

VF broth: No growth.

Yeast-potato mash: Turbid; gas; yellowish-green sediment, becoming orange; pigment maximum at 30°C, very poor at 37° C.

Gelatin: Rapid liquefaction.

Milk: Rapid coagulation, becoming yellowish-green, then orange.

Coagulated egg-white: Partial digestion.

Carbohydrates: Glucose, fructose, maltose, sucrose, galactose, lactose and starch are fermented.

Biochemistry: Nitrites formed from nitrates; produces alcohols, ketones, acetoin, NH_3, acetic, butyric, lactic and succinic acids; final pH $=$ 4.5; Pectin digested to the extent of 95% in 7 days; 3 adaptative enzymes: an endopolygalacturodinase (pH 3.5), an endopolymethylgalacturonidase (pH 5.5), and less active, a pectinesterase. Galacturonic acid digested to the extent of 100% in 7 days.

3. *Clostridium roseum* McCoy and McClung 1935.

Habitat: Isolated from German corn; found again in the soil of Tropical Africa. Quite uncommon.

Morphology: Straight rods, 0.8 μ $\times$ 4 μ; actively motile; clostridial spore, either subterminal or free, 0.6 to 0.7 μ $\times$ 1.5 μ; granulose-positive on starch media; Gram-positive.

Physiology: Strict anaerobe. Opt. T. $=$ 37°C. (20-47°C). Resists 20 minutes at 80° C and 10 minutes at 100°C. Neutral red temporarily reduced.

Cultural characters: Gas and slightly fetid odor produced.

Deep agar: Pink, lenticular colonies, even in the deeper layers. Pigment occurs at 26°C only.

Glucose broth: Turbid; gas; H_2S formed; indole not formed.

Gelatin: Liquefaction in 48 hours.

Milk: Coagulated; gas; hydrolysis of casein.

Potato: Butylic fermentation.

Carbohydrates: Acid and gas from arabinose, xylose, glucose, mannose, fructose, galactose, lactose, maltose, sucrose, raffinose, dextrin, glycogen and starch; pectin is digested.

Biochemistry: Nitrites formed from nitrates; produces NH_3, H_2S, acetone, butanol, ethanol, volatile amines, formic, butyric and lactic acids, aldehydes and acetylmethylcarbinol.

Serology: Specific agglutination (shares a common antigen with *Cl. acetobutylicum*).

4. *Clostridium haumanni* (Soriano) Prévot 1938.

Synonym: Bacillus haumanni Soriano 1930.

Habitat: Water and mud from retting vats in Argentina.

Morphology: Straight rods, 0.8 μ × 4 to 8 μ; motile; large-sized, oval, subterminal spore; yellow (never blue) iodophilic granules: Gram-positive.

Physiology: Strict anaerobe. Resists 1 minute at 100°C.

Cultural characters: Gas produced. Isolation on carrot-agar.

Carrot-agar: Canary-yellow, lenticular colonies, becoming brick-red; gas.

Carrot juice: Gassy fermentation; pigment.

Gelatin: No liquefaction.

Potato: Gassy fermentation; red pigment.

Flax fibers: Liberated by pectinolysis; retting.

Carbohydrates: Acid and gas from glucose, fructose, mannose, galactose, sucrose, maltose, lactose, arabinose, salicin, and xylose.

Pectin: Lyzed.

Serology: Specific agglutination.

5. *Clostridium flavum* McClung and McCoy 1951.

Synonym: Type IV of pectinolytic *Clostridium* Laniganii 1951.

Habitat: Australian flax, soil.

Morphology: Straight or slightly-curved rods, 0.4 μ × 2 to 7 μ; with rounded ends; occurring singly, in pairs or as palissades; short filaments; elliptical, subterminal spore, formed early, 0.8 μ × 2.5 μ; motile; Gram-positive.

Physiology: Strict anaerobe. Opt. T. = 30-37°C.

Cultural characters: No growth on agar media.

Yeast-extract agar: Circular, convex or umbonate, smooth, opaque, viscous, canary-yellow colonies.

Deep agar: Canary-yellow, lenticular colonies; gas.

Gelatin: Liquefaction in 7 to 11 days.

Glucose peptone broth; Abundant turbidity; gas; yellow sediment; butylic odor.

Milk: Spongy clot; acid and gas.

Coagulated egg-white: Softening.

Potato: Fermentation; canary-yellow pigment.

Brain-medium: Not blackened, nor digested.

Carbohydrates: Acid and gas from glucose, galactose, maltose, sucrose, lactose, starch and pectin.

Biochemistry: Nitrites not formed from nitrates; nitrites reduced; indole not formed; produces H_2S (traces) and butyric acid. Active retting agent of flax.

6. *Clostridium rubrum* Ng and Vaughn 1963.

Habitat: Soil.

Morphology: Rods measuring 0.9 μ × 6 to 23 μ; motile; oval, subterminal or eccentric spore, swelling the rod; Gram-positive.

Physiology: Strict anaerobe. Opt. T. = 35°C.

Cultural characters: Gas produced.

Starch-agar slant: Pale-red colonies in the center, greyish on the sides; pigment does not diffuse.

Wheat mash-agar: Pale-red colonies.

Potato mash: Pale-red, turbid growth.

Wheat mash: Pink or colorless, turbid growth.

Gelatin: No liquefaction.

Milk: Unchanged.

Coagulated egg-white: Not attacked.

Carbohydrates: Acid and gas from flucose, lactose, sucrose, mannitol and starch.

Pectin: Liquefied. Pectic acid liquefied to the extent of 3 to 6%. Galacturonic acid fermented to 87%.

Biochemistry: Nitrites not formed from nitrates; from galacturonic acid, produces: CO_2, H_2, acetic and butyric acids.

7. *Clostridium corallinum* Prévot and Raynaud 1944.

Habitat: Soil from France and Senegal. Frequent.

Morphology: Rods with rounded ends, 0.8 μ × 3 to 4 μ; occurring singly, in pairs or in short chains; motile by means of 1-4 peritrichous flagella; filamentous, granular forms; in wet preparations, the bacterial body is pink; subterminal, clostridial spores, sometimes free, 1 μ × 1.5 to 2.0 μ; Gram-positive.

Physiology: Strict anaerobe, may become microaerophilic by mutation; Opt. T. = 37°C; growth begins at 17°C. Resists 1 minute at 100° C. Opt. pH = 7.4. Neutral red and phenosafranin reduced.

Cultural characters: Gas and fetid odor produced.

Deep agar: Fluffy and arborescent colonies, coral-red in the upper layers, colorless in the deeper layers; gas.

Agar slant (in vacuo): Circular colonies, with irregular border; become red upon re-entry of air.

Peptone water: Slight, flaky turbidity.

Glucose VF broth: Abundant turbidity; coherent viscid sediment; gas and fetid odor. No pigment in vacuum; after re-entry of air, coral-red or purple pigment sediments with the bacterial bodies.

Gelatin: Liquefaction in 24 hours; black sediment.

Milk: Coagulation in 24 hours; then slowly digested.

Coagulated serum: Attacked very slowly.

Carbohydrates: Glucose, fructose, maltose, galactose, sucrose, lactose, arabinose, xylose, mannitol, sorbitol, dulcitol, glycerol, starch and inulin are fermented.

Biochemistry: Nitrites formed from nitrates; produces NH_3, H_2S, volatile amines, alcohols (butanol), acetone, acetic, butyric and formic acids. Active retting agent of textile plants, although pectin is not attacked *in vitro*.

Pigment: Soluble in ethanol, methanol, ether, acetone, chloroform, benzine and iso-propyl oxide; broken down by chromatography into 6 different pigments.

Pathogenicity: Non-pathogenic for mouse and guinea pig. Poorly active hemolysin *in vitro*.

7 bis. *Cl. corallinum* var. *durieuxi* Prévot and Sansonnens.

Lightly-pigmented colonies; milk digested in 1 month; carbohydrates barely fermented; nitrites not formed from nitrates; produces formic, butyric and lactic acids.

7 ter. *Cl. corallinum* var. *joncherei* Prévot and Sansonnens.

Highly pigmented, lenticular colonies; milk digested in 10 days; no single carbohydrate is fermented; nitrites not formed from nitrates; produces acetic, iso-butyric and lactic acids.

8. *Clostridium saturni-rubrum* Prévot 1946.

Habitat: Soil of marsh forests on the Ivory Coast.

Morphology: Straight rods with rounded ends, 0.8 μ $\times$ 4 to 5 μ; occuring singly, in pairs or in short chains, sometimes as filaments; weakly motile; internal, granular structure with spiral chromatic filament; rare subterminal, clostridial spore, often free, oval in shape but sometimes quite elongated; Gram-positive.

Physiology: Strict anaerobe. Opt. T. $= 26°C$ (18-37°C). Resists 1 hour at 60°C and 5 minutes at 70°C. Survives more than 3 months. Opt. pH $= 7.4$. Neutral red and safranin reduced.

Cultural characters: Gas, but no fetid odor produced.

Deep agar: Fluffy, irregular colonies which becomes saturn-red in 2 to 3 days at 26°C; abundant gas, breaking up the agar.

Glucose VF broth: Rapid, abundant turbidity; explosive gas; saturn-red pigment which sediments with the bacterial bodies.

Peptone water: Meager growth; slight gas production.

Gelatin: No liquefaction.

Milk: Unchanged.

Coagulated proteins: Not attacked.

Carbohydrates: Glucose, fructose, maltose, galactose, lactose, sucrose, arabinose, mannitol and starch are actively fermented.

Biochemistry: Nitrites not formed from nitrates; produces NH_3, volatile amines, alcohols, aldehydes, propionic, valerianic, caproic and lactic acids, CO_2 and H_2 in the ratio of 1:1.

Pigment: Stimulated by carbohydrates, especially fructose and starch. Extractible by chloroform and benzine.

Retting activity: Marked for flax, hemp and hollyhocks.

Pathogenicity, experimental: The guinea pig dies in 4 to 5 days with no apparent lesion after intramuscular injection: the germ cannot be recuperated. No toxin, or hemolysin.

9. *Clostridium acetobutylicum*
McCoy, Fred, Peterson and Hastings 1926.

Synonym: Clostridium acetonobutylicum Weizamnn 1912.

Habitat: Soil, plants. Frequent.

Morphology: Similar to *Cl. butyricum;* numerous iodophilic granules.

Physiology: Strict anaerobe. Opt. T. $= 20$-$47°$C. Killed after 10-30 minutes at $82°$C.

Cultural characters: Large amounts of gas produced.

Deep agar: Lenticular colonies.

Glucose broth: Abundant turbidity; gas produced; indole not formed.

Glucose gelatin: Liquefaction.

Milk: Coagulated; casein hydrolyzed.

Potato: Creamy growth; yellowish foam.

Carbohydrates: Arabinose, xylose, rhamnose, glucose, mannose, fructose, sucrose, maltose, lactose, raffinose, melezitose, starch, dextrin, inulin, glycogen, salicin and amygdalin are fermented. Cellulose not attacked. The authors who first described this species did not report the attack of pectin; however, the strain having been deposited with ATCC, it was studied subsequently by other authors who found that it has a marked pectinolytic activity.

Biochemistry: Fixes atmospheric nitrogen; produces mainly acetone and butanol, secondarily acetic and butyric acids, ethanol, CO_2, H_2 and acetoin.

10. *Clostridium laniganii* McClung and McCoy 1951.

Habitat: Soil, mud.

Morphology: Straight rods with rounded ends, 0.8 $\mu \times$ 4 to 6 μ; motile by means of peritrichous flagella; subterminal, cylindrical spore, 0.9 $\mu \times$ 2 μ, swelling the rod; Gram-positive.

Physiology: Strict anaerobe. Opt. T. $=$ 30-37°C. Resists 5 minutes at 80°C. Janus green and safranin reduced, neutral red temporarily reduced.

Deep agar: White, lenticular colonies 1-1.5mm in diameter; gas.

Yeast-potato agar: Abundant, whitish turbidity; gas; white sediment.

VF broth: Growth possible only after transfer from glucose-yeast.

Peptone medium: Abundant, whitish turbidity, gas; white sediment.

Peptone water: No growth.

Gelatin: Liquefaction.

Milk: Coagulated; white, retracted clot. Not digested.

Coagulated egg-white in DBM medium: Unchanged.

Carbohydrates: Xylose, arabinose, fructose, galactose, glucose, sucrose, maltose, lactose and starch are fermented. Glycerol is not attacked.

Pectin: Digested to the extent of 60 to 92% in 7 days, according to the strains. Three enzymes: mainly, a constituent endopolygalacturonidase (pH 7.5), small amounts of a constituent endopolymethllgalacturonidase (pH 7.5) and an adaptive, fleeting pectin-methylesterase (pH 7.5) from young cultures. Galacturonic acid fermented to 100% in 7 days.

Biochemistry: Nitrites not formed from nitrates; amines, phenol and indole not formed; produces (from potato mash) NH_3 (0.068gm/1.), aldehydes, alcohols, ketones; total volatile acidity (0.57gm 1.): formic, acetic and butyric acids in the ratio 1:3.5, and lactic acid. Terminal pH 4.5.

11. *Clostridium omnivorum* Prévot, Thouvenot and Kaiser 1957.

Habitat: Intestinal tract of the tench and of the perch.

Morphology: Straight rods with rounded ends, 0.9 μ $\times$ 3 to 5 μ; occurring singly, in pairs or in short chains; slight motility; by means of peritrichous flagella; clostridial spores formed in large numbers, often free; Gram-positive.

Physiology: Strict anaerobe. Resists 10 to 15 minutes at 100°C. Survives more than 4 years. Neutral red and safranin reduced irreversibly.

Cultural characters: Large amounts of gas, and fetid odor produced.

Deep agar: Irregular colonies, either arborescent or made up by a complex of lenticular colonies; abundant gas.

Glucose VF broth: Rapid, abundant turbidity; abundant gas; highly fetid odor; bacteriogloea.

Peptone water: Turbid; gas; fetid odor; bacteriogloea.

Gelatin: Liquefaction in 48 hours to 1 month.

Milk: Digested, without previous coagulation, in 2 to 6 days.

Coagulated proteins: Not attacked.

Carbohydrates: Glucose, fructose, maltose, starch and pectin are fermented.

Biochemistry: Nitrites not formed from nitrates; sulfites reduced; produced NH_3, H_2S, volatile amines, aldehydes, ketones, phenols, acetoin, acetic, iso-butyric (or valerianic) and lactic acids. Ca pectate and d-galacturonate are fermented. The pectinolytic activity is complete and rapid for some strains, incomplete and sluggish for others.

Pathogenicity: Non-pathogenic for mouse and guinea pig.

12. *Clostridium pectinolyticum* Saissac, Brugière and Raynaud.

Synonym: Cl. butyricum "C8" Saissac, Brugière and Raynaud 1952.

Habitat: Natural retting mash of the grass-cloth plant.

Morphology: Large-sized rods, 1.2 μ $\times$ 5 to 6 μ; actively motile; subterminal spore, often spear-headed; by means of peritrichous flagella Gram-positive.

Physiology: Strict anaerobe. Opt. T. $= 37°C$ (20-40°C). Resists 1 minute at 100°C. Neutral red reduced.

Cultural characters: Large amounts of explosive gas and intense butyric odor. No growth on meat or peptone media.

Potato-agar: Colorless, lenticular colonies which become brown with age; abundant gas.

Potato mash: Abundant growth and gas; the fragments of potato are broken up. Added with yeast extract or autolysate, this medium is ideal for growing this species.

Gelatin: No liquefaction.

Milk: Slow coagulation (10 days).

Carbohydrates: Glucose, fructose, maltose, galactose, sucrose, lactose, mannitol and starch are fermented. Pectin is entirely degraded in a very short time (100% in 6 days at 37°C).

Biochemistry: Fermentation of potato mash produces CO_2 and H_2, acetic and butyric acids in the ratio 1:4, acetone (traces). Indole not formed, nor H_2S, nor acetoin.

13. *Clostridium gurfelii* (Gürfel) nov. comb.

Synonym: Clostridium innominate of Gürfel, Kaiser 1961.

Habitat: Stalks of *Abutilon aviceannae.* Uncommon.

Morphology: Rods measuring 2 μ $\times$ 6 to 9 μ; occurring singly or in pairs; motile in young cultures; iodophilic granules; clostridial spore; Gram-positive.

Physiology: Strict anaerobe. Opt. pH 6.5-7.5.

Cultural characters: No gas produced.

Deep agar: Colorless, lenticular colonies.

Potato mash: Fermentation, neither mucoid nor pigmented.

Gelatin: Liquefaction in the presence of carbohydrate.

Milk: Coagulation.

Carbohydrates: Arabinose, glucose, fructose, galactose, sucrose, maltose, lactose, raffinose, mannitol, dextrin and starch are fermented. Cellulose is weakly fermented.

Biochemistry: Fermentation of *Abutilon aviceannae* decoction produces acetic and butyric acids.

Retting activity: Marked with flax, hemp and other textile plants.

Pathogenicity: Non-pathogenic.

14. *Clostridium kaneboi* Nakahama and Harada 1949.

Habitat: Soil, sugar cane.

Morphology: Straight rods with rounded ends, 0.3 to 0.8 μ $\times$ 2 to 7μ;

occurring singly or in short chains of 2-4 elements; motile; central or subterminal spore; fusiform sporangia, 1.5 μ to 2.5 μ; Gram-positive.

Physiology: Strict anaerobe. Opt. T. = 37°C. Opt. pH = 5.6-6.7.

Agar: Yellowish-white, moist, smooth colonies, 2 to 5 mm. in diameter.

Sugar cane broth: Abundant turbidity; acid; strong odor; abundant spore formation.

Corn or soya broth: Turbid; gas.

Milk: Coagulation; gas.

Potato: Yellowish-brown colonies, 2 mm. in diameter.

Carbohydrates: Xylose, arabinose, glucose, fructose, mannose, galactose, maltose, lactose, starch, dextrin, inulin, glycogen and mannitol are fermented. Trehalose and pectin are weakly fermented.

Biochemistry: Nitrites not formed from nitrates; indole not formed; produces H_2S, acetone, butanol and ethanol.

15. *Clostridium macerans* (Schardinger) Prévot 1957.

Synonym: Bacillus macerans Schardinger 1904; Aerobacillus macerans (S.) Donker 1926; Zymobacillus macerans (S.) Kluyver and van Niel 1936.

Habitat: Soil, water; fermenting starchy plants, retting flax, retting vats. Very frequent.

Morphology: Rods measuring 0.6 to 1.0 μ × 2.5 to 6 μ; occurring singly or in pairs; motile; lipid inclusions; ellipsoidal, clostridial spore; Gram-positive (easily decolorized).

Physiology: Microaerophilic or facultative anaerobe. Opt. T. = 37°C (22-45). Moderately thermoresistant.

Cultural characters: Gas produced.

Agar slant: Small, whitish, transparent, irregular, smooth colonies.

Broth: Turbid; slight sediment. In glucose broth: sometimes viscid sediment. Terminal pH 5.0-5.5.

Gelatin: Liquefaction.

Milk: Acidified, but not coagulated.

Potato: Napiform growth; gas; disintegrated.

Carbohydrates: Glucose, fructose, galactose, sucrose, maltose, lactose, xylose, arabinose, rhamnose, mannose, trehalose, cellobiose, raffinose, melezitose, dextrin, inulin, salicin, mannitol, glycerol, sorbitol, starch and pectin are fermented.

Biochemistry: Nitrites formed from nitrates; produces acetone and ethanol.

16. *Clostridium polymyxa* Prazmowski 1880.

Synonym: Bacillus polymyxa (P.) Migula; Granulobacter polymyxa (P.) Beijerinck; Aerobacillus polymyxa (P.) Donker.

Habitat: Soil, water, milk, feces, fermenting plants, seeds. Very frequent.

Morphology: Rods measuring 0.6 to 1.0 μ $\times$ 2.5 to 6.0 μ; occurring singly or in short chains; motile; lipid inclusions; clostridial spore; Gram-positive (easily decolorized).

Physiology: Microaerophilic or facultative anaerobe. Opt. T. = 30°C (20-33).

Cultural characters: Gas produced.

Agar slant: Delicate, whitish, lobate, extensive, rough colonies.

Broth: Uniform turbidity, granular or flaky, sedimenting into a viscid sediment. Terminal pH 5.2-6.8.

Gelatin: Slow liquefaction.

Milk: Casein hydrolyzed, but not coagulated.

Potato: Gassy distintegration.

Carbohydrates: Glucose, fructose, galactose, maltose, mannose, sucrose, lactose, trehalose, cellobiose, raffinose, melzitose, dextrin, inulin, salicin, glycerol, mannitol, arabinose and xylose are fermented. Starch is hydrolyzed. Pectin and hemicellulose are fermented.

Biochemistry: Nitrites formed from nitrates; produces ethanol, butylene-glycol, acetoin, acetone and butanol.

SUB-GENUS IV: *CLOSTRIDIUM SEPTICUM.*

(Agents of malignant hemorrhagic edema and of blackleg).

This group comprises 6 highly related species:

1. Rods of average size; filamentous forms; arborescent or grenade-like colonies; gas produced; gelatin liquefied; milk coagulated; saccharolytic; neutral red reduced; no H_2S formed; hemolytic; toxic; pathogenic (red malignant edema); specific antitoxin.

   1. *Clostridium septicum,* page 254

2. Rods of average size; punctiform or lenticular colonies; gelatin liquefied; broth turbid, then auto-agglutination; milk coagulated; saccharolytic; indol (traces) formed; hemolytic; pathogenic (blackleg).

   2. *Clostridium chauvoei,* page 255

3. Long, filamentous rods or short thick rods; punctiform or branching colonies; gas produced; gelatin liquefied; milk coagulated; neutral red reduced; H_2S formed; hemolytic; pathogenic (blackleg of Sardinian sheep).

   3. *Clostridium sardiniensis,* page 256

4. Similar to *Cl. chauvoei;* arborescent colonies; gas produced; fetid odor; milk coagulated; saccharolytic; proteolytic; indole, scatole and NH_3 produced; pathogenic.

   4. *Clostridium balaenae,* page 256

5. Pleomorphic rods; filamentous forms; heart- or grenade-shaped colonies; non-proteolytic; milk coagulated; saccharolytic; hemolytic; pathogenic (malignant edema).

   5. *Clostridium tumefaciens,* page 257

6. Lenticular, heart- or powder puff-shaped colonies; gas produced; non-proteolytic; milk coagulated; indole not formed; hemolytic; saccharolytic; pathogenic.

   6. *Clostridium multifermentans,* page 257

7. Growth only on media containing 0.5% agar; agent of diarrhea of the young rabbit, accompanied by fatal tympanism.

   7. *Clostridium tympani-cuniculi,* page 258

1. *Clostridium septicum* (Pasteur) Macé, Ford.

Synonym: Vibrion septique Pasteur and Joubert 1877; *Bacillus septicus* Macé; *Clostridium septique* Topley and wilson. It is known as *Clostridium oedematis maligni,* but since this term is being discussed anew, we prefer *Cl. septicum* adopted by Bergey *et al.*

Habitat: Soil, dung, intestinal tract of herbivorous animals and man, infected wounds. Frequent.

Morphology: Rods with rounded ends, 0.6 to 0.8 μ $\times$ 3 to 5 μ; occurring in short chains or filaments; motile by means of peritrichous flagella; subterminal or central spore often swelling the rod; free ovoid spore of large size; Gram-positive.

Physiology: Strict anaerobe. Opt. T. $= 37°$C. Resists a few minutes at $80°$C. Survives several years. Neutral red definitely and safranin temporarily reduced.

Cultural characters: Gas, but no fetid odor produced.

Deep agar: Fluffy, arborescent or grenade-shaped colonies; gas.

Glucose broth: Abundant rubidity; acid.

Peptone water: Slight turbidity; gas; indole not formed.

Gelatin: Slow liquefaction.

Milk: Acidified; coagulated; gas.

Coagulated proteins: Not attacked.

Brain-medium: Not blackened.

Carbohydrates: Butyric acid and gas from glucose, fructose, maltose, lactose and salicin; sucrose not fermented.

Pathogenicity, natural: Gas gangrene; septicemia, infected wounds, malignant hemorrhagic edema.

Pathogenicity, experimental: Injection of 0.1 ml. into the guinea pig produces a hemorrhagic gaseous edema which is fatal in 24 hours.

Specific toxin: Highly active, 0.005 ml. killing the guinea pig, and 0.002 ml. killing the mouse.

Hemolysin: Very active *in vitro*.

Septicum toxin is a complex substance: it contains a lethal factor, a hemolytic factor and a deoxyribonuclease, also a non-hemolytic, lethal factor common to *histolyticum* toxin.

Serology: Specific agglutination at 1:20,000.

Specific antitoxin: 0.002 ml. will neutralize 10 MLD (mouse); the antitoxin corresponding to the common factor in *histolyticum* toxin is present.

Biochemistry: Nitrites formed from nitrates in the presence of some carbohydrates, N_2 formed in the presence of others; sulfites reduced to sulfides; produces NH_3, volatile amines, acetylmethylcarbinol, acetic, butyric and lactic acids.

2. *Clostridium chauvoei* (Arloing *et al.*) Holland.

Synonym: Bacillus chauvoei Arloing, Cornevin and Thomas 1887; *Bacillus carbonis* Migula; *Bacillus anthracis symptomatici* Kruse; *Clostridium feseri* 1885[1].

Habitat: Intestinal tract of cattle; pig, whale, fish, dung, soil of infected regions, waters where fish suffer from blackleg.

Morphology: Straight rods, 1 μ $\times$ 3 to 8 μ; occurring singly, in short chains of 3 to 4 elements, exceptionally in filaments; motile by means of 6-8 peritrichous flagella; clostridial spore; Gram-positive.

Physiology: Strict anaerobe. Opt. T. $= 37°$C. Resists 30 minutes at 100°C. Neutral red and safranin reduced.

Cultural characters: Gas produced.

Deep agar: No growth or very small punctiform colonies.

Serum-deep agar: Lenticular or arborescent colonies.

Glucose broth: Meager growth; turbid; gas; flaky sediment; traces of indole formed.

Gelatin: Liquefaction.

Coagulated proteins: Not attacked.

Milk: Coagulated; gas.

Carbohydrates: Acid and gas from glucose, fructose, sucrose and lactose. Salicin not fermented.

Biochemistry: Nitrites formed from nitrates; sulfites reduced to sulfides; produces NH_3, volatile amines, acetylmethylcarbinol, acetic, butyric and lactic acids.

Pathogenicity, natural: Blackleg or symptomatic anthrax of cattle, sheep and fish.

Pathogenicity, experimental: Intramuscular injection of 0.025 ml. into

---

[1] The synonymy between the terms *feseri* and *chauvoei* is not absolutely certain. The toxins have not been compared. Similar but different types of toxins can be in action.

the guinea pig produces blackleg, followed by death in a few days.

Toxin: Specific; contains hemolysin, aggressin and precipitinogen; kills the mouse rapidly.

Serology: Specific agglutination at 1:4000; cross-reaction with *Cl. septicum.*

Antitoxin: Specific, but neutralizes partially *septicum* toxin.

Systematics: Species closely related to *Cl. septicum,* but nonetheless different (fermentation, pathogenicity and antigenicity).

3. *Clostridium sardininensis* (Altar) P. 1938.

Habitat: Isolated from blackleg in sheep of Sardinia by Altara (Bradsot of Sardinia); African soil. Quite frequent.

Morphology: Short, thick rods with rounded ends, 1.0 to 1.5 μ $\times$ 2 to 5 μ; pleomorphic; filamentous; occurring singly; motile by means of peritrichous flagella; central or subterminal spore; Gram-positive.

Physilogy: Strict anaerobe. Opt. T. $= 22\text{-}37°C$. Resists 1 hour at 80°C. Neutral red reduced.

Cultural characters: Gas produced.

Deep agar: Circular or ramified, punctiform colonies.

Glucose broth: Turbid; gas; acidified; H_2S formed.

Peptone water: Flaky growth, sedimenting rapidly.

Gelatin: Liquefaction.

Milk: Coagulated; gas formed.

Brain-medium: Abundant growth; not blackened.

Coagulated proteins: Not attacked, except coagulated serum which is very slightly attacked.

Carbohydrates: Acid and gas from glucose, maltose, galactose, sucrose, lactose, glycerol, dextrin and starch.

Biochemistry: Nitrites not formed from nitrates; sulfites reduced to sulfides; produces NH_3, H_2S, acetic, butyric and lactic acids.

Pathogenicity, natural: Bradsot of sheep in Sardinia.

Pathongenicity, experimental: Intramuscular injection of 0.25 to 0.5 ml. of culture into the guinea pig or sheep produces fatal gaseous edema.

Specific toxin: Kills the guinea pig at 0.3 ml.; not neutralized by anti-*septicum* or anti-*chauvoei* serum. Active hemolysin.

Systematics: Species closely related to *Cl. chauvoei,* from which it differs by the antigenic structure of its toxin.

4. *Clostridium balaenae* (Nielsen) Prévot 1938.

Habitat: Sea-water from Norway, plankton, intestinal tract of sardines and herrings from America, copepods, schizopods, shrimps; blackleg of whale. Frequent.

Morphology: Similar to *Cl. chauvoei;* motility is lost rapidly; spherical or oval, subterminal spore; Gram-positive.

Physiology: Strict anaerobe. Opt. T. $= 25\text{-}33\,^{\circ}$C. Resists 10 minutes at 100°C.

Cultural characters: Gas and fetid odor produced.

Glucose broth: Turbid; gas and fetid odor.

Milk: Coagulated.

Coagulated proteins: Gaseous fermentation.

Carbohydrates: Acid and gas from glucose and lactose.

Biochemistry: Produces NH_3, volatile amines, indole and scatole.

Pathogenicity, natural: Blackleg of whale following harpoon wounds.

Pathogenicity, experimental: Non-pathogenic.

Systematics: Species closely related to *Cl. chauvoei,* but more markedly proteolytic and non-pathogenic for laboratory animals.

5. *Clostridium tumefaciens* (Wilson) Hauduroy *et al.*

Synonym: Bacillus tumefaciens Wilson 1919.

Habitat: Isolated from gas gangrene cases. Uncommon.

Morphology: Large rods with rounded ends; pleomorphic, sometimes filamentous; motile; central or subterminal spore; Gram-positive.

Physiology: Strict anaerobe. Opt. T. $= 37\,^{\circ}$C. Resists 10 minutes at 100°C. Slight reducing powers.

Cultural characters: Gas produced.

Deep agar: Lenticular or grenade-shaped colonies.

Gelatin: No liquefaction.

Milk: Coagulated.

Carbohydrates: Glucose, fructose, galactose, maltose, lactose, sucrose, inulin, glycerol and salicin are fermented.

Biochemistry: Nitrites not formed from nitrates; sulfites not attacked; produces NH_3, H_2S, formic and butyric acids.

Pathogenicity, natural: Gas gangrene, enterotoxemia of cattle.

Pathogenicity, experimental: Subcutaneous injection of 1 ml. into the guinea pig produces death in 24 hours following gaseous hemorrhagic edema. The rabbit is equally susceptible.

Toxin: Not completely neutralized by anti-*septicum* serum. Active hemolysin.

Systematics: Species closely related to *Cl. septicum.*

6. *Clostridium multifermentans* (Stoddard) Bergey.

Synonym: Bacillus multifermentans tenalbus Stoddard 1919.

Habitat: Isolated from a case of gas gangrene; found in soil and milk. Quite frequent.

Morphology: Similar to *Cl. septicum.*

Physiology: Strict anaerobe. Opt. T. $= 30\text{-}35\,^{\circ}$C.

Cultural characters: Gas produced.

Deep agar: Lenticular or heart-shaped colonies; gas.

Glucose broth: Turbid; gas; indole not formed.

Milk: Coagulated.

Coagulated proteins: Not attacked.

Carbohydrates: Acid and gas from glucose, fructose, galactose, maltose, lactose, sucrose, raffinose, starch, salicin, inulin and glycerol.

Pathogenicity, natural: Gas gangrene.

Pathogenicity, experimental: Non-pathogenic in pure culture; in association with *Cl. sporogenes,* produces gas gangrene.

Systematics: Species closely related to *Cl. septicum.*

7. Clostridium tympani-cuniculi Morcos 1949.

Synonym: B. tympani-cuniculi Morcos 1932.

Habitat: Intestinal tract of young rabbits.

Morphology: Straight rods, 0.3 to 0.5 μ $\times$ 3 to 6 μ; actively motile; clostridial spore, difficult to observe; Gram-positive.

Physiology: Strict anaerobe.

Cultural characters: Grows only in media containing 0.5% agar; gas produced in media containing fresh albuminous compounds.

Agar-erum: No growth.

Agar-broth: Abundant, gaseous growth; inflammable gas (H_2).

Milk: Acidified; partly coagulated.

Coagulated serum: Not liquefied.

Animal tissue-media: Blackened; inflammable gas (H_2).

Carbohydrates: Sucrose, glucose, mannitol and lactose are fermented.

Pathogenicity, natural: Fatal meteorism of the young rabbit, accompanied by diarrhea (tympanism).

Pathogenicity, experimental: Guinea pig, rabbit, white rat, grey rat killed by injection of cultures. The pigeon is refractory.

Immunology: Toxin has not been studied.

Serology: Anti-*chauvoei* serum has no effect upon the cultures of this species; hyperimmunization of the rabbit produces a serum which does not afford protection; but young rabbits immunized with culture filtrates or with infected tissue material are protected against the inoculation of a fatal dose.

SUB-GENUS V: CLOSTRIDIUM NOVYI

(Agents of pink, gelatinous, malignant edema).

This groups comprises 9 species which are closely related:

1. Arborescent colonies; gas produced; auto-agglutination in broth; gelatin liquefied; pathogenic.

2. Species closely related to the preceding; arborescent colonies; gas produced; auto-agglutination in broth; gelatin liquefied; milk coagulated; fetid odor; proteins not attacked; indole not formed, or H₂S; saccharolytic; pathogenic (pink, gelatinous, malignant edema); toxin; hemolysin; specific antitoxin.

   2. *Clostridium oedematiens,* page 260

3. Lenticular or arborescent colonies; flaky growth in broth; putrid odor; gas produced; gelatin liquefied; milk digested; saccharolytic; pathogenic.

   3. *Clostridium bellonensis,* page 261

4. Hazy colonies; broth turbid; gas and H₂S produced; gelatin liquefied; milk coagulated; casein attacked; brain-medium blackened; saccharolytic; pathogenic.

   4. *Clostridium sarcoemphysematodes,* page 261

5. Large rods; arborescent colonies; obligate serophile; milk unchanged; gelatin liquefied; saccharolytic; pathogenic; toxic.

   5. *Clostridium gigas,* page 262

6. Arborescent colonies; flaky growth in broth; gelatin liquefied; milk coagulated; non-saccharolytic; pathogenic (osteomyelitis of the buffalo); hemolysin.

   6. *Clostridium bubalorum,* page 262

7. Arborescent colonies; broth turbid; gelatin liquefied; milk coagulated; saccharolytic; indole formed; toxin; hemolysin; pathogenic.

   7. *Clostridium oedematis-benigni,* page 263

8. Arborescent solonies; broth turbid; gas produced; gelatin liquefied; milk coagulated; non-proteolytic; saccharolytic; active toxin; pathogenic.

   8. *Clostridium toxinogenes,* page 263

9. Lenticular colonies; gas produced; abundant growth in broth; gelatin liquefied; milk digested; coagulated egg-white attacked; fetid odor; saccharolytic; hemolytic; toxin; pathogenic.

   9. *Clostridium hemolyticum,* page 264

     1. **Clostridium novyi** (Novy) Bergey *et al.*

Synonym: Bacilus oedematis II Novy; *Bacillus novyi* Migula.

Habitat: Guinea pigs dying from gelatinous, malignant edema. Quite frequent.

Morphology: Rods measuring 0.8 μ × 2 to 5 μ; sometimes filamentous; motile by means of peritrichous flagella; subterminal, clostridial spore; Gram-positive.

Physiology: Strict anaerobe. Opt. T. = 37°C. Resists 1 hour at 58°C.

Cultural characters: Gas produced.

Deep agar: Arborescent colonies; gas and fetid odor produced.

Glucose broth: Turbid, then flaky with sediment: acidified.

Gelatin: Liquefaction in 12 to 18 hours; gas.

Milk: Acidified.

Carbohydrates: Glucose, maltose, fructose, xylose, starch and glycerol are fermented.

Pathogenicity, natural: Malignant edema in guinea pigs inoculated with milk nuclein.

Pathogenicity, experimental: Intramuscular injection of 0.1 to 0.25 ml. into the rabbit, guinea pig, mouse, rat, pigeon and cat, produces colorless or pink, gelatinous edema, with pleural exsudate and peritoneal hemorrhages followed by death in 36 hours.

2. *Clostridium oedematiens* (Weinberg and Séguin) Bergey.

Synonym: Bacillus oedematiens W. and S. 1915.

Habitat: Soil, dung, intestinal tract of sheep, infected war wounds. Frequent.

Morphology: Thick rods with rounded ends, 1 μ $\times$ 4 to 8 μ; straight or slightly-curved filaments up to 15 μ; motile by means of 20 peritrichous flagella; voluminous, clostridial spore, oval and subterminal; Gram-positive.

Physiology: Strict anaerobe. Opt. T. $= 22$-$37°$C. Resists 30 minutes at 100°C. Survives more than 10 years. Neutral red and safranin are reduced.

Cultural characters: Gas and fetid odor produced.

Deep agar: Fluffy or arborescent colonies; gas.

Glucose broth: Slight turbidity and auto-agglutination; gas and fetid odor; acidified; H_2S not formed.

Peptone water: Very meager growth; little or no indole formed.

Glucose gelatin: Slow liquefaction; gas.

Milk: Coagulated; acidified; not digested.

Coagulated proteins: Not attacked.

Carbohydrates: Acid and gas from glucose, fructose, maltose, sucrose, galactose, lactose.

Pathogenicity, natural: Toxic gas gangrene in man; hepatic necrosis in sheep ("black disease") and man.

Pathogenicity, experimental: Injection of 0.25 ml. into the guinea pig produces pink, gelatinous edema, followed by death in 18 to 24 hours.

Toxin: Highly active: 200-8000 MLD (mouse, subcutaneous); complex structure: $a,\beta,\gamma,\delta,\sigma,\epsilon$, where a is a lethal factor, β, a necrotizing lecithinase, γ a non-necrotizing lecithinase, d an oxygenlabile hemolysin, σ an oxygen-stable hemolysin, and ϵ a factor responsible for the pearly zone. Hemolysin active *in vitro*. At least two toxic types are known; A $= \epsilon,\delta,\gamma,a$; B $= a,\beta,\sigma$, and one unknown type, C.

Specific antitoxin: 0.001 ml. will neutralize 100MLD of toxin.

Biochemistry: N_2 formed from nitrates; sulfites not reduced; produces NH_3, aldehydes, alcohols, acetylmethylcarbinol, acetic, butyric, lactic and succinic acids.

3. *Clostridium bellonensis* (Sacquépée) Prévot 1938.

Synonym: Bacillus bellonensis Sacquépée 1915.

Habitat: Infected war wounds; putrefying dead cats. Uncommon.

Morphology: Straight, pleomorphic, filamentous rods, 0.5 μ $\times$ 3 μ; motile by means of peritrichous flagella; oval, subterminal spore; Gram-positive.

Physiology: Strict anaerobe. Opt. T. $=37°$C. Resists 15 minutes at 95°C and 2 minutes, sometimes 5 minutes at 100°C. Marked longevity. Neutral red and safranin reduced.

Cultural characters: Gas and slightly fetid odor produced.

Deep agar: Lenticular or arborescent colonies; gas.

Glucose broth: Flaky growth; putrid odor.

Gelatin: Slow liquefaction.

Milk: Coagulated and slowly digested.

Coagulated egg-white: Not attacked.

Carbohydrates: Acid and gas from glucose, maltose, fructose, lactose, mannitol, and dulcitol.

Biochemistry: Nitrites not formed from nitrates; sulfites not reduced; produces NH_3, volatile amines, aldehydes, ketones, phenol, H_2S, acetic, propionic and lactic acids.

Pathogenicity, natural: Edematous gas gangrene.

Pathogenicity, experimental: In the guinea pig, rabbit and mouse, produces local gaseous edema, followed by death.

Toxic: Active; not neutralized by anti-*oedematiens* serum.

Antitoxin: Specific; does not neutralize *oedematiens* toxin.

Systematics: Species very closely related to *Cl. oedematiens,* from which it differs, however, by its toxin.

4. *Clostridium sarcoemphysematodes* (Conradi and Bieling) Prévot 1938.

Synonym: Bacillus sarcoemphysematodes hominis C. and B. 1916.

Habitat: Gas gangrene. Uncommon.

Morphology: Long, thick, pleomorphic rods; motile by means of peritrichous flagella; club-shaped spore; Gram-positive.

Physiology: Strict anaerobe. Opt. T. $=37°$C. Resists 1 hour at 100°C.

Cultural characters: Gas produced.

Deep agar: Fluffy, cloudy colonies.

Glucose broth: Turbid; gas and H_2S produced; acidified.

Gelatin: Liquefaction.

Milk: Coagulated; casein partly digested.

Coagulated serum: Digested.

Brain-medium: Blackened; H_2S formed.

Carbohydrates: Glucose, maltose, fructose, galactose, sucrose, lactose and arabinose are fermented.

Pathogenicity, natural: Gas gangrene.

Pathogenicity, exeperimental: In the guinea pig, pink, gaseous, toxic edema.

5. *Clostridium gigas* (Zeissler and Rassfeld) Prévot 1938.

Synonym: Bacillus gigas Z. and R.

Habitat: Sheep suffering from bradsot. Quite frequent.

Morphology: Rods measuring 1 to 2 μ $\times$ 4 to 20 μ; motile by means of peritrichous flagella; clostridial, central or subterminal spore; Gram-positive.

Physiology: Strict anaerobe. Opt. T. $= 37°C$. Resists 5-20 minutes at 100°C. Neutral red reduced temporarily.

Cultural characters: Obligate serophile; gas and fetid odor produced.

Serum-deep agar: Irregular colonies.

Serum-glucose-liver broth: Abundant turbidity; gas and putrid odor.

Gelatin: Meager growth; doubtful liquefaction.

Serum-gelatin: Liquefaction.

Liver-milk: Flaky coagulation, then peptonized.

Brain-medium: Blackened.

Carbohydrates: Glucose and fructose are fermented; sometimes, galactose, arabinose and xylose are also fermented.

Biochemistry: Nitrites not formed from nitrates; produces NH_3, H_2S, volatile amines, ketones, propionic, butyric and lactic acids.

Pathogenicity, natural: Bradsot of sheep in Germany; malignant edema of the pig.

Pathogenicity, experimental: In the guinea pig, mouse, rabbit and sheep, pink or colorless, gelatinous edema.

Toxin: Active, thermolabile, not neutralized by anti-*oedematiens* serum.

Antitoxin: Specific.

Systematics: Species quite different from *Cl. oedematiens,* because of its large size, serophile character, and absence of cross-neutralization.

6. *Clostridium bubalorum* (Kraneveld) Prévot 1938.

Synonym: Bacillus osteomyelitis bubalorum Kraneveld 1930.

Habitat: Buffalos suffering from osteomyelitis in Dutch Indies.

Morphology: Rods with rounded ends, 1.5 to 1.8 μ $\times$ 3 to 11 μ; motile; clostridial, central or subterminal spore; Gram-positive.

Physiology: Strict anaerobe. Opt. T. $= 37°C$. Resists 3 minutes at 100°C. Marked longevity. Neutral red reduced permanently.

Cultures characters: Gas and slightly fetid odor produced (H_2S).

Deep agar: Very small, fluffy, transparent colonies.
Albumin-liver broth: Abundant, flaky growth, sedimenting rapidly.
Peptone water: Meager growth; black sediment.
Gelatin: Liquefaction.
Milk: Coagulated.
Coagulated egg-white: Not attacked.
Carbohydrates: Not fermented.
Biochemistry: Nitrites not formed from nitrates; sulfites not reduced; produces NH_3, H_2S, volatile amines, ketones, formic, acetic, propionic and lactic acids.
Pathogenicity, natural: Osteomyelitis of the buffalo and the mule.
Pathogenicity, experimental: Non-pathogenic or feebly pathogenic for the guinea pig. Weak hemolysin.
Systematics: Species closely related to *Cl. gigas.*

7. *Clostridium oedematis-benigni* (Ukil) Prévot 1938.

Habitat: Appendix, pig, water from the Congo. Quite uncommon.
Morphology: Straight rods with rounded ends, 1 μ $\times$ 2 to 8 μ; rapidly becomes non-motile; distribution of flagella unknown; oval, subterminal spore; Gram-positive.
Physiology: Strict anaerobe. Opt. T. $=$ 37°C. Resists 4 minutes at 100°C. sometimes 30 minutes. Marked longevity. Neutral red is reduced.
Cultural characters: Gas and slightly fetid odor produced.
Deep agar: Arborescent, fluffy colonies.
Glucose broth: Turbid; disagreeable odor.
Peptone water: Meager growth; indole formed.
Gelatin: Liquefaction.
Milk: Slowly coagulated; casein incompletely digested after 3 weeks.
Coagulated serum: Slightly attacked.
Carbohydrates: Acid and gas from glucose, maltose, fructose and galactose.
Biochemistry: Nitrites formed from nitrates by some strains; sulfites reduced by some strains; produces NH_3, H_2S, volatile amines, ethanol, acetoin, acetic, butyric and lactic acids.
Toxin: Active. Weak hemolysin.
Pathogenicity, natural: Isolated in appendicitis and gaseous edema of the pig.
Pathogenicity, experimental: Subcutaneous injection into the guinea pig and mouse produces an edema which heals spontaneously.
Systematics: Species closely related to *Cl. oedematiens.*

8. *Clostridium toxinogenes* (Kojima) Prévot 1938.

Habitat: Mammals. Uncommon.
Morphology: Rods measuring 1 μ $\times$ 3 to 4 μ; motile by means of

12-13 peritrichous flagella; central or subterminal spore; Gram-positive.

Physiology: Strict anaerobe. Opt. T. = 37° C. Resists 20 minutes at 100°C. Neutral red and safranin reduced.

Cultural characters: Gas produced.

Deep agar: Arborescent colonies; some varieties produce lenticular colonies.

Glucose broth: Turbid; acidified; no odor.

Gelatin: Liquefaction; gas.

Milk: Slowly coagulated; some varieties produce rapid coagulation and retraction of the clot.

Coagulated serum: Not attacked.

Carbohydrates: Sucrose only is fermented; sometimes, glucose, fructose, maltose, lactose, galactose and glycerol.

Biochemistry: Nitrites not formed from nitrates; sulfites not reduced; produces NH_3, ethanol, acetic, butyric and lactic acids.

Pathogenicity, natural: Isolated in mixed culture from a case of blackleg in Japan, and from a fatal enzootic disease of sheep in France.

Pathogenicity, experimental: Injection of 0.01 ml. kills the guinea pig in 2 to 4 days, following the formation of a gelatinous edema.

Toxin: Highly active: 0.005 ml. kills the rabbit. Active hemolysin.

Antitoxin: Specific.

Systematic: Species related to *Cl. oedematiens,* but differs by its toxin.

9.   *Clostridium hemolyticum* (Vawter and Records) Hauduroy *et al.*

Synonym: Cl. hemolyticus bovis Vawter and Records 1926; *Bacillus hemolyticus* Hall 1926.

Habitat: Isolated from South American cattle dying of icterohemoglobinuria; soil of Equatorial Africa.

Morphology: Long rods, 0.8 μ $\times$ 3.5 to 9 μ; occurring in chains of 4-5 elements; clostridial, subterminal spore; Gram-positive. Motile by means of peritrichous flagella.

Physiology: Strict anaerobe. Opt. T. = 32-37°C. Resists 5 minutes at 100°C. Survives several years. Neutral red and safranin reduced.

Cultural characters: Gas produced.

Deep agar: Lenticular colonies.

Glucose broth: Abundant turbidity; gas, fetid odor and H_2S produced; indole not formed.

Gelatin: Liquefaction.

Milk: Digested without previous coagulation.

Coagulated egg-white: Partly digested.

Carbohydrates: Acid and gas from glucose, fructose, maltose, inositol, mannose, galactose, sucrose, arabinose, xylose, dulcitol, sorbitol and starch.

Pathogenicity, natural: Icterohemoglobinuria of cattle (Sierra Nevada, Andes, Chile).

Pathogenicity, experimental: Intramuscular injection of 0.1 to 1.5 ml. into the guinea pig causes hemoglobinuria and death in 16 to 24 hours; no gas.

Biochemistry: Nitrites not formed from nitrates; sulfites reduced by strains from the soil; produces NH_3, H_2S, volatile amines, indole, acetyl-methylcarbinol, acetic, propionic, valerianic and lactic acids; some strains produce butyric acid.

Toxin: Active: 1 ml. kills the guinea pig and rabbit; mouse killed by 0.1 ml. Hemolysin; Very active against the red blood cells of several animals species.

Serology: Specific agglutination.

Systematics: Species related to *Cl. oedematiens,* but neatly distinct on account of the absence of any cross-reaction.

SUB-GENUS VI: *CLOSTRIDIUM BOTULINUM*
(Agents of botulism).

These five species are highly related, and differ from each other by the antigenic structure of their toxin and by some differences in the nature and degree of their metabolism.

1. Colonies occurring as thin disks; gas produced; gelatin liquefied; milk coagulated, then digested; H_2S formed; indole not formed; saccharolytic; hemolysin; neurotoxin; specific antitoxin; cause of botulism in man and animals.

   1. *Clostridium botulinum* A, page 266

2. Less proteolytic than type A; toxin not neutralized by type A antitoxin.

   2. *Clostridium botulinum* B, page 267

3. Irregular colonies; saccharolytic; proteolytic; toxin not neutralized by types A and B antitoxins.

   3. *Clostridium botulinum* C, page 267

4. Non-proteolytic; saccharolytic; highly toxic; toxin not neutralized by types A, B, and C antitoxins.

   4. *Clostridium botulinum* D, page 268

5. Non-proteolytic; toxin less active than that of the preceding, but not neutralized by types A, B, C and D antitoxins.

   5. *Clostridium botulinum* E, page 268

6. Proteolytic; saccharolytic; toxin not neutralized by types A, B, C, D and E antitoxins.

   6. *Clostridium botulinum* F, page 269

1. *Clostridium botulinum* A (van Ermengen) Holland.

Synonym: Bacillus botulinus van Ermengen 1896.

Habitat: Soil, vegetables, fruit, human and animal feces, preserved meat and vegetables. Very frequent.

Morphology: Long rods, 0.9 to 1.2 μ $\times$ 4 to 6 μ; occurring singly, in pairs or in short chains; motile by means of 6-20 peritrichous flagella; oval, subterminal spore, fusiform or club-shaped; Gram-positive.

Physiology: Strict anaerobe. Opt. T. $=$ 25-33°C (20-40). Thermoresistance quite marked, but varies with the strains: some are moderately thermoresistant, others resist 2 to 3 hours at 100°C, 15 to 20 minutes at 105°C and 2 to 3 minutes at 120°C. Neutral red and safranin reduced.

Cultural characters: Gas and fetid odor produced.

Deep agar: Thin disk-like colonies, riddled with gaseous alveoli; some strains have fluffy colonies; gas.

Blood-deep agar: Irregular, hemolytic colonies.

Glucose broth: Turbid; gas; rancid odor; indole not formed.

Meat-broth: Abundant turbidity; gas and putrid odor.

Gelatin: Liquefaction; H_2S formed.

Milk: Coagulated, then digested; H_2S formed.

Coagulated egg-white: Digested; H_2S formed; some strains do not attack egg-white.

Carbohydrates: Acid and gas from glucose, fructose, maltose, dextrin, salicin and glycerol.

Biochemistry: Nitrites not formed from nitrates; sulfites not reduced; produces NH_3, H_2S, volatile amines, alcohols, ketones, acetylmethylcarbinol, acetic, butyric and lactic acids.

Pathogenicity, natural: Botulism (toxi-infection and food poisoning); a few human cases of botulism are known to have occurred from infected wounds. Type A botulism in animals is quite rare, but always food-borne.

Pathogenicity, experimental: Injection or ingestion of fluid cultures or of filtrates produces fatal botulism in numerous animal species. Injection of washed cells may also produce botulism; the MLD varies with the strains. The result is a neuro-vegetative paralytic syndrome.

Toxin: Of protein nature, its molecular weight is around 1,000,000; it is an integral part of the bacterial body, and may be extracted with suitable solvents. As a result of autolysis, it may be found in the fluid portion of the culture medium after 3 to 6 days; the guinea pig is killed by 1/200,000-1/500,000, the mouse by 1/1,000,000-1/2,000,000. 1 gm. of the purified toxin may contain 32 billion mouse MLD.

Hemolysin: Appears early, disappears rapidly; has been identified as a lecithinase related to the α factor of *W. perfringens*. Easily transformed into toxoid.

Antitoxin: Specific, highly active: 1 ml. may neutralize 75,000-100,000 MLD.

2. *Clostridium botulinum* B (Leuchs) Dickson.

Habitat, Morphology: Similar to type A, more particularly in the intestinal tract of the pig.

Physiology: Spore slightly less thermoresistant than that of type A. Proteolytic activity less marked than that of type A. Slightly less marked reducing power than type A (neutral red only is reduced). Human and animal type B botulism is similar to type A.

Toxin: Highly active; not neutralized by type A antitoxin.

Hemolysin: Appears early.

Antitoxin: Strictly specific, neutralizing only type B toxin.

Biochemistry: Nitrites not formed from nitrates; sulfites not reduced; produces NH_3, H_2S, volatile amines, alcohols, ketones, acetic, butyric and lactic acids.

3. *Clostridium botulinum* C Bengston 1922.

Synonym: Clostridium luciliae Bergey *et al.* 1923.

Habitat: Isolated from larvae of *Luciliae caesar* and from chicken dying of limberneck; soil, intestinal tract of the cat, the sheep, and the rat, spoiled silage.

Morphology: Similar to type A; 10-20 peritrichous flagella; rapidly becomes motile.

Physiology: Spore slightly-less thermoresistant than that of types A and B. Low reducing power (neutral red not reduced).

Deep agar: Irregular colonies; no gas.

Glucose broth: Flaky growth; no gas.

Gelatin: Liquefaction.

Milk: Coagulated, then digested.

Coagulated proteins: Not attacked.

Carbohydrates: Glucose, fructose, maltose, lactose are fermented by all strains; galactose, sucrose, starch and glycerol are feebly attacked by some strains.

Biochemistry: Nitrites not formed from nitrates; sulfites not reduced; produces NH_3, H_2S, volatile amines, ketones, acetic, propionic, butyric and lactic acids.

Pathogenicity, natural: Mainly animal botulism, human cases being seldom met; this type of food-poisoning results from spoiled silage or meat: domestic fowl, wild ducks, horses, donkey, mule, cattle, ranch mink.

Pathogenicity, experimental: Injection of filtrates will reproduce botulism in a wide variety of animals.

Toxin: Different from types A and B; not neutralized by types A and B antitoxins. Highly active: the mouse is killed by 1/100,000 ml.

Note.—Type C may be subdivided into types Cα and Cβ which share a common toxic factor, but type Cα has a specific minor toxic factor; thus,

Cα antitoxin will neutralize Cα and Cβ toxins, while Cβ antitoxin neutralizes Cα partly.

4. *Clostridium botulinum* D Theiler 1927.

Habitat: Carcasses of animals dying from Lamsiekte (South African cattle), soil of infected regions, intestinal tract of healthy carriers.
Morphology: Similar to type A.
Physiology: Spore less thermoresistant than that of the preceding types.
Cultural characters: Small amounts of gas and fetid odor produced.
Deep agar: Small, translucent, irregular colonies.
Broth: Flaky growth.
Gelatin: No liquefaction.
Milk: Coagulated by some strains, but never digested.
Coagulated proteins: Not attacked.
Carbohydrates: Glucose, fructose, maltose, galactose, and lactose are fermented by all strains; some strains ferment in addition: glycerol, starch and dulcitol.
Biochemistry: Nitrites not formed from nitrates; sulfites not reduced; produces NH_3, volatile amines, alcohols, acetic, butyric and lactic acids.
Pathogenicity, natural: Highly toxic form of botulism in cattle and horses.
Toxin: Not neutralized by A and B antitoxins, partially neutralized by C antitoxin.

5. *Clostridium botulinum* E Gunnison, Cummings and Meyer 1936 (fish type).

Habitat: Intestinal tract of marine and soft-water fish; marine sediments.
Morphology: Similar to the preceding species.
Physiology: Strict anaerobe. Very poorly thermoresistant: resists 5 minutes at 70°C, 1 to 2 minutes at 100°C; killed after 10 minutes at 80°C, or 3 minutes at 100°C. Neutral red and phenosafranin partially reduced.
Cultural characters: Gas and slightly fetid odor produced.
Liver-deep agar: Small, flat, lenticular colonies.
Beef heart broth: Turbid; gas; meat is reddened.
Gelatin: Liquefaction in 2 to 3 days.
Milk: Slowly and incompletely coagulated.
Carbohydrates: Glucose, fructose, maltose, sucrose and lactose are actively fermented; arabinose, xylose, glycerol, starch and mannitol are feebly fermented.
Biochemistry: Nitrites not formed from nitrates; sulfites not reduced; produces NH_3, aldehydes, ketones, indole, acetic, butyric and lactic acids.
Coagulated proteins: Not attacked or feebly attacked.
Pathogenicity, natural: Botulism from preserved fish.

Toxin: Less active than that of the preceding types; not neutralized by types A, B, C and D antitoxins.

Antitoxin: Specific; does not neutralize A, B, C and D toxins.

Note.—The varieties described under the name of *Cl. parabotulinum* exhibit only differences of degree in their proteolytic activity. At the Rome Congress of 1953, the subcommittee on the nomenclature of the clostridia has recommended that it be dropped.

To these 5 classical types, we add an E sub-type, discovered in 1960 and provisionally designated as type F.

6. *Clostridium botulinum* type F. Møller and Scheibel 1960.

Habitat: Unknown. Isolated from preserved liver paste from Langeland (Denmark).

Morphology: Similar to the preceding species.

Physiology: Strict anaerobe. Unstable and highly thermoresistant spore. Opt. T. = 30°C.

Cultural characters: Proteolytic and saccharolytic activity similar to that of types A and B.

Pathogenicity, natural: Severe human botulism (one fatal case) following ingestion of contaminated liver paste.

Toxin: Relatively weak: 30,000 mouse MLD per ml. appear in 3 to 4 days; highly unstable (strains lose easily their toxigenicity); not neutralized by types A, B, C, D and E antitoxins, although highly active type E antitoxin may neutralize it partly. Not activated by trypsin.

Antitoxin: Specific (neutralizes type E toxin only).

SUB-GENUS VII: *CLOSTRIDIUM SPOROGENES.*

(Proteolytic species, pathogenic either in pure or in mixed culture)
This group actually comprises 21 species.

A) Species producing gas and putrid odor:
  1. Fluffy and arborescent colonies; highly putrid gas formed; actively proteolytic; coagulated egg-white, milk, coagulated serum and meat are digested; lipolytic; saccharolytic; H_2S and indole (traces) formed; black pigment; toxin; feebly hemolytic; pathogenic (putrid gas gangrene); resists 15 to 60 minutes at 100°C.
  1. *Clostridium sporogenes,* page 272
  1 bis. Varieties of *Clostridium sporogenes:*
    a) Less proteolytic (casein not completely digested), non-pathogenic.
    Variety A, page 273

b) Larger size than A; more actively proteolytic than A (casein completely digested).
Variety B, page 273

c) Lenticular colonies.
Variety *parasporogenes,* page 273

d) Less putrid; tart odor.
Variety of A. P. Marie, page 273

e) Non-pathogenic.
Equine variety, page 273

f) Produces crystals of tyrosine.
Variety *tyrosinogenes,* page 274

g) Very highly thermoresistant (up to 8½ hours at 100°C).
Variety *stavangerensis,* page 274

2. Flabellate spore; irregular, fluffy colonies; broth turbid, then auto-agglutination; fetid gas; gelatin liquefied (viscous colonies); milk digested; proteolytic; saccharolytic; non-pathogenic.

2. *Clostridium flabelliferum,* page 274

3. Large, thick rods; encapsulated; lenticular colonies; actively proteolytic (coagulated egg-white, gelatin and meat are digested); saccharolytic; H₂S and indole formed; highly pathogenic (putrid gas gangrene); very active toxin, not neutralized by anti-*sporogenes* serum.

3. *Clostridium saprotoxicum,* page 275

4. Lenticular colonies; gas and putrid odor; gelatin not liquefied; milk coagulated; casein partially digested; coagulated egg-white partly digested; saccharolytic; H₂S formed; pathogenic for the rabbit; weak toxin.

4. *Clostridium gallii,* page 275

5. Irregular colonies; putrid gas; broth turbid with viscid zoogloea; intensely putrid odor; actively proteolytic (gelatin, milk, coagulated serum and coagulated egg-white are digested; meat is attacked); saccharolytic; neutral red reduced; indole not formed; highly pathogenic (putrid gas gangrene, gangrenous appendicitis); very active toxin, not neutralized by other antigangrenous antitoxins; very active urease.

5. *Clostridium sordelli,* page 276

6. Irregular, akene-shaped colonies; putrid gas; broth turbid; with viscid zoogloea; proteolytic (gelatin, milk, coagulated egg-white and coagulated serum are digested); saccharolytic; non-pathogenic in pure culture, but pathogenic in association; non-hemolytic; no toxin, nor urease.

6. *Clostridium bifermentans,* page 276

6 bis. Hemolytic variety (lecithinase).

    6 bis. *Cl. bifermentans* var *milesi,* page 277

    6 ter. Thermoresistant and pyogenic variety.

    6 ter. *Cl. bifermentans* var. *pyogenes,* page 277

7. Granular colonies; viscid zoogloea in broth; fetid odor; gelatin liquefied; milk coagulated, then digested; coagulated serum digested; H_2S and caproic acid formed; non-pathogenic.

    7. *Clostridium caproicum,* page 277

8. Highly thermoresistant variety (4 hours at 100°C).

    8. *Cl. caproicum* var. *strasbourgensis,* page 278

9. Morphologically and physiologically similar to the *bifermentans-caproicum* group, but sulfate-reducer on isolation (endocellular reductase which disappears during transfers).

    9. *Clostridium cauteretsensis,* page 278

10. Lenticular colonies; fetid gas; proteolytic (gelatin, milk and coagulated serum are digested; coagulated egg-white is attacked); saccharolytic; indole (traces) formed; feebly pathogenic (gelatinous edema); no toxin, nor hemolysin.

    10. *Clostridium aerofoetidum,* page 279

11. Black, lenticular colonies (becoming colorless and irregular in subsequent cultures); proteolytic, saccharolytic; non-pathogenic.

    11. *Clostridium saccharolyticum,* page 280.

12. Starred colonies; gelatin liquefied; milk coagulated; fibrin digested; putrid odor (H_2S, indole scatole); non-pathogenic.

    12. *Clostridium carnofoetidum,* page 280

13. Encapsulated rods; punctiform or snowy colonies; broth turbid; gas and fetid odor; gelatin liquefied; milk coagulated, then digested; indole and H_2S formed; pathogenic (peritonitis).

    13. *Clostridium ghoni,* page 281

    13 bis. Non-pathogenic variety.

        13 bis. *Cl. ghoni var. fructicosum,* page 281

14. Circular and arborescent colonies; gas produced; milk coagulated, then digested; neutral red reduced; gelatin liquefied; saccharolytic; pathogenic; toxic.

    14. *Clostridium mitelmani,* page 281

15. Proteolytic; saccharolytic, thiamine attacked by means of an aneurinase I.

    15. *Clostridium thiaminolyticum,* page 282

16. Irregular colonies; gelatin liquefied; milk coagulated, then digested; not saccharolytic; indole not formed, nor H_2S; non-pathogenic.

    16. *Clostridium hastiforme,* page 283

B) Gaseous, but not fetid species:
  17. Lenticular fluffy colonies; feebly proteolytic; non- or feebly saccharolytic; feebly or non-pathogenic.
    17. *Clostridium subterminale,* page 283

C) Species producing no gas in gelatin-free media; not putrid:
  18. Irregular, arborescent colonies; gas not produced in broth; gas produced in the presence of gelatin; milk digested; gelatin liquefied; muscle fibrin and crude tendon are digested; coagulated serum digested; H_2S formed; saccharolytic (no gas produced); pathogenic; very active, hemolytic toxin; specific antitoxin.
    18. *Clostridium histolyticum,* page 284

D) Species producing no gas, but with a fetid odor:
  19. Lenticular colonies; proteolytic; feebly saccharolytic; non-pathogenic.
    19. *Clostridium limosum,* page 284
  20. Irregular, flaky colonies; slowly proteolytic; saccharolytic; feebly or non-pathogenic.
    20. *Clostridium regulare,* page 285

E) Species producing no gas, nor fetid odor:
  21. Lenticular colonies; heavy zoogloea; feebly proteolytic; glucose only is fermented; non-pathogenic.
    21. *Clostridium zoogleicum,* page 285

1.   *Clostridium sporogenes* (Metchnikoff) Bergey.

Synonym: Bacillus sporogenes Metchnikoff 1908.

Habitat: Soil, dung, feces of man and animals; methane-producing mud, infected war wounds. Very frequent (member of original universal microflora).

Physiology: Strict anaerobe. Opt. T. = 22-37°C. Resists 15 minutes to 1 hour at 100°C. Survives more than 10 years. Neutral red reduced definitely, safranin reduced temporarily.

Cultural characters: Gas and putrid odor produced.

Deep agar: Fluffy, arborescent, flaky colonies.

Glucose broth: Abundant flaky growth; intensely putrid odor; gas; black pigment.

Gelatin: Liquefaction; gas and H_2S produced.

Milk: Digested without previous coagulation; gas and H_2S formed.

Coagulated serum: Digested and blackened; H_2S formed.

Coagulated egg-white: Digested; H_2S formed.

Meat: Digested; abundant black sediment.

Lipids: Broken down into fatty acids and glycerol.

Carbohydrates: Glucose, fructose, maltose, galactose, mannitol, dextrin, glycerol and sorbitol are fermented.

Biochemistry: Nitrites formed from nitrates; sulfites reduced to sulfides by some strains; produces NH_3, H_2S, volatile amines, (trimethylamine), indole (traces), acetic, butyric and lactic acids ($+$ traces of valerianic and caproic acids).

Pathogenicity, natural: Appendicitis, gas gangrene, food poisoning.

Pathogenicity, experimental: Some strains produce putrid gas gangrene in the guinea pig; other strains are pathogenic on account of the large amounts of NH_3 formed; still others are non-pathogenic.

Soluble toxic substance: Kills the rabbit and guinea pig by intravenous injection; identified as NH_3.

Hemolysin: Feebly active. No real toxin.

Serology: Specific agglutination at 1-1,000.

1 bis. Varieties of *Cl. sporogenes.*

a) Variety A (Metchnikoff).

Habitat: Intestinal tract of man.

Morphology: Similar to the normal species.

Physiology: Less proteolytic; non-pathogenic.

b) Variety B (Metchnikoff).

Habitat: Intestinal tract of man suffering from colitis.

Morphology: Similar to the normal species, except that it is slightly larger than variety A.

Physiology: More actively proteolytic than variety A; non-pathogenic.

c) Variety *parasporogenes* (McIntosh).

Synonym: Bacillus parasporogenes McIntosh; *Clostridium parasporogenes.*

Habitat: Isolated from cases of gas gangrene.

Morphology: Similar to *Cl. sporogenes.*

Cultural characters: Lenticular colonies in deep agar; proteolytic and saccharolytic (glucose, fructose and maltose). Pathogenic for the young guinea pig.

Serology: Specific agglutination.

d) Variety of A.P. Marie 1925.

Habitat: Pork meat macerating in water at 18° C.

Morphology: Similar to the normal species.

Cultural characters: Similar to *Cl. sporogenes,* except non putrid, tart odor.

Pathogenicity, experimental: Produces large abscess in the guinea pig.

e) Equine variety of Choukévitch 1911.

Habitat: Intestinal tract of the horse.

Morphology: Similar to the normal species.

Physiology: Cultural characters: Similar to the normal species.
Pathogenicity: Non-pathogenic.

f) Variety *tyrosinogenes* (Hall) Bergey *et al.*
Synonym: Bacillus tyrosinogenes (Hall) 1922.
Habitat: Unknown.
Morphology: Similar to *Cl. sporogenes.*
Physiology: Similar to *Cl. sporogenes.*
Carbohydrates: Acid and gas from glucose, fructose and maltose. Other carbohydrates are feebly fermented.
Pathogenicity: Non-pathogenic.
Main characteristic: Produces large amounts of crystalline tyrosine.

g) Cl. sporogenes var. *stavangerensis* Prévot, Raynaud and Tataki 1951.

Habitat: Isolated from preserves in Stavanger (Norway).
Morphology: Similar to the normal species.
Physiology: Resists 6 to 8 hours at 100°C, 15 to 30 minutes at 105°C, 5 to 10 minutes at 110°C, and some strains, 5 min. at 115°C. Contains a substance which, primarily endocellular, eventually diffuses into the surrounding medium and confers by prolonged contact a high thermo-resistance to bacteria which are normally poorly resistant.

2. *Clostridium flabelliferum* Sturges and Reddish 1926.

Habitat: Brine and salted meat, pond mud. Quite uncommon.
Morphology: Rods measuring 0.5 μ $\times$ 3 to 5 μ; motile by means of peritrichous flagella; oval, subterminal spore; that part of the protoplasm next to the spore spreads out fan-like after the third day; Gram-positive.
Physiology: Strict anaerobe. Opt. T. $= 37°C$. Resists 10 minutes at 100°C. Neutral red reduced.
Cultural characters: Gas and putrid odor produced.
Deep agar: Irregular, flaky fluffy colonies.
Glucose broth: Turbid, then auto-agglutination; gas and putrid odor produced.
Gelatin: Liquefaction in 24 hours; viscous colonies.
Milk: Digested in 4 days; putrid odor.
Coagulated proteins: Not attacked.
Carbohydrates: Acid and gas from flucose, fructose, galactose, maltose, sucrose, mannitol and sorbitol.
Biochemistry: Nitrites not formed from nitrates; sulfites reduced to sulfides, sometimes sulfates equally (endocellular reductase); produces NH_3, H_2S, volatile amines, aldehydes, formic, butyric and lactic (traces) acids.
Pathogenicity: Non-pathogenic.
Systematics: Species closely related to *Cl. sporogenes.*

3. **Clostridium saprotoxicum** (Sordelli and Soriano) Prévot 1938.

Synonym: Bacillus saprotoxicus S. and S. 1934.

Habitat: Infected wounds, soil of the Ivory Coast, gorilla feces. Quite uncommon.

Morphology: Short, thick rods, 1.5 μ $\times$ 3 to 5 μ; encapsulated; motile by means of peritrichous flagella; oval, central or subterminal spore; Gram-positive.

Physiology: Strict anaerobe. Opt. T. = 37°C. Resists 1 minute at 100°C. Neutral red and safranin reduced.

Cultural characters: Gas and putrid odor formed.

Deep agar: Lenticular colonies with delicate projections.

Glucose broth: Turbid; gas, putrid odor, H_2S and indole formed.

Gelatin: Liquefaction.

Milk: Coagulated, then partly digested; fat hydrolyzed.

Coagulated egg-white: Digested.

Meat: Digested and blackened.

Carbohydrates: Acid and gas from glucose, fructose, maltose, galactose, sucrose, arabinose, xylose and starch.

Biochemistry: Nitrites not formed from nitrates; produces NH_3, H_2S, volatile amines, ethanol, aldehyde, acetone, indole, acetylmethylcarbinol (traces), acetic, butyric and lactic acids.

Pathogenicity, natural: Gas gangrene in man.

Pathogenicity, experimental: Intramuscular injection into the guinea pig produces local swelling and putrid edema, followed by death from intoxication; intraperitoneal injection produces fatal peritonitis.

Toxin: Active; produces convulsions and death. Not neutralized by anti-*sporogenes* nor by anti-*sordellii* sera.

Antitoxin: Specific.

Systematics: Autonomous species on account of the antigenic structure of its toxin.

4. **Clostridium gallii** (Galli) Prévot 1938.

Habitat: Rabbit. Uncommon.

Morphology: Straight or slightly-curved rods; pleomorphic, motile; central or subterminal spore; Gram-positive.

Physiology: Strict anaerobe. Opt. T. = 37-40°C. Resists 10 minutes at 70°C.

Cultural characters: Gas and putrid odor formed.

Deep agar: Lenticular colonies; gas.

Glucose broth: Turbid; gas, putrid odor and H_2S formed.

Gelatin: No liquefaction.

Milk: Coagulated; casein slowly digested.

Coagulated egg-white: Attacked; putrid odor.

Carbohydrates: Glucose, maltose, sucrose and lactose are fermented.

Pathogenicity, natural: Isolated from necrotic lesions of the rabbit.

Pathogenicity, experimental: Diffuse phlegmon; peritonitis.

Toxin: Appears on the eighth day; active: kills the guinea pig in 3 days.

5. *Clostridium sordellii* (Sordelli) Hall and Scott 1927.

Synonym: Bacillus oedematis sporogenes Sordelli 1922.

Habitat: Soil, putrid gangrene, appendicitis. Quite frequent.

Morphology: Rods measuring 1.2 to 1.5 μ $\times$ 3 to 5 μ; filaments up to 45 μ; short chains of 4-5 elements; motile by means of peritrichous flagella; clostridial spore; Gram-positive.

Physiology: Strict anaerobe. Opt. T. $= 37°$C. Resists 1 hour at 100°C. Survives more than 10 years. Neutral red reduced.

Cultural characters: Gas and putrid odor produced.

Deep agar: Arborescent colonies; gas.

Blood agar: Dew-drop colonies; little or no hemolysis.

Glucose broth: Turbid; filaments and viscous zoogloea; repulsive odor; acidified; indole formed.

Gelatin: Liquefaction.

Milk: Coagulated then digested.

Coagulated serum: Slowly digested.

Meat: Disintegrated.

Carbohydrates: Glucose, fructose and maltose are fermented.

Biochemistry: Nitrites not formed from nitrates; sulfites reduced to sulfides; produces NH_3, H_2S, volatile amines, ethanol, aldehyde, ketone, indole, acetylmethylcarbinol (traces), acetic, butyric, valerianic and lactic acids. Very active urease.

Pathogenicity, natural: Gas gangrene, appendicitis, icterohemo-globinuria of cattle.

Pathogenicity, experimental: Highly pathogenic. Intramuscular injection of 0.1 ml. into the rabbit produces death in 24 hours. Intramuscular injection of 0.01 ml. into the guinea pig produces death in 24 hours following non-putrid, gaseous, red edema; sometimes putrid lesions.

Toxin: Highly active: guinea pig killed by 1/500 ml. in 48 hours; mouse killed by 1/10,000 ml. Thermolabile. Not neutralized by diverse anti-gas gangrene sera. Hemolytic lecithinase.

Antitoxin: Specific. No cross-reaction with the other pathogenic clostridia.

Antigenicity: A complex polysaccharide shared in common with *Cl. bifermentans.*

6. *Clostridium bifermentans* (Tissier and Martelly) Bergey.

Synonym: Bacillus bifermentans sporogenes Tissier and Martelly 1902;

Bacillus centrosporogenes Hall 1922.

Habitat: Soil, putrefying butcher's meat, infected war wounds, mud from rivers and ponds. Very frequent.

Morphology: Straight rods with rounded ends, 0.8 to 1.0 $\mu \times$ 5 to 6 μ; occurring singly or in short chains; motile in young cultures by means of peritrichous flagella; oval, central or subterminal, clostridial spore, numerous, often free; Gram-positive.

Physiology: Strict anaerobe. Opt. T. $= 37°$C. Resists 1½ minutes at 100°C. Survives more than 10 years. Neutral red and safranin reduced.

Cultural characters: Gas and putrid odor produced.

Deep agar: Strawberry-shaped colonies made up of agglomerated lenticular colonies; gas and putrid odor.

Glucose broth: Abundant turbidity; viscous sediment; putrid odor, gas, indole, NH_3, H_2S, tyrosine, leucine, proteoses and amines formed.

Gelatin: Liquefaction.

Milk: Digested.

Coagulated egg-white: Attacked; slowly digested.

Coagulated serum: Digested.

Carbohydrates: Acid and gas from glucose, maltose, fructose, glycerol and sorbitol.

Biochemistry: Nitrites not formed from nitrates; sulfites reduced to sulfides; urease not present; produces NH_3, H_2S, volatile amines, ethanol, aldehyde, acetone, indole, acetic, butyric, valerianic and lactic acids. acetylmethylcarbinol (traces), CO_2, H_2 and, under certain conditions, CH_4.

6 bis. *Cl. bifermentans* var. *milesi*
(Miles and Miles 1947) Prévot and Capponi 1949.

This variety differs from the normal species only by the presence of a lecithinase C which is immunologically related to the a factor of *W. perfringens;* it is not lethal, slightly toxic for the guinea pig, and does not require Ca ions.

6 ter. *Cl. bifermentans* var. *pyogenes* Sartory and Meyer 1941.

Habitat: Semi-preserves.

Physiology: Marked thermoresistance (2 hours at100°C). Markedly thermophilic (45-55°C). Neutral red not reduced.

Cultural characters: Feeble fermentation of carbohydrates.

Biochemistry: Nitrites formed from nitrates.

Pathogenicity: Pyogenic in laboratory animals.

7. *Clostridium caproicum* (Rodella) Prévot 1938.

Synonym: Bacillus anaerobicus caproicus Rodella 1906.

Habitat: Isolated from Italian cheese; intestinal tract of man, pond mud, soil of Africa. Frequent (part of the original universal microflora).

Morphology: Rods with square ends; 3 to 5 μ; occurring in long chains; actively motile; oval spore, clostridial or free; Gram-positive.

Physiology: Strict anaerobe. Opt. T. $= 24\text{-}28°C$ (22-37). Resists 5 minutes at $100°C$. Survives more than 2 years. Neutral red definitively reduced, safranin temporarily reduced.

Cultural characters: Gas and fetid odor produced.

Deep agar: Circular or starred colonies, sometimes fluffy or arborescent; gas.

Plain broth: Growth occurring as a membrane, then as a viscous zoogloea; gas and fetid odor.

Gelatin: Liquefaction.

Milk: Mucoid growth, then coagulated and finally digested; gas, H_2S and caproic acid.

Coagulated serum: Liquefaction; strong odor, black pigment.

Coagulated proteins: Partly digested.

Carbohydrates: Glucose, fructose, maltose and sorbitol are fermented.

Biochemistry: Nitrites not formed from nitrates; sulfites reduces to sulfides; produces NH_3, H_2S, indole, aldehydes, alcohols, acetic, iso-butyric or optically active valerianic acids; under certain conditions, may produce CH_4.

Pathogenicity, experimental: Non-pathogenic in pure culture.

Pathogenicity, natural: Isolated in acute appendicitis. Some strains are hemolytic, due to the presence of a lecithinase.

8. *Cl. caproicum* var. *strasbourgensis*
Meyer, Malgras and Aladame 1952.

Habitat: Contaminated preserves (swelled sauerkraut with sausages from Strasbourg).

Morphology: Similar to the normal species.

Physiology: Resists 4 hours at $100°C$.

Carbohydrates: Lactose, galactose and sucrose not fermented.

Biochemistry: Produces ketones, alcohol, aldehydes, isovalerianic and formic acids in the ratio 1:1.

9. *Clostridium cauteretsensis* Prévot 1949.

Habitat: Cauteretsins, daxins and gleins from the Pyrenees.

Morphology: Similar to *Cl. bifermentans* (0.8 to 1.0 $\mu \times$ 3 to 4 μ); motility varies with the strains: sometimes very active, sometimes weak, but always by means of peritrichous flagella; spores formed freely; numerous free spores; Gram-positive.

Physiology: Strict anaerobe. Resists 6 to 15 minutes at $100°C$. Neutral red and safranin reduced.

Cultural characters: Gas and fetid odor produced.

Deep agar: Fluffy colonies of average size; large amounts of gas.

Iron-sulfate-deep agar: Black colonies in the few days following isolation; no gas formed.

Glucose VF broth: Abundant turbidity; gas; very fetid odor; abundant zoogloea.

Peptone water: Abundant turbidity sedimenting as a viscous zoogloea.

Gelatin: Liquefaction in 1 to 2 days.

Milk: Digested in 1 to 2 days without previous coagulation; fat hydrolyzed.

Coagulated serum: Partly or completely digested.

Other coagulated proteins: Partly digested.

Carbohydrates: Glucose, fructose, maltose, starch and glycerol are fermented.

Biochemistry: Nitrites not formed from nitrates; sulfites reduced to H_2S during the first generations; produces NH_3, H_2S, indole, scatole (traces), volatile amines, aldehydes, ketones, alcohols, iso-butyric, acetic and sometimes formic acids.

Pathogenicity: Non-pathogenic. No toxin, no hemolysin, no lecithinase.

10. **Clostridium aerofoetidum** (Weinberg and Séguin) Bergey *et al.*

Synonym: Bacillus aerofoetidus Weinberg and Séguin 1917.

Habitat: Intestinal tract (appendix), infected wounds, soil. Quite frequent.

Morphology: Rods measuring 0.6 to 0.7 μ $\times$ 3 to 5 μ; occurring in short chains; motile by means of peritrichous flagella; oval, subterminal spore, seldom observed; Gram-positive.

Physiology: Strict anaerobe. Opt. T. $=$ 30-37°C. Resists 1 to 10 minutes at 70°, 80° or 100°C. Survives indefinitely. Neutral red and safranin reduced.

Cultural characters: Gas and fetid odor produced.

Deep agar: Lenticular or irregular colonies, heart-shaped; gas.

Glucose broth: Abundant turbidity; gas and fetid odor.

Gelatin: Slow liquefaction.

Milk: Coagulated, then digested.

Coagulated serum: Rapid or slow liquefaction.

Coagulated egg-white: Attacked (softened and amber-colored).

Carbohydrates: Glucose, maltose, fructose, lactose, salicin and glycogen are fermented.

Biochemistry: Nitrites not formed from nitrates; sulfites reduced to sulfides; produces NH_3, H_2S, volatile amines, aldehydes, ketones, acetylmethylcarbinol, acetic, butyric, valerianic and lactic acids. Traces of indol formed.

Pathogenicity, natural: Gas gangrene, appendicitis.

Pathogenicity, experimental: Intramuscular injection into the guinea pig will produce a gaseous phlegmon with transparent, gelatinous edema. No toxin, nor hemolysin.

11. *Clostridium saccharolyticum* (Distaso) Bergey.

Synonym: B. sporogenes saccharolyticus Distaso 1911.

Habitat: Intestinal tract of man, chimpanzé, cat and sardine. Quite uncommon.

Morphology: Rods measuring 0.8 μ $\times$ 3 μ with rounded ends; occurring singly, in pairs or in short chains; motile; large, oval, clostridial subterminal spore; Gram-positive.

Physiology: Strict anaerobe. Opt. T. $= 37°$C. Resists 2 to 3 minutes at 100°C. Neutral red, phenosafranin and safranin reduced.

Cultural characters: Gas and fetid odor produced (fecaloid+butyric).

Glucose-deep agar: Greyish, lenticular colonies, becoming black. The black color of the colonies disappears upon transfer into VF deep agar, but reappears in semi-solid peptone water at 26°C. The colonies may become irregular and surrounded by small satellite colonies; gas produced.

Glucose VF broth: Turbid.

Gelatin: Liquefaction in 24 hours.

Milk: Curdled, casein precipitated, then digested; transparent, amber-yellow fluid.

Coagulated proteins: Slowly digested.

Carbohydrates: Glucose, lactose and sucrose are fermented.

Pathogenicity: Non-pathogenic.

Biochemistry: Produces NH_3, H_2S, volatile amines, indole, aldehydes, alcohol, ketones, iso-valerianic and acetic, sometimes lactic acids.

12. *Clostridium carnofoetidum* (Salus) McCrudden 1910.

Synonym: Cl. foetidum carnis Salus 1904.

Habitat: Soil, putrefying corpses, feces, soils of Africa. Quite frequent.

Morphology: Straight rods, 2 to 4 μ; occurring singly or in short chains; motile; clostridial spore, central or subterminal, skittle-shaped; Gram-positive.

Physiology: Strict anaerobe. Opt. T. $= 37°$C. Resists 1 minute at 100°C. Neutral red not reduced.

Cultural characters: Gas and fetid odor produced.

Deep agar: Starred, mossy or lenticular colonies; gas.

Glucose broth: Abundant turbidity; sediment; fetid gas.

Gelatin: Arborescent colonies; liquefaction.

Milk: Coagulated, then digested in part.

Fibrin: Putrid digestion (H_2S, NH_3, CO_2); indole and scatole.

Coagulated proteins: Slightly attacked.

Carbohydrates: Glucose, fructose, maltose and glycerol are fermented; sorbitol and mannitol are feebly fermented.

Biochemistry: Nitrites not formed from nitrates; produces NH_3, H_2S, volatile amines, alcohols, acetone, propionic, valerianic and lactic acids.

Pathogenicity: Non-pathogenic.

13. *Clostridium ghoni* (Ghon and Mucha) Prévot 1938.

Habitat: Genital tract of the woman, soil, pond mud. Quite frequent.

Morphology: Straight or slightly-curved rods, 0.6 $\mu \times$ 3 to 7 μ; occurring singly or in short chains; filaments; motile by means of peritrichous flagella; oval, central or subterminal spore, sometimes clostridial; Gram-positive.

Physiology: Strict anaerobe. Opt. T. $= 21\text{-}37°C$. Resists 20 minutes at 70°C and 3 minutes at 80°C. Survives more than 1 year. Neutral red reduced.

Cultural characters: Gas and putrid odor produced.

Deep agar: Circular, brownish, punctiform colonies with fluffy, irregular border; sometimes arborescent; small amounts of gas.

Glucose broth: Abundant turbidity; gas, indole; H_2S; not coherent, viscous sediment; putrid odor.

Petone water: Slight turbidity; no gas formed.

Gelatin: Slow liquefaction.

Milk: Coagulated, then digested; gas.

Coagulated ascitic fluid: Complete digestion.

Coagulated serum: Digested.

Coagulated egg-white: Not attacked, or partly and slowly attacked.

Carbohydrates: Glucose and sucrose fermented with the production of butyric and lactic acids, CO_2, H_2 and N_2. Some strains ferment also fructose, maltose, galactose, lactose, sorbitol, mannitol and glycerol.

Biochemistry: Nitrites not formed from nitrates; produces NH_3, H_2S, volatile amines, alcohol, aldehyde, indole, acetylmethylcarbinol, formic, butyric and lactic acids.

Pathogenicity, natural: Fibrino-hemorrhagic peritonitis.

Pathogenicity, experimental: Feeble: large doses are required to kill the guinea pig by local edema and visceral degeneration.

Intraperitoneal injection produces fibrino-purulent peritonitis.

13 bis *Cl. ghoni,* var. *fructicosum* (Zeetti).

Synonym: Bacillus fructicosus Zeetti 1934.

We relate to *Cl. ghoni* the strains described by Zeetti in 1934 under the name of *Bacillus fructicosus;* they differ only by their non-pathogenicity.

14. *Clostridium mitelmani* (Mitelman) P. 1938.

Habitat: Intestinal tract of diarrheal cases; pond mud, mummies. Quite uncommon.

Morphology: Rods measuring 0.8 to 1.0 μ × 2 to 5 μ; motile; oval spore; Gram-positive.

Physiology: Strict anaerobe. Opt. T. = 37°C. Resists 10 minutes at 80°C, and sometimes 3 minutes at 100°C. Phenosafranin reduced.

Cultural characters: Gas and fetid odor produced.

Deep agar: Small, circular colonies, sometimes lenticular.

Glucose broth: Turbid; gas; fetid odor.

Gelatin: Liquefaction.

Milk: Coagulated, then digested.

Coagulated egg-white and serum: Not attacked.

Carbohydrates: Glucose, fructose, maltose, galactose, sucrose, lactose, mannitol and glycerol are fermented.

Biochemistry: Nitrites not formed from nitrates; sulfites reduced to sulfides; produces NH_3, H_2S, ethanol, aldehyde, indole (traces), acetic, valerianic and lactic acids.

Pathogenicity, experimental: Very weak: slight edema which heals spontaneously.

Toxin: Weak: produces edema, then an eschar.

15. *Clostridium thiaminolyticum* Kimura and Liao 1953.

Habitat: Feces from healthy carriers and sick persons in Kyoto. Quite frequent.

Morphology: Rods with rounded ends, 0.8 to 1.0 μ × 2 to 3.5 μ; occurring singly, never in chains; motile by means of peritrichous flagella; ellisoidal, subterminal spore, swelling the rod; Gram-positive.

Physiology: Strict anaerobe. Neutral red reduced.

Cultural characters: Gas and fetid odor produced.

VF broth: Turbid; gas; fetid odor.

Tarrozzi broth: Turbid; gas; fetid odor.

Gelatin: Liquefaction.

Milk: Rapid digestion.

Coagulated egg-white: Attacked and partly digested.

Liver: Blackened.

Carbohydrates: Glucose, maltose and glycerol actively fermented; fructose and mannose feebly fermented.

Biochemistry: Produces H_2S, acetoin; thiamine decomposed by fluid cultures and by centrifugates; the enzyme does not dialyze through cellophane. Opt. pH = 7.5. Opt. T. = 30°C. Destroyed after 20 minutes at 90-100°C. Under optimum conditions, 1 ml. of supernatant will decompose 77 μg of thiamine en 1 hour. Aniline, homosulfamine, pyridine, niacine, 2-methyl-4-amino-5-hydroxymethyl-pyrimidine and cystein act as activators: therefore, it is an aneurinase I.

Pathogenicity: Non-pathogenic. No toxin, nor hemolysin.

16. *Clostridium hastiforme*
(Cunningham and Jenkins) MacLennan 1939.

Habitat: Soil of England and Africa.

Morphology: Thin rods with rounded ends, 0.3 to 0.6 μ $\times$ 2 to 6 μ; occurring singly or in pairs, seldom in short chains; motile by means of peritrichous flagella; oval, subterminal spore, spear head-shaped; Gram-positive.

Physiology: Not very strict anaerobe. Opt. T. $= 30°C$ (22-37). Resists 30 minutes at 70°C. Neutral red reduced.

Cultural characters: Very small amounts of gas; slightly fetid.

Deep agar: Small, circular, irregular colonies; little gas.

Glucose broth: Diffuse turbidity, followed by flaky sediment; cheesy odor; indole not formed.

Gelatin: Liquefaction in 7 to 10 days.

Coagulated proteins: Not attacked.

Milk: Coagulated, then digested; cheesy odor; alkaline.

Brain-medium: Not digested, nor blackened.

Carbohydrates: Not fermented.

Biochemistry: Nitrites not formed from nitrates; produces NH_3, H_2S, volatile amines, aldehydes, alcohols, formic, butyric and lactic acids.

Pathogenicity: Non-pathogenic. No toxin, nor hemolysin.

Serology: Specific agglutination; antigenically homogeneous.

17. *Clostridium subterminale* (Hall and Whitehead) Bergey.

Synonym: Bacillus subterminalis H. and W. 1927.

Habitat: African manioc, spoiled meat, soil.

Morphology: Rods occurring singly, in pairs or in short chains; motile; clostridial, oval, subterminal spore; Gram-positive.

Physiology: Strict anaerobe. Opt. T. $= 30°C$. Resists 2 minutes at 100°C. Neutral red and phenosafranin definitively reduced, safranin temporarily reduced.

Cultural characters: Gas, but no fetid odor; slightly aromatic.

Deep agar: Lenticular colonies, sometimes fluffy; gas.

Glucose broth: Abundant turbidity; gas.

Peptone water: Slight turbidity.

Gelatin: Slow liquefaction; black sediment.

Milk: Slowly coagulated, then slowly digested.

Coagulated proteins: Not attacked or very lightly so.

Brain-medium: Slight turbidity; gas; slow and incomplete digestion.

Iron-brain medium: Blackened.

Carbohydrates: Glucose, maltose, sucrose and lactose sometimes fermented.

Biochemistry: Nitrites not formed from nitrates; sulfites reduced to sulfides; H_2S not formed; indole not formed; produces NH_3, aldehydes, ethanol, ketones, lecithinase, caproic, propionic or acetic, butyric and lactic (large quantities) acids.

Pathogenicity: Non-pathogenic or feebly pathogenic (diarrhea).

18. *Clostridium histolyticum* (Weinberg and Séguin) Bergey *et al.*

Synonym: Bacillus histolyticus Weinberg and Séguin 1917.

Habitat: Soil, tannery water, human feces, intestinal tract (appendix), infected wounds. Frequent.

Morphology: Rods measuring 0.5 to 0.8 μ $\times$ 3 to 5 μ; motile; clostridial, oval, subterminal spore; Gram-positive.

Physiology: Strict anaerobe. Opt. T. $= 37°C$. Resists 10 minutes at 105°C; killed after 1 hour at 100°C. Survives more than 10 years. Neutral red definitively reduced, safranin temporarily reduced.

Cultural characters: No gas produced in gelatin-free media; no fetid odor.

Deep agar: Fluffy or arborescent colonies.

Glucose broth: Turbid; very slightly fetid odor.

Peptone water: Slight turbidity; traces of indole.

Gelatin: Liquefaction; gas production is a function of the strains.

Milk: Very rapidly and completely digested.

Coagulated egg-white and serum: Digested.

Fibrin: Digested.

Fresh muscle and fresh tendon: Digested.

Carbohydrates: Acid, but no gas from glucose, lactose and maltose.

Biochemistry: Nitrates more or less reduced or destroyed; produces NH_3 H_2S, acetic, butyric and lactic acids, acetylmethylcarbinol (traces). In addition to the proteases, presence of a true collagenase which dissolves Kanagy's true collagen.

Pathogenicity, natural: Gangrene (myolysis), appendicitis.

Pathogenicity, experimental: Intramuscular injection of 0.2 ml. into the guinea pig produces dissecting edema and complete histolysis, followed by death in 24 to 48 hours.

Toxin: Highly active: Mouse killed by 0.1 ml. Shares a common antigen with *Cl. septicum.*

Hemolysin: In vitro production of an active hemolysin.

Antitoxin: Specific; contains an antibody which neutralizes an antigen from *Cl. septicum.*

19. *Clostridium limosum* André 1948.

Habitat: Mud from the Ebrié laguna on the Ivory Coast.

Morphology: Rods with rounded ends, 0.7 μ $\times$ 3 μ; occurring singly, in pairs, sometimes in short chains; motile; clostridial, subterminal spore, sometimes free; Gram-positive.

Physiology: Strict anaerobe. Opt. T. = 37°C. Resists 10 minutes at 100°C. Survives several months. Neutral red partially reduced.

Cultural characters: No gas produced, but fetid odor.

Deep agar: Very small, lenticular colonies.

Glucose VF broth: Abundant turbidity; sediment; very slightly acidified.

Peptone water: Abundant growth; indole not formed.

Gelatin: Liquefaction.

Milk: Digested in 4 days.

Coagulated proteins: Not attacked.

Carbohydrates: Glucose and galactose are fermented.

Biochemistry: Nitrites not formed from nitrates; produces NH_3, H_2S, volatile amines, alcohols, acetic, propionic and lactic acids.

Pathogenicity: Non-pathogenic; active hemolysin *in vitro,* neutralized by anti-*perfringens* and anti-*septicum* sera.

20. *Clostridium regulare* (Distaso) Bergey *et al.*

Synonym: Bacillus sporogenes regularis Distaso 1911.

Habitat: Intestinal tract; semi-preserves.

Morphology: Long rods with rounded ends; occurring singly or in pairs; motile; small, oval, subterminal spore, slightly clostridial; Gram-positive.

Physiology: Strict anaerobe. Opt. T. = 37°C. Resists 40 minutes at 100°C. Neutral red and phenosafranin are reduced, safranin is partly reduced.

Cultural characters: No gas, but fetid odor produced (scatole and valerianic acid).

Deep agar: Small, opaque, irregular, fluffy colonies.

Glucose broth: Abundant turbidity.

Gelatin: Liquefaction.

Milk: Acidified, slowly coagulated, then slowly digested.

Coagulated proteins: Slowly digested.

Carbohydrates: Glucose, lactose and sucrose are fermented.

Biochemistry: Produces NH_3, H_2S, indole (traces), amines, aldehydes, ethanol, ketones, phenol, acetic and formic acids.

Pathogenicity: Non-pathogenic for the guinea pig, feebly pathogenic for the mouse.

21. *Clostridium zoogleicum* (Distaso) Bergey *et al.*

Synonym: Bacillus sporogenes zoogleicus Distaso 1911.

Habitat: Intestinal tract of man.

Morphology: Long rods; occurring singly, in pairs or in short chains; motile; large, oval, subterminal spore; Gram-positive.

Physiology: Strict anaerobe. Opt. T. = 37°C.

Cultural characters: No gas, or fetid odor produced.

Deep agar: Small, greyish, heart-shaped colonies, slightly opaque; no gas formed.

Glucose broth: Turbid, then clarifying with zoogleic sediment.

Gelatin: Very likely, liquefied.

Milk: Slowly coagulated, then digested.

Coagulated egg-white: Digested; zoogloea.

Carbohydrates: Acid, but no gas from glucose; lactose and sucrose. are not fermented.

Biochemistry: Traces of indole formed.

Pathogenicity: Non-pathogenic.

APPENDIX

We place here provisionnally one proteolytic species still not sufficiently described.

Clostridium maebashi Iseki, Furukawa and Yamamoto 1959.

Habitat: Soil (Japan, Maebashi).

Morphology: Rods with rounded ends; motile; central spore; Gram-positive.

Physiology: Anaerobic. Resists 30 minutes at 60°C.

Cultural characters: No gas produced.

Glucose deep agar: Fluffy colonies.

Blood agar: Thin, translucid, dew-drop or tressed colonies; no hemolysis.

Milk: Coagulated.

Brain-medium: Blackened, but not liquefied.

Coagulated serum: Liquefied.

Carbohydrates: Not fermented.

Biochemistry: Nitrites not formed from nitrates; produces indole; blood group B substance is destroyed with the liberation of 8% galactose, with the help of an enzyme related to galactosidase.

SUB-GENUS VIII: *CLOSTRIDIUM FALLAX*
(Feebly pathogenic, non-proteolytic agents).

This group comprises actually 20 species.

A) Species producing gas, but no fetid odor.
1. Encapsulated rods; lenticular colonies; gas produced; gelatin not liquefied; milk coagulated; saccharolytic; pathogenic; weak toxin; no hemolysin; acetic and valerianic acids produced.
   1. *Clostridium fallax,* page 288

2. Similar to the preceding species; produces formic and butyric acids.
   2. *Clostridium pseudo-fallax,* page 289

3. Encapsulated rods; lenticular colonies; gas produced; gelatin liquefied; milk unchanged; non-pathogenic; produces formic, propionic and lactic acids.
   3. *Clostridium lacunarum,* page 289

4. Flat, discoid colonies; gas produced; milk unchanged; saccharolytic; pathogenic; toxigenic; unencapsulated.
   4. *Clostridium difficile,* page 289

5. Stickland positive.
   5. *Clostridium sticklandi,* page 290

6. Lenticular, then arborescent colonies; gas produced; gelatin not liquefied; milk unchanged; indole not formed; saccharolytic; pathogenic; unencapsulated.
   6. *Clostridium sextum,* page 290

7. Unencapsulated; lenticular or globular colonies; gelatin not liquefied; milk coagulated; produces butyric and propionic acids.
   7. *Clostridium fissum,* page 291

8. Unencapsulated rods; lenticular colonies; gelatin not liquefied; milk coagulated; saccharolytic; pathogenic.
   8. *Clostridium gummosum,* page 292

9. Unencapsulated rods; very small spore; lenticular colonies; gelatin not liquefied; milk unchanged.
   9. *Clostridium microsporum,* page 292

B) Species producing gas and fetid odor.

10. Unencapsulated rods; irregular, arborescent colonies; gelatin not liquefied; milk unchanged; pathogenic.
    10. *Clostridium septimum,* page 293

11. Highly pleomorphic rods, encapsulated; microaerophilic; diffuse colonies; gas and fecaloid odor; gelatin liquefied; milk coagulated; pathogenic (necrosis).
    11. *Clostridium necrosans,* page 293

12. Unencapsulated rods; lenticular colonies; gelatin liquefied; milk coagulated; saccharolytic; non-pathogenic.
    12. *Clostridium nauseum,* page 294

13. Lenticular colonies; milk unchanged; saccharolytic; indole formed; non-pathogenic
    13. *Clostridium lactopropylbutylicum,* page 294

14. Lenticular or irregular colonies; non-proteolytic; milk acidified, but not coagulated; gelatin not liquefied; saccharolytic; non-pathogenic.
    14. *Clostridium innominatum,* page 295

15. Lenticular colonies; gelatin not liquefied; milk unchanged; markedly aromatic odor.

   15. *Clostridium aromaticum,* page 295

16. Circular colonies; gelatin liquefied; milk coagulated; indole formed; H₂S produced.

   16. *Clostridium tonkinensis,* page 296

C) Species producing no gas.

17. Ramified colonies; gelatin not liquefied; milk unchanged; urea hydrolyzed; non-pathogenic.

   17. *Clostridium ureolyticum,* page 296

18. Lenticular colonies; milk unchanged; gelatin not liquefied; saccharolytic; non-pathogenic.

   18. *Clostridium irregularis,* page 297

19. Flat colonies; milk coagulated; gelatin liquefied; saccharolytic; non-pathogenic.

   19. *Clostridium pruchii,* page 297

20. Irregular colonies; fecaloid odor; indole and scatole produced.

   20. *Clostridium scatologenes,* page 298

1. **Clostridium fallax** (Weinberg and Séguin) Bergey *et al.*

Synonym: Bacillus *fallax* Weinberg and Séguin 1915.

Habitat: Infected war wounds; gas gangrene, appendicitis, blackleg of sheep, soil of Africa, marine sediment. Frequent.

Morphology: Rods measuring 0.6 μ $\times$ 1.2 to 5 μ; may show spheroids; encapsulated; motile by means of peritrichous flagella; subterminal spore; Gram-positive.

Physiology: Strict anaerobe. Opt. T. $= 37°C$. Killed at $100°C$. Survives several years. Neutral red definitively reduced, safranin temporarily reduced.

Cultural characters: Large amounts of gas produced, but not fetid.

Deep agar: Lenticular or heart-shaped colonies; gas.

Glucose broth: Abundant turbidity, then auto-agglutination; gas.

Peptone water: Turbid, then auto-agglutination.

Gelatin: No liquefaction.

Milk: Coagulated.

Coagulated serum: Not attacked.

Carbohydrates: Acid and gas from glucose, fructose, maltose, sucrose, lactose, inulin and glycogen.

Biochemistry: Nitrites not formed from nitrates; sulfites reduced to sulfides; produces NH₃, volatile amines, aldehydes, ketones, acetylmethylcarbinol, acetic, valerianic and lactic acids.

Pathogenicity, natural: Gas gangrene, appendicitis, parietal dissecting phlegmon.

Pathogenicity, experimental: Intramuscular injection into the guinea pig produces gaseous red edema.

Toxin: Weak, non-hemolytic.

2. *Clostridium pseudo-fallax* Prévot and Loth 1941.

Habitat: Soil, gangrenous wounds, appendicitis, gleins from Dax.

Morphology: Straight or slightly-curved rods with rounded ends,

Physiology: Entirely similar to *Cl. fallax.* Neutral red definitively reduced, safranin temporarily reduced.

Cultural characters: Similar to *Cl. fallax.*

Biochemistry: Nitrites not formed from nitrates; sulfites reduced to sulfides; produces NH_3, volatile amines, aldehydes, ketones, acetylmethylcarbinol, formic, butyric and lactic acids.

Pathogenicity, natural: When associated, participates in gas gangrene.

Pathogenicity, experimental: Non-pathogenic.

3. *Clostridium lacunarum* Robin 1948.

Habitat: Mud from Ebrié laguna on the Ivory Coast.

Morphology: Straight or slightly-curved rods with rounded ends, 0.9 μ $\times$ 4 μ; occurring singly or in short chains; feebly motile; oval, clostridial, subterminal spore, 1.5 to 3.0 μ; encapsulated; Gram-positive.

Physiology: Strict anaerobe. Opt. T. $= 37°$C. Resists 3 minutes at 100°C. Neutral red definitively reduced.

Cultural characters: Gas, but no fetid odor produced.

Deep agar: Lenticular colonies; gas.

Glucose VF broth: Abundant turbidity clearing rapidly to a flaky sediment; stale odor.

Peptone water: Slight turbidity.

Gelatin: Liquefaction.

Milk: Unchanged.

Coagulated proteins: Not attacked.

Carbohydrates: Glucose, fructose, maltose, lactose, galactose, and sucrose are actively fermented; mannitol weakly fermented.

Biochemistry: Nitrites formed from nitrates in the presence of mannitol; produces NH_3, H_2S, volatile amines, acetylmethylcarbinol, formic, propionic and lactic acids.

4. *Clostridium difficile* (Hall and O'Toole) P. 1938.

Synonym: Bacillus difficilis Hall and O'Toole 1935.

Habitat: Intestinal tract of new-born. Quite frequent.

Morphology: Short, thick rods; actively motile by means of 5-6 peritrichous flagella; elongated, subterminal spore; Gram-positive.

Physiology: Strict anaerobe. Opt. T. = 37°C. Survives 3 years.

Cultural characters: Gas produced.

Deep agar: Flat, discoid colonies; no gas.

Glucose broth: Turbid; gas.

Gelatin: No liquefaction.

Milk: Unchanged.

Coagulated serum: Not digested.

Brain-medium: Blackened; H_2S.

Carbohydrates: Acid and gas from glucose, fructose, mannitol, salicin and xylose.

Pathogenicity, experimental: Highly pathogenic for guinea pig and mouse: local edema, convulsions and death.

Toxin: Reproduces the above symptoms (enterotoxin).

5. *Clostridium sticklandi* Stadman and McClung 1957.

Habitat: Black mud from San Francisco bay, associated with *Methanococcus vannieli.*

Morphology: Slender rods with rounded ends, 1 to 2 μ long, sometimes 4 μ; occuring singly, in pairs, sometimes in short chains; actively motile; clostridial spore, seen only in old cultures; Gram-positive.

Physiology: Strict anaerobe. Opt. T. = 30-38°C.

Cultural characters: Gas and fetid odor produced. Obtained by enrichment on formate media.

Deep agar: Lenticular colonies, 1-3mm in diameter.

Egg-yolk agar slant (in vacuo): Moist, punctiform or irregular colonies, sometimes larger.

Blood agar: Greyish colonies; no hemolysis.

Gelatin: No liquefaction.

Milk: Unchanged.

Coagulated egg-white: Not attacked.

Coagulated serum: Not attacked.

Carbohydrates: Glucose, galactose and maltose slightly fermented.

Biochemistry: Nitrites not formed from nitrates; produces NH_3, putrescin, cadaverin and traces of scatole. Several amino acids utilized, among which proline and arginine; positive Stickland reaction; proline reduced to d-amino-valerianic acid.

Pathogenicity: Non-pathogenic.

Systematics: Closely related to *Cl. difficile.*

6. *Clostridium sextum* (von Hibler) Heller Prévot 1940.

Synonym: Bacillus VI von Hibler 1905. Not to be confused with *Plectridium carnis* (Klein) P. 1938 which has terminal spores.

Habitat: Soil, rabbit from injection of earth; poto-poto of the Ivory Coast; gleins from Dax.

Morphology: Rods measuring 0.5 to 0.7 μ $\times$ 2 to 5 μ; occurring singly, in pairs, seldom in short chains of 3-4 elements; motile by means of peritrichous flagella; oval, subterminal spore; Gram-positive.

Physiology: Microaerophilic. Opt. T. = 22-37°C. Resists 3 minutes at 100°C.

Cultural characters: Gas produced.

Deep agar: Lenticular colonies, becoming arborescent.

Glucose broth: Turbid; gas; indole not formed, nor H_2S.

Gelatin: No liquefaction.

Milk: Unchanged; large amounts of gas.

Coagulated proteins: Not attacked.

Brain-medium: Not blackened; H_2S not formed.

Carbohydrates: Acid and gas from glucose, galactose, fructose, maltose, lactose, sucrose, amygdalin, salicin and dextrin.

Biochemistry: Nitrites formed from nitrates; produces NH_3, H_2S, ethanol, acetylmethylcarbinol, acetic, butyric and lactic acids.

Pathogenicity, experimental: Guinea pig, rabbit and rat are susceptible: edema, necrosis and death.

Exotoxin: Moderately active.

Hemolysin: Very active.

7. *Clostridium fissum* (Debono) Bergey *et al.*

Synonym: Bacillus fissus Debono 1912.

Habitat: Intestinal tract of man.

Morphology: Slightly-curved rods with rounded or square ends; occurring singly, in pairs, in short chains or in filaments; motile; small, oval, subterminal spore, slightly clostridial; Gram-positive.

Physiology: Strict anaerobe. Opt. T. = 22-37°C. Resists 5 minutes at 80°C. Neutral red and phenosafranin reduced.

Cultural characters: Gas and markedly butyric odor produced.

Glucose deep agar: Small, white, globular or lenticular colonies.

Glucose broth: Turbid.

Gelatin: No liquefaction.

Milk: Coagulated in 5 days.

Coagulated proteins: Not attacked.

Carbohydrates: Acid and gas from glucose, fructose and glycerol; acid but no gas from lactose and sucrose.

Biochemistry: Nitrites formed from nitrates; sulfites not reduced; indole not formed; produces NH_3, H_2S, iso-butyric and propionic acids.

Pathogenicity, natural: Isolated in a case of suppurative arthritis of the wart-hog.

Pathogenicity, experimental: Local gaseous edema with suppuration and slow evolution towards death in the guinea pig. No toxin. Weak hemolysin.

8. *Clostridium gummosum* Spray 1947.[1]

Habitat: Intestinal tract of man.

Morphology: Rods measuring 0.8 to 1.0 $\mu \times$ 4 to 8 μ; occurring singly or in pairs; motile; large, oval, eccentric or subterminal spore, swelling the rod; Gram-positive.

Physiology: Strict anaerobe. Opt. T. = 18-37°C.

Cultural characters: Gas, but no fetid odor.

Agar slant: Large, circular, convex colonies with clear-cut border; highly mucoid.

Blood-agar: No hemolysis.

Deep agar: Mucoid, elastic, lenticular colonies.

Gelatin: No liquefaction.

Milk: Slow fermentation with bubbles of gas; coagulated in 18 to 20 hours.

Coagulated egg-white: Not attacked.

Coagulated serum: Not attacked.

Brain-medium: Unchanged.

Carbohydrates: Acid and gas from glucose, maltose, galactose and mannitol; lactose slowly fermented.

Biochemistry: Nitrites not formed from nitrates; indole not produced; H_2S not formed.

Pathogenicity, natural: Isolated in a case of gas gangrene.

Pathogenicity, experimental: Non-pathogenic for mouse, guinea pig and rabbit.

9. *Clostridium microsporum* Spray 1947.

Habitat: Intestinal tract.

Morphology: Rods measuring 0.8 $\mu \times$ 2 to 4 μ; filaments; distinct vacuoles, especially in old cultures; occurring singly or in pairs; navicular forms with pointed ends; actively motile: spinning movement with slow translation movement; small, spherical, central or subterminal spore, swelling the rod; Gram-positive.

Physiology: Strict anaerobe. Opt. T. = 37°C. Resists 10 minutes at 80°C.

Cultural characters: Gas, but no fetid odor.

Agar slant (in vacuo): Very small, dew-drop colonies.

Deep agar: Lenticular colonies.

Blood agar: No hemolysis.

Gelatin: No liquefaction.

Milk: Acid and gas, but no coagulation.

---

[1] Spray has described this species as a member of the "butyric group", but he brought forth no chemical proof of this assertion.

Carbohydrates: Acid and gas from glucose, maltose and galactose.

Brain medium: Unchanged.

Biochemistry: Nitrites not formed from nitrates; indole not formed; H_2S not formed.

Pathogenicity, natural: Isolated in a case of putrid fatal peritonitis.

Pathogenicity, experimental: Non-pathogenic for mouse and guinea pig.

10. *Clostridium septimum* (von Hibler) Prévot 1938.

Synonym: Bacillus VII von Hibler.

Habitat: Soil, pond mud, oysters. Quite frequent.

Morphology: Rods with rounded ends, occurring singly or in pairs; motile; ellipsoidal, central or subterminal spore; Gram-positive.

Physiology: Strict anaerobe. Opt. T. $= 37°$C. Resists 10 minutes at 70°C, but is killed at 97-98°C. Survives 6 months. Phenosafranin reduced.

Cultural characters: Gas and fetid odor produced.

Deep agar: Irregular colonies with arborescent projections.

Glucose broth: Turbid; gas; viscous sediment; fetid odor.

Gelatin: No liquefaction or very slowly liquefied (20 days).

Milk: Very slowly coagulated (1 month) or not coagulated.

Coagulated serum: No liquefaction.

Fibrin: Not attacked.

Brain-medium: Acidified; gas; no blackening.

Carbohydrates: Glucose, fructose, maltose, galactose, sucrose, arabinose, xylose, dulcitol, mannitol, glycerol, sorbitol and starch are fermented.

Biochemistry: Nitrites not formed from nitrates; sulfites reduced to sulfides; produces NH_3, H_2S, aldehydes, acetylmethylcarbinol, acetic and valerianic acids.

Pathogenicity, experimental: Pathogenic for rabbit, guinea pig, cat and pigeon; lesions unknown. Numerous strains are non-pathogenic.

11. *Clostridium necrosans* (Schupfer) Prévot 1938.

Synonym: Bacillus aerogenes necrosans Schupfer 1905.

Habitat: Intestinal tract and natural cavities of man. Uncommon.

Morphology: Straight rods, 0.8 to 0.9 μ $\times$ 2.4 to 4.5 μ; occurring singly, in pairs or in short chains; motile by means of peritrichous flagella; encapsulated; oval, subterminal, clostridial spore, 0.8 to 2 μ $\times$ 1.2 to 1.4 μ; Gram-positive.

Physiology: Strict anaerobe upon isolation, becoming microaerophilic. Opt. T. $= 22$-37°C.

Cultural characters: Gas and fecaloid odor.

Deep agar: Confluent colonies; no gas.

Glycerol agar: Confluent colonies; gas and fecaloid odor.

Glucose broth: Turbid; fecaloid odor.

Gelatin: Liquefaction.

Milk: Coagulation.

Pathogenicity, natural: Isolated from a thoracic, necrotizing, gaseous abscess.

Pathogenicity, experimental: Fatal gaseous abscess in the guinea pig.

12. *Clostridium nauseum* Spray 1947.

Habitat: Soil of Virginia.

Morphology: Rods with rounded ends, 0.8 to 1.0 $\mu \times$ 6 to 12 μ; occurring singly, in pairs or in short chains of 4-6 elements; actively motile by means of peritrichous flagella; ellipsoidal, subterminal, clostridial spore; Gram-positive in young cultures.

Physiology: Strict anaerobe. Opt. T. $= 18$-$37\,^{\circ}$C. Resists 10 minutes at $80\,^{\circ}$C.

Cultural characters: Gas and putrid odor.

Agar surface (in vacuo): Small, flat, transparent colonies.

Deep agar: Small, creamy-white, lenticular colonies.

Blood agar: No hemolysis.

Gelatin: Very slowly liquefied (30 days).

Milk: Coagulated in 4 to 5 days; slow retraction.

Coagulated egg-white: Not attacked.

Coagulated serum: Not attacked.

Brain-medium: Blackened, but not attacked.

Carbohydrates: Acid and gas from glucose, fructose, maltose.

Biochemistry: Nitrites not formed from nitrates; produces H_2S, large amounts of indole and scatole, mercaptans. The odor is due to an unidentified aromatic nitrogenous compound.

Pathogenicity, experimental: Non-pathogenic for mouse, guinea pig and rabbit.

13. *Clostridium lactopropylbutylicum*
(Tissier and Gashing) Prévot 1938.

Synonym: Bacillus lactopropylbutylicus non liquefaciens T. and G. 1903.

Habitat: Sugar milk. Uncommon.

Morphology: Thick, short rods; motile; clostridial, central or subterminal spore; Gram-positive.

Physiology: Strict anaerobe. Opt. T. $= 20$-$37\,^{\circ}$C. Resists 5 minutes at $100\,^{\circ}$C.

Cultural characters: Gas produced.

Deep agar: Lenticular colonies; gas.

Glucose broth: Abundant turbidity; gas; sediment; traces of indole.

Gelatin: No liquefaction.
Milk: Unchanged.
Glucose or sucrose milk: Coagulated.
Carbohydrates: Glucose and sucrose are fermented.
Biochemistry: Produces NH_3, propanol, butanol and lactic acid.
Pathogenicity: Non-pathogenic.

14. *Clostridium innominatum* (Adamson) Prévot 1938.

Synonym: Bacillus E Adamson 1919.
Habitat: Isolated from war wounds, soil, preserves. Quite uncommon.
Morphology: Short, thick rods; motile; spherical, clostridial, subterminal spore; Gram-positive.
Physiology: Strict anaerobe. Opt. T. = 37°C. Resists 5 minutes at 100°C. Survives more than 1 year. Neutral red and safranin reduced.
Cultural characters: Gas produced.
Deep agar: Small, circular or irregular colonies; gas.
Glucose broth: Turbid; gas.
Gelatin: No liquefaction.
Milk: Acidified, but not coagulated.
Coagulated proteins: Not attacked.
Carbohydrates: Glucose, maltose, lactose, mannitol, fructose, arabinose, xylose and galactose are fermented.
Biochemistry: Nitrites not formed from nitrates; sulfites reduced to sulfides; produces NH_3, H_2S, ketones, acetylmethylcarbinol, acetic, butyric and lactic acids.
Pathogenicity: Non-pathogenic.

15. *Clostridium aromaticum* Lebert 1948.

Habitat: Gruyère cheese.
Morphology: Straight rods with rounded ends, 1.0 to 1.2 μ × 1.8 to 4.0 μ; occurring singly, in pairs or in short chains; motile; oval, clostridial, subterminal spore, 1.3 μ × 1.5 μ; Gram-positive.
Physiology: Strict anaerobe. Opt. T. = 37°C. Resists 1 minute at 100°C. Survives 4 to 5 months in culture media, more than 6 months in cheese. Requires a growth factor found in gruyère cheese. Neutral red reduced in 5 days.
Cultural characters: Gas and aromatic odor produced (gruyère cheese).
Cheese-deep agar: Lenticular colonies; gas. Slow liquefaction of the agar.
Cheese-glucose VF broth: Abundant turbidity; gas; strong odor characteristic of gruyère cheese.
Cheese-peptone water: Diffuse turbidity; gas.
Gelatin: No liquefaction.
Milk: Unchanged.

Coagulated proteins: Not attacked.

Carbohydrates: Glucose and fructose only are fermented.

Biochemistry: Nitrites not formed from nitrates; indole not formed, nor H_2S produced; produces NH_3, propionic and valerianic acids, traces of lactic acid.

Pathogenicity, experimental: Non-pathogenic for guinea pig. No toxin, nor hemolysin.

16. *Clostridium tonkinensis* Bruneau 1941.

Habitat: Probably, soil of Tonkin, forest humus of the Ivory Coast.

Morphology: Rods of varying size with rounded ends; occurring singly or in short chains of 2-5 elements; feebly motile and only in capillary tubes; ovoid, subterminal spore swelling the rod; Gram-positive.

Physiology: Strict anaerobe. Resists 1 hour at 80°C and 2 minutes at 100°C. Neutral red and safranin reduced.

Cultural characters: Gas and fetid odor produced.

Deep agar: Plumose, fluffy, circular colonies; gas.

Glucose broth: Abundant turbidity; fetid gas.

Peptone water: Abundant turbidity; small amounts of gas with odor of burnt horn; indole formed.

Gelatin: Partly liquefied in 4 days.

Milk: Massive coagulation; gas.

Meat: Not attacked.

Carbohydrates: Glucose, maltose and sucrose actively fermented; lactose, mannitol and glycerol feebly fermented.

Blood-broth: Intense hemolysis.

Lead-agar: Blackened.

Biochemistry: Nitrites not formed from nitrates; produces NH_3, H_2S, indole, volatile amines, acetone, aldehydes, o-cresol, acetic, butyric and lactic acids.

Pathogenicity, natural: Isolated from war wounds in Tonkin.

Pathogenicity, experimental: Fleeting tumefaction in the guinea pig and pigeon, from which the germ may be recovered but which heals spontaneously.

17. *Clostridium ureolyticum* (Geilinger) Prévot 1938.

Habitat: Soil, dung.

Morphology: Slender rods with rounded ends; actively motile; spherical spore; Gram-positive.

Physiology: Strict anaerobe. Opt. T. $= 30°C$.

Cultural characters: No gas produced.

Deep agar: Arborescent colonies.

Glucose broth: Slow, meager growth.

Urea-broth: Turbid; urea hydrolyzed with formation of free N_2, and $CO_3 (HN_4)_2$.

Gelatin: Very meager growth.

Milk: No growth.

Pathogenicity: Non-pathogenic.

18. *Clostridium irregularis* (Choukévitch) Prévot 1938.

Synonym: Bacillus irregularis (Choukévitch) 1911.

Habitat: Intestinal tract of the horse. Uncommon.

Morphology: Rods with rounded ends, 0.5 μ × 4 to 7 μ; occurring singly or in pairs; feebly motile; involution forms; clostridial, central or subterminal spore; Gram-positive.

Physiology: Strict anaerobe. Opt. T. = 37°C. Neutral red and safranin reduced.

Cultural characters: No gas produced.

Deep agar: Lenticular colonies.

Gelatin: No liquefaction.

Milk: Unchanged.

Coagulated proteins: Not attacked.

Carbohydrates: Glucose only is fermented.

Biochemistry: Produces NH_3, volatile amines, aldehydes, acetylmethyl-carbinol, acetic, valerianic and lactic acids.

Pathogenicity: Non-pathogenic.

19. *Clostridium pruchii* (Conn, Esten and Hammer) Bergey *et al.*

Synonym: Bacillus lactic pruchi C., E. and H. 1906; *Bacillus pruchii* Buchanan and Hammer 1915.

Habitat: Viscous milk, soil of Africa.

Morphology: Rods of varying size, 0.8 μ × 5 to 6 μ; motile by means of peritrichous flagella; subterminal or central spore; Gram-positive.

Physiology: Strict anaerobe. Opt. T. = 30°C. Resists 1 minute at 100°C. Phenosafranin reduced.

Cultural characters: No gas produced.

Deep agar: Lenticular colonies, may become somewhat arborescent.

Glucose broth: Turbidity which secondarily becomes flaky and sediments as a viscid mass; acidified; indole noy formed.

Gelatin: Liquefaction.

Milk: Acidified, then coagulated; becomes yellow; indole not formed.

Coagulated proteins: Not attacked.

Biochemistry: Nitrites not formed from nitrates in the presence of glucose, but formed in the presence of lactose; produces NH_3, H_2S, volatile amines, ethanol, propionic, butyric and lactic acids.

Pathogenicity: Non-pathogenic.

20. *Clostridium scatologenes* Fellers 1923.

Habitat: Isolated from contaminated preserved food (macaroni and salmon).

Morphology: Rods measuring 4 to 7 μ; slowly motile; ellipsoidal, clostridial, subterminal spore; Gram-positive.

Physiology: Strict anaerobe. Opt. T. $= 37°$C. Opt. pH $= 7.0$. Not very thermoresistant.

Cultural characters: No gas produced, but fecaloid odor.

Deep agar: Irregular, granular, translucent colonies with opaque center.

Plain broth: Turbid; H_2S; fecaloid odor.

Peptone water: Turbid; blackened; H_2S.

Carbohydrates: Acid, but no gas from most of the carbohydrates.

Biochemistry: Produces H_2S, indole, phenol, large amounts of scatole, scatol-carbonic acid, acetic, propionic, butyric, valerianic, caproic, lactic and succinic acids.

GROUP IX: CHROMOGENIC SPECIES
NOT CLASSIFIED IN THE PRECEDING GROUPS.

This residual group actually comprises 5 species.

1. Red colonies; no gas formed; gelatin liquefied; non-pathogenic.

   1. *Clostridium rubellum,* page 298

2. Red, lenticular colonies; gas and fecaloid odor; gelatin liquefied; milk coagulated; saccharolytic; feebly pathogenic.

   2. *Clostridium chromogenes,* page 299

3. Slightly pink-colored, lenticular colonies; gelatin liquefied; produces p-cresol.

   3. *Clostridium cresologenes,* page 299

4. Greyish, lenticular colonies; gas, but no odor; non-proteolytic; milk coagulated; saccharolytic; non-pathogenic.

   4. *Clostridium partum,* page 300

5. Thermophilic; black colonies; no gas; gelatin not liquefied; H_2S formed; non-saccharolytic; non-pathogenic.

   5. *Clostridium nigrificans,* page 300

1. *Clostridium rubellum* (Okada) Prévot 1938.

Synonym: Bacillus rubellus Okada 1892.

Habitat: Soil, dust. Uncommon.

Morphology: Rods with rounded ends, 0.7 to 0.8 $\mu \times$ 3 to 7 μ; united by 2-3 filaments; encapsulated; actively motile by means of peritrichous flagella; clostridial, central or subterminal spore, tadpole-shaped; Gram-positive.

Physiology: Strict anaerobe. Opt. T. = 18-37°C. Resists 30 minutes at 80°C. Killed after 5 minutes at 100°C.

Cultural characters: Pigment formed; no gas produced.

Deep agar: Reddish colonies.

Glucose broth: Turbid; red pigment.

Gelatin: Red, arborescent colonies; liquefaction.

Pathogenicity: Non-pathogenic.

2. *Clostridium chromogenes* (Ghon and Mucha) Prévot 1938.

Habitat: Isolated from a sub-phrenic abscess. Very uncommon.

Morphology: Pleomorphic rods of average size: short and long forms; encapsulated; motile by means of peritrichous flagella; clostridial, subterminal spore; Gram-positive.

Physiology: Strict anaerobe. Opt. T. = 21-37°C. Survives indefinitely. Neutral red reduced.

Cultural characters: Gas and fetid odor produced; pigment formed.

Deep agar: Lenticular colonies; gas; diffuse red pigment.

Glucose broth: Turbid; gas; fecaloid odor; H_2S.

Peptone water carbohydrates: Abundant formation of red pigment.

Gelatin: Liquefaction; gas; red pigment.

Milk: Coagulated, then digested; gas.

Coagulated hydrocele fluid: Digested; gas.

Human blood: Hemolysis.

Carbohydrates: Acid and gas from sucrose, lactose, fructose, maltose, galactose and mannitol.

Biochemistry: Red pigment formed only in the presence of peptone.

Pathogenicity, natural: Peri-nephritic abscess.

Pathogenicity, experimental: Feebly pathogenic for mouse: edema and exsudative peritonitis, followed by fatal toxic infection.

Systematics: Closely related to *Cl. rubellum,* but nonetheless different.

3. *Clostridium cresologenes* (Rhein) Prévot 1938.

Synonym: Bacillus cresologenes Rhein 1922.

Habitat: Putrefying brain broth. Uncommon.

Morphology: Rods measuring 0.5 to 0.7 μ × 2 to 4 μ; motile by means of peritrichous flagella; oval, clostridial, central or subterminal spore; Gram-positive.

Physiology: Strict anaerobe. Opt. T. = 37°C. Resists 15 minutes at 100°C. Survives several years.

Cultural characters: Gas and fetid odor produced; pigment formed.

Deep agar: Lenticular colonies; pinkish color in the upper layers.

Glucose broth: Turbid; production of p-cresol in 24 hours, scatole in

8 days; gas and nauseous odor.

Gelatin: Liquefaction.

Coagulated proteins: Not attacked.

Brain-medium: Not blackened.

Biochemistry: Produces NH_3, scatole (traces) and p-cresol.

Pathogenicity: Non-pathogenic.

4. *Clostridium partum* (Levens) Prévot 1938.

Habitat: Isolated as a saprophyte in postpartum anthrax. Quite uncommon.

Morphology: Rods measuring 0.5 to 0.7 μ $\times$ 3 to 4 μ: feebly motile by means of peritrichous flagella; central or subterminal spore; Gram-positive.

Physiology: Strict anaerobe. Opt. T. $= 25\text{-}37°C$. Killed after 5 minutes at 100°C.

Cultural characters: Gas and pigment produced.

Deep agar: Lenticular or fluffy, greyish colonies; gas, but no odor.

Gelatin: No liquefaction.

*Milk:*Slowly coagulated; no gas.

Coagulated proteins: Not attacked.

Coagulated serum: Greyish-green, cloudy colonies.

Carbohydrates: Glucose, lactose, sucrose, and maltose are fermented.

Pathogenicity: Non-pathogenic.

5. *Clostridium nigrificans* Werkman and Weaver 1927.

Habitat: Preserved peas and corn showing sulfur-stinker spoilage; soil, manure.

Morphology: Rods measuring 0.5 μ $\times$ 3 to 6 μ; motile; clostridial, subterminal spore; chromaffinic granules; Gram-positive.

Physiology: Strict anaerobe. Opt. T. $= 55°C$ (32-70° C). Resists several hours at 100°C. but destroyed after 8 hours at 110°C; resists 50 minutes at 118° C. Opt. pH $= 5.8$ - 7.6.

Cultural characters: No gas, but fetid odor produced.

Beef heart agar: Dark colonies surrounded by a black zone.

Pea broth $+$ $FeCl_3$: Black growth; indole not formed.

Gelatin: No liquefaction.

Coagulated serum: Not atttacked.

Carbohydrates: Not fermented.

Biochemistry: Nitrites not formed from nitrates.

Pathogenicity: Non-pathogenic.

Systematics: Perfectly individualized species, although all of its biochemical characters have not been determined. Some authors have wrongly identified as *Sporovibrio desulfuricans* authentic strains of *Cl. nigrificans,* simply on account of the black colonies. This has resulted in a state of confusion which has thrown some doubt as to the existence of sporeforming strains of sulfate-reducing virios. But the existence of the latter is now well-acknowledged and we maintain their systematical position as fixed by Starkey.

APPENDIX

We add here, provisionally and with all the necessary reserve, a germ which has been insufficiently described and wrongly classed under the not too well-defined term of *Methanobacterium,* whereas it could well be a *Clostridium* or an anaerobic *Bacillus.* This distinction will become possible only when pure cultures have been obtained.

Clostridium propionicum Stadtman and Barker *nov. comb. prov.*

Synonym: Methanobacterium propionicum Stadtman and Barker 1951.
Habitat: Black mud from San Francisco bay.
Morphology: Short, thick rods; occurring singly or in pairs; actively motile; central spore not swelling the rod; irregular bipolar staining with erythrosine or methylene blue; Gram-positive.
Physiology: Anaerobic. Grows at 30° C. Has not been obtained in pure culture. Produces methane from propionate.
Fluid media: Abundant uniform turbidity.
Biochemistry: Oxidizes propionic acid in such a way that the carbon atom from CO_2, as well as the a and β carbons, are found in an acetate molecule. CH_4 produced entirely from CO_2.

We place here a recently described species which is presently the only alginolytic anaerobe known; it, therefore, cannot be placed in any other known group.

Clostridium alginolyticum Billy 1965.

Habitat: Black, sulfhydric, marine mud where it is found symbiotically with *D. desulfuricans.*
Morphology: Straight rods, 0.8 to 1.0 μ $\times$ 6 to 8 μ; motile by means of peritrichous flagella; clostridial, subterminal spore; Gram-positive.
Physiology: Strict anaerobe and obligate halophile. Opt. T. $= 30°C$. Opt. pH $= 7$-8. Resists 5 minutes at 80°C. Survives a few days in agar-free media, and a few months in the presence of agar.
Cultural characters: Gas and odorless. Isolation possible only in sea water added with algin and filtrate of *D. desulfuricans.*
Sea water-algin-fitrate deep agar: Fluffy, whitish colonies.
Sea water-algin-filtrate silicogel: Liquefied in 24 hours and decomposed to uronides by means of an exo-alginase.

Lactate media: Meager growth; no gas.

Usual media (gelatin, milk, carbohydrates, proteins, cellulose, pectin, agar): No growth.

Biochemistry: Nitrates, sulfates and sulfites not reduced; citrate not attacked; terminal pH is acid (acetic and lactic acids, uronids); produces ethanol and acetoin. Active exoalginase, liquefying algin in 18 hours.

Pathogenicity: Non-pathogenic.

Chapter 7

ORDER II: PLECTRIDIALES P. 1938.

Definition.—Sporulales with terminal spores. This important order is sub-divided into two families:

1. Gram-negative *Plectridiales: Terminosporaceae.*
2. Gram-positive *Plectridiales: Plectridiaceae.*

FAMILY I: *TERMINOSPORACEAE* P. 1938.

The *Terminosporaceae,* or Gram-negative *Plectridiales,* comprise two genera:

Genus I: Motile *Terminosporaceae: Terminosporus,* page 303

Genus II: Non-motile *Terminosporaceae: Caduceus,* page 310

GENUS I: *TERMINOSPORUS* P. 1938.

Definition: Straight or slightly-curved rods, motile, with terminal spore, Gram-negative.

This genus comprises presently 11 species:

A) Species producing no gas:
1. Gelatin not liquefied; non-protolytic; saccharolytic; non-pathogenic.
   1. *Terminosporus raabi,* page 304

B) Species producing gas:
2. Spherical spores; lenticular colonies; gas produced; milk coagulated; saccharolytic; non-pathogenic.
   2. *Terminosporus thermosaccharolyticus,* page 304
3. Spherical spores; lenticular colonies; gas produced; cellulolytic, saccharolytic.
   3. *Terminosporus cellobioparus,* page 305
4. Thermophilic (65°C); no growth on usual media; saccharolytic (pentoses); cellulolytic.
   4. *Terminosporus thermocellulolyticus,* page 305

1. *Terminosporus raabi* (Raab) P. 1938.

Habitat: Tap water in Minneapolis. Quite uncommon.

Morphology: Long, slender rods; motile in young cultures; terminal spore; Gram-negative.

Physiology: Strict anaerobe. Killed after 20 minutes at 85°C.

Cultural characters: No gas produced.

Glucose broth: Abundant turbidity; butyric odor.

Gelatin: No liquefaction.

Milk: Unchanged.

Coagulated egg-white and serum: Not attacked.

Carbohydrates: Acid, but no gas, from glucose, fructose, galactose, maltose, sucrose, lactose, raffinose, mannitol, dulcitol, inulin, salicin, xylose and starch.

Pathogenicity: Non-pathogenic.

1 bis. *T. raabi,* variety *saigonensis* Reynes.

Microaerophilic; thermoresistant; no odor.

2. *Terminosporus thermosaccharolyticus* (McClung) P. 1938.

Synonym: Clostridium thermosaccharolyticum McClung 1935.

Habitat: Spoiled preserves, soil, Quite frequent.

Morphology: Long, slender, granular rods, 0.4 to 0.7 μ × 3.5 to 7.5 μ;

occurring singly or in pairs; motile by means of peritrichous flagella; spherical, teminal spore; Gram-negative.

Physiology: Strict anaerobe, Thermophilic: Opt. T. = 55-60°C (grows also at 30°C).

Cultural characters: Gas produced.

Deep agar: Small, lenticular colonies; gas.

Glucose broth: Turbid; gas.

Milk: Coagulated; gas.

Gelatin: No liquefaction.

Coagulated proteins: Not attacked.

Carbohydrates: Acid and gas from glucose, fructose, arabinose, galactose, mannose, xylose, cellobiose, lactose, maltose, sucrose, trehalose, dextrin, glycogen and starch.

Biochemistry: Produces CO_2 and H_2 (from glucose and xylose), acetic, butyric and lactic acids.

3. *Terminosporus cellobioparus* (Hungate) P. 1938.

Synonym: Clostridium cellobioparus Hungate 1944.

Habitat: Rumen.

Isolation: In deep agar with cellulose.

Morphology: Slightly-curved or spirally curved rods, 0.3 to 0.4 μ × 3 to 5 μ; motile by means of peritrichous flagella (spiral or rotatory movement); terminal spore, 0.9 μ, sometimes free; Gram-negative.

Physiology: Strict anaerobe. Opt. T. = 38°C. Resists 12 hours at 85°C. Opt. pH = 7.4.

Cultural characters: Gas produced.

Glucose deep agar: Lenticular colonies; gas.

Cellulose deep agar: Irregular colonies.

Fluid media (inorganic salts + cellulose): Less abundant growth; requires biotin.

Carbohydrates: Glucose, fructose, maltose, xylose, arabinose, mannose, cellobiose, melibiose and hemicellulose are fermented.

Biochemistry: Produces H_2 and CO_2 (in a ratio less than 1), ethanol, acetic, formic and lactic acids. Produces cellobiose, ethanol, acetic formic and lactic acids. Produces cellobiose from cellulose, but not glucose from cellobiose. Transfers on carbohydrate media do not cause disappearance of cellulolytic activity.

4. *Terminosporus thermocellulolyticus* Pochon 1942.

Habitat: Manure.

Isolation: Progressively on mineral media containing NH_3 + NH_2 as nitrogen source, added with cellulose, with heating for 5 minutes at 100°C at each transfer, then incubating at 65°C.

Morphology: Pleomorphic rods, 0.5 μ × 5 μ; motile; spherical, terminal spore, becoming free, 1.5 μ; Gram-negative. Formation of long chains and filaments, hair-like, around cellulose fibers.

Physiology: Strict anaerobe. Opt. T. = 65° (42-70).

Cultural characters: Very difficult to grow in the absence of cellulose. Carbohydrates: Pentoses are actively fermented (xylose, arabinose and rhamnose), hexoses feebly and temporarily fermented. Cellulolytic activity is preserved after transfers on pentose media.

Biochemistry: Cellulose is destroyed to the extent of 95% in 6 days, with formation of abundant gas (CO_2, H_2 and CH_4), alcohols, acetic and butyric acids; yellow pigment. The first stage in the destruction of cellulose is glucose.

5. *Terminosporus cellulosam-fermentans* (Werner) P. 1938.

Synonym: Bacillus cellulosam-fermentans Werner 1925; *Clostridium werneri* Bergey *et al.*

Habitat: Intestinal tract of the larvae of *Potosia cuprea.*

Morphology: Straight or slightly-curved, slender rods, 0.5 to 0.7 μ × 1.5 to 4.0 μ; may reach 7 μ; occurring singly, in pairs or in short chains; feebly motile by means of peritrichous flagella; oval, terminal spore; Gram-negative.

Physiology: Strict anaerobe. Opt. T. = 33-37°C (21-39°). Resists 5 minutes at 100°C.

Cultural characters: Gas produced.

Cellulose-agar: Small, irregular colonies; blackened; H_2S.

Glucose broth: No growth.

Usual Media: No growth.

Celulose (rose-bush or filter-paper): Slowly digested; progressive disintegration; blackening; production of CO_2 and H_2.

Carbohydrates: Not fermented.

Pathogenicity: Non-pathogenic

6. *Terminosporus thermocellus* (Viljoen, Fred and Peterson) P. 1938.

Synonym: Clostridium thermocellum V., F. and P. 1926:

Habitat: Manure. Quite uncomon.

Morphology: Rods measuring 0.4 μ × 5 μ; motile; oval, terminal spore, 0.6 μ × 0.9 μ; Gram-negative.

Physiology: Strict anaerobe. Thermophilic: Opt. T. = 43-65°C (38-72°). Resists 30 minutes at 115°C.

Cultural characters: Gas produced .

Deep agar: Irregular colonies; gas.

Glucose broth and usual media: No growth on isolation; after training, meager growth.

Cellulose-peptone water: Growth at 43-65°C, with destruction of cellulose.

Milk: Acidified and coagulated; gas.

Carbohydrates: Cellulose, starch, raffinose, sucrose, maltose, lactose, mannose, galactose, fructose, glucose, xylose and arabinose are fermented.

Biochemistry: Cellulose broken down to CO_2, H_2, ethanol, acetic and butyric acids, and a yellow pigment (lipidic) soluble in ether.

Pathogenicity: Non-pathogenic.

6 bis. *Terminosporus ellipsosporus* (Rotmistrow) 1957.

Synonym: Clostridium ellipsosporus Rotmistrow 1939.

This species is closely related to the preceding. Thermophilic; grows on potato cellulose *in vacuo* and with CO_2, or on cellophane. 80-90% of the cellulose destroyed with the production of ethanol, formic, acetic, butyric and lactic acids.

7. *Terminosporus thermocellulaseum* (Enebo) nov. comb.

Synonym: Clostridium thermocellulaseum Enebo 1951.

Habitat: Grass and decaying leaves.

Morphology: Rods with rounded ends, 0.3 to 0.4 μ $\times$ 2 to 4.8 μ; occurring singly or in pairs; motile by means of few peritrichous flagella; terminal spore, often free, 1.0-1.2 μ; Gram-negative.

Physiology: Strict anaerobe. Opt. T. = 55-60°C. Opt. pH = 8.0. Catalase-negative.

Cellulose-agar: Small, yellowish, convex, translucent colonies.

Gelatin: No liquefaction at 55°C.

Milk: Unchanged.

Carbohydrates: Acid and gas from glucose, fructose, mannose, maltose, cellobiose, arabinose and xylose. Cellulose hydrolyzed to cellobiose and glucose.

Biochemistry: Indole not formed; produces (from reducing sugars) ethanol, CO_2, H_2, formic, acetic, lactic and succinic acids (sometimes malic and fumaric acids). Cellulase which decomposes cellulose.

Pathogenicity: Non-pathogenic.

8. *Terminosporus kluyveri* (Barker and Taha) P. 1948.

Synonym: Clostridium kluyveri Barker and Taha 1942.

Habitat: Soft water and marine muds.

Morphology: Rods measuring 0.9 to 1.1 μ $\times$ 3 to 11 μ; occurring singly, in pairs or in short chains; motile by means of peritrichous flagella; oval, terminal spore; Gram-negative.

Physiology: Strict anaerobe. Opt. T. = 34°C. Opt. pH = 6.8.

Cultural characters: No growth on usual media; small amounts of gas produced, but no fetid odor; slow growth.

Isolation and conservation media: Yeast autolyzate + mineral salts and ethanol. Yeast autolyzate may be replaced by a mixture of biotin + vitamin H'.

Yeast autolyzate agar: Fluffy or lenticular colonies.

Carbohydrates: Not fermented.

Biochemistry: Ethanol used as source of carbon; its fermentation produces caproic acid. May also produce butyric acid.

Pathogenicity: Non-pathogenic.

9. *Terminosporus tartarivorus* (Mercer and Vaughn) P. 1957.

Synonym: Clostridium tartarivorum Mercer and Vaughn 1951.

Habitat: Vineyard soil, spontaneous fermentation of wine tartar.

Morphology: Long, slender rods, 0.4 to 0.6 μ $\times$ 5 to 6 μ; motile by means of peritrichous flagella; spherical, terminal spore, 0.7 μ $\times$ 2.0 μ; Gram-negative.

Physiology: Strict anarobe. Opt. T. $= 55$-$60°$C, minimum $= 30$-$37°$C. Opt. pH $= 6.2 — 7.2$.

Group I: eurythermic: no growth at $30°$C.

Group II: stenothermic: growth at $30°$C.

Cultural characters: Gas, but no fetid odor; tartrates fermented (Ca d-tartrate).

Meat-medium: No growth.

Brain-medium: Slight turbidity; gas.

Coagulated egg-white: Not attacked.

Gelatin: No liquefaction.

Carbohydrates: Arabinose, xylose, glucose, fructose, galactose, mannose, maltose, lactose, sucrose, trehalose, cellobiose, aesculin, amygdalin, salicin, mannitol, sorbitol, dextrin, glycogen and starch are fermented.

Biochemistry: Nitrites not formed from nitrates; H_2S and indole not formed; produces CO_2, H_2, acetic and butyric acids in the ratio 16:1; pyruvate and lactate also fermented.

Pathogenicity: Non pathogenic.

10.   *Terminosporus indologenes* Bezjak 1952.

Habitat: Intestinal tract of man. Very uncommon.

Morphology: Straight or slightly-curved rods, 0.6 μ $\times$ 3 to 4 μ; pleomorphic; metachromatic granules; sometimes bipolar staining; motile; spherical, terminal spore; Gram-negative.

Physiology: Strict anaerobe. Opt. T. $= 37°$C. Weak thermoresistance. Slight reducing powers.

Cultural characters: Gas and slightly fetid odor produced.

Deep agar: Small, lenticular colonies.

Blood agar slant (in vacuo): Circular, moist, greyish colonies with irregular margin invading the entire surface.

Glucose broth: Diffuse turbidity; disagreeable odor.

Tryptophane-broth: Turbid; indole and H_2S produced.

Gelatin: No growth.

Milk: Acidified, coagulated; gas.

Coagulated proteins: Not attacked.

Carbohydrates: Acid and gas from sucrose, maltose, glucose, and lactose.

Biochemistry: Produces H_2S and indole.

Pathogenicity, natural: Isolated in a case of post-operative septicemia (intestinal cancer) with wall abscess.

Pathogenicity, experimental: Non-pathogenic for the mouse.

11. *Terminosporus uracilicus* (Campbell 1957) nov. comb.

Synonym: Clostridium uracilicus Campbell 1957.

Habitat: Black mud from San Francisco bay; garden soil; uracil-containing media. Frequent.

Morphology: Rods measuring 0.4 to 0.8 μ $\times$ 2.0 to 2.8 μ; occurring singly, in pairs or in short chains; motile by means of peritrichous flagella; oval, terminal spore; granulose-positive; Gram-negative.

Physiology: Anaerobic. Opt. T. $=$ 30-35°C. Still grows at 45°C.

Cultural characters: Gas produced.

Deep agar: Irregular colonies with opaque center.

Agar slant (in vacuo): Circular, convex, opaque, nonpigmented colonies.

Blood agar: No hemolysis.

Broth: Turbidity diffuse with viscous sediment.

Gelatin: No liquefaction.

Milk: Coagulated.

Coagulated egg-white: Digested.

Heart: Digested after reddening.

Brain-medium: Blackened.

Carbohydrates: Acid and gas from glucose, fructose, mannose, glycerol, salicin, cellobiose, dextrin and starch.

Biochemistry: Nitrites not formed from nitrates; produces H_2S, CO_2, H_2, ethanol, formic, acetic, butyric, lactic and succinic acids. Utilizes uracil and 8 amino acids. Requires biotin.

Pathogenicity: Non pathogenic.

Systematics: Considered wrongly to be a *Clostridium* by Campbell, it really belongs to the genus *Terminosporus,* since it is Gram-negative and has a terminal spore. Among these, it should be located with the gas-producing species, closely related to *T. kluyveri.*

APPENDIX

We place here, with all the necessary reserve, the germ discovered by Omelianski in 1916 and redescribed by Barker under the name of *Methano-*

bacterium omelianskii; since it is a sporeformer, it is definitely not a *Bacterium* and cannot remain with the *Bacteriaceae* as can be seen in Bergey's 6th edition.

Terminosporus omelianskyi (Barker) nov. comb.

Synonym: Methanobacterium omelianskyi Barker 1936.

Habitat: Organic matter decomposing under anaerobic conditions in a neutral medium, soil, mud from soft and marine waters, sewage, rabbit feces.

Morphology: Straight or slightly-curved, not branching, rods, 0.6 to 0.7 μ $\times$ 3 to 6 μ, sometimes 10 μ; weakly motile; spherical spore terminal swelling the rod; Gram-negative.

Physiology: Strict anaerobe. Opt. T. $= 37\text{-}40°C$, maximum $= 46\text{-}48°C$. Weakly thermoresistant. Opt. pH $= 6.5\text{-}8.1$.

Biochemistry: Utilizes NH_3 as source of N; oxidizes ethanol and other alcohols (propanol, n-butanol, n-amyl) to the corresponding fatty acids. Secondary alcohols are oxidized to ketones. H_2 is oxidized; CO_2 is reduced to CH_4. Growth is directly proportional to the amount of CO_2 supplied at low concentration.

Note.—This species could be responsible for the production of CH_4 in the mixed culture of *C. cellulosae-methanicus* studied by Clausen in 1931; CO_2 and H_2 recorded could be produced by the associated cellulolytic anaerobe: *Caduceus, Terminosporus* or *Plectridium.*

GENUS II: *CADUCEUS* P. 1938.

Definition.—Non-motile, Gram-negative *Terminosporaceae.* This genus comprises actually 5 species:

1. Oval spores; circular colonies; gas produced; gelatin not liquefied; non-proteolytic; saccharolytic; amylolytic; thermophilic; non-pathogenic.

    1. *Caduceus thermoaerogenes,* page 311.

2. Circular, nebulous colonies; abundant gas formed; gelatin liquefied; milk coagulated, then digested; coagulated proteins digested; saccharolytic; non-pathogenic.

    2. *Caduceus thermophilus,* page 311

3. Oval spores; cellulose not attacked; gas produced; yellowish pigment.

    3. *Caduceus cellulosae-dissolvens,* page 311

4. Spherical spores; ferments cellulose and some carbohydrates, except glucose; gas formed.

    4. *Caduceus cellulosolvens,* page 312

5. Oval spores; milk coagulated and digested; saccharolytic and cellulolytic.
  5. *Caduceus leptinotarsae,* page 312

1. *Caduceus thermoaerogenes* (Damon and Feirer) P. 1938.

Synonym: Clostridium thermoaerogenes Damon and Feirer 1925.
Habitat: Horse dung. Uncommon.
Morphology: Rods with rounded ends, 1.8 μ $\times$ 7 μ; granular cytoplasm; non-motile; oval, terminal spore; Gram-negative.
Physiology: Strict anaerobe. Thermophilic: Opt. T. $=$ 45-55°C. Killed after 10 minutes at 110-115°C.
Cultural characters: Gas produced.
Deep agar: Circular colonies; gas.
Glucose broth: H_2S not formed, nor odor; indole not produced.
Gelatin: No liquefaction.
Coagulated proteins: Not attacked.
Carbohydrates: Acid and gas from maltose, inulin, and starch.
Biochemistry: Nitrites formed from nitrates at 55°C in 48 hours.
Pathogenicity: Non-pathogenic.

2. *Caduceus thermophilus* (R. Veillon) P. 1938.

Synonym: Bacillus thermophilus R. Veillon 1922.
Habitat: Horse dung. Uncommon.
Morphology: Long, thick rods with square ends; occurring singly or in pairs; non-motile; terminal spore; Gram-negative.
Physiology: Strict anaerobe. Thermophilic: Opt. T. $=$ 37-55°C. Vegetative forms killed at temperatures above 58°C. Resists 30 minutes at 80°C.
Cultural characters: Gas produced.
Deep agar: Circular colonies, at first punctiform, then spherical and nebulous; at 55°C, become voluminous, powder puff-shaped; large amounts of gas produced.
Plain broth: Abundant turbidity; sediment; gas.
Gelatin: No liquefaction.
Milk: Coagulated, then digested.
Coagulated egg-white: Digested at 37°C.
Carbohydrates: Glucose, fructose, galactose, sucrose, lactose and maltose are fermented; cellulose is not attacked.
Biochemistry: Produces NH_3, H_2S, CO_2, acetic, propionic and butyric acids.
Pathogenicity: Non-pathogenic.

3. *Caduceus cellulosae-dissolvens* (Khouvine) P. 1938.

Synonym: Bacillus cellulosae dissolvens Khouvine 1923; *Clostridium dissolvens* Bergey et al.

Habitat: Feces of man (frequency = 60%), digestive tract of herbivorous animals and of the guinea pig; soil. Frequent.

Morphology: Straight or slightly-curved rods, 0.8 μ $\times$ 2.5 to 12.5 μ, occurring singly or in pairs; chromaffinic granules; non-motile; oval, terminal spore, 2.0 μ $\times$ 2.5 μ; Gram-negative.

Physiology: Strict anaerobe. Opt. T. = 35-50°C. Resists 50 minutes at 100°C.

Cultural characters: Gas produced. No growth on usual media; requires presence of an extract of human feces + cellulose (filter-paper).

Deep agar: No growth.

Cellulose-fecal extract-broth: Slow digestion of cellulose which, before disappearing, takes on an orange-yellow tinge.

Carbohydrates: Not fermented, except cellulose.

Biochemistry: From cellulose, produces CO_2, H_2, ethanol, acetic, butyric and lactic (traces) acids. Yellow non-diffusible pigment.

3 bis. Thermophilic races of *Caduceus cellulosae-dissolvens*.

Better growth at 55°C; spores more thermoresistant: 1 hour at 100°C, 10 minutes at 110°C.

4. *Caduceus cellulosolvens* (Cowles and Rettger) P. 1938.

Synonym: Clostridium cellulosolvens Cowles and Rettger 1931.

Habitat: Horse feces. Quite uncommon.

Morphology: Straight or slightly-curved rods, 0.5 μ $\times$ 2 to 6 μ; occurring singly or in pairs; non-motile; spherical, terminal spore; Gram-negative.

Physiology: Strict anaerobe. Opt. T. = 37°C. Resists 15 minutes at 85°C.

Cultural characters: Growth in media added with an extract of fecal matter and cellulose.

Dextrin-deep agar: Rare, small colonies.

Carbohydrates: Acid and gas from cellulose, dextrin, arabinose, xylose and soluble starch.

Biochemistry: Produces H_2, CO_2 and organic acids.

5. *Caduceus leptinotarsae* (Sartory and Meyer) P. 1948.

Synonym: Clostridium leptinotarsae Sartory and Meyer 1941.

Habitat: Intestinal tract of the doryphora (potato beetle).

Morphology: Straight or slightly-curved rods, 0.5 to 0.7 μ $\times$ 1.5 to 4.0 μ; occurring often in pairs; undulating, spermatozoidal forms; non-motile; large, oval, terminal spore, 0.6 to 1.2 μ $\times$ 1.0 to 1.8 μ, germinating apically; Gram-negative.

Physiology: Strict anaerobe. Opt. T. = 27-37°C. Resists 50-60 minutes at 100°C. Neutral red not reduced.

Cultural characters: Gas produced.

Peptone water: Turbid; indole formed.

Gelatin: No liquefaction.

Milk: Coagulated, then digested.

Carbohydrates: Acid and gas from glucose, maltose, sucrose, galactose, lactose, and mannitol. Cellulose is actively fermented, even in the presence of other carbohydrates.

Biochemistry: Nitrites not formed from nitrates; produces CO_2, H_2, butyric and lactic acids.

FAMILY II. *PLECTRIDIACEAE* Fischer emend.

Gram-positive *Plectridiales.*

This family is sub-divided into two genera which are defined as follows:
1. Rods with terminal spore; Gram-positive; motile by means of peritrichous flagella.
   1. *Plectridium* Fischer, page 313
2. Rods with terminal spore; Gram-positive; non-motile.
   2. *Acuformis* Prévot, page 334

GENUS I: *PLECTRIDIUM* Fischer 1895 emend.

This genus comprises the motile Plectridiaceae, a total of 29 species, 26 of which are strict anaerobes and 1 is facultatively anaerobic. Here is the key to the determination of these species:
   I. Species producing gas:

A) Non-proteolytic:

   a) Gelatinolytic:
   1. Free spherical spores; fluffy colonies; gas produced; saccharolytic; milk unchanged: indole and H_2S produced; specific toxin reproducing tetanus; hemolysin; specific antitoxin.
      1. *Plectridium tetani,* page 316
   2. Spherical spores; irregular colonies; gas produced; milk unchanged; saccharolytic; non-pathogenic.
      2. *Plectridium tetanomorphoum,* page 317
   3. Microaerophilic; punctiform colonies; gas produced; milk coagulated; H_2S and putrid odor formed; indole not produced; saccharolytic; pathogenic (hemorrhagic, gaseous edema); toxin and hemolysin produced.
      3. *Plectridium hemolysans,* page 317
   4. Oval spores; lenticular or spherical colonies; gas produced; broth

turbid; milk coagulated; butyric odor; putrefactive agent; non-pathogenic.

4. *Plectridium saprogenes,* page 318

b) Not gelatinolytic:

5. Oval spores; arborescent colonies; broth turbid; gas produced; milk unchanged; no odor formed; saccharolytic; pathogenic (sero-hemorrhagic edema.)

5. *Plectridium carnis,* page 318

6. Oval spores; lenticular colonies; gas produced; broth turbid; milk unchanged; saccharolytic; indole and putrid odor produced; non-pathogenic.

6. *Plectridium indologenes,* page 319

7. Spherical spores; circular or lenticular colonies; gas produced; broth turbid; H_2S formed; milk unchanged or slowly coagulated; saccharolytic; non-pathogenic.

7. *Plectridium fluxum,* page 319

8. Oval spores; lenticular or irregular colonies; broth turbid; gas produced; milk coagulated, saccharolytic; hemolytic; non-pathogenic.

8. *Plectridium tertium,* page 320

9. Very marked thermoresistance; lenticular colonies; gas produced; milk unchanged; saccharolytic.

9. *Plectridium caloritolerans,* page 321

10. Oval spores; irregular colonies; gas produced; milk unchanged; broth turbid; fetid odor; non-pathogenic.

10. *Plectridium pseudo-tetanicum,* page 321

11. Oval spores; fluffy colonies; no putrid odor; gelatin not liquefied; milk unchanged; non-proteolytic; non-saccharolytic; indole not formed; H_2S produced.

11. *Plectridium cochlearium,* page 322

12. Oval spores; lenticular colonies; no fetid odor; gelatin not liquefied; milk coagulated; requires growth factor from pepper.

12. *Plectridium causophilum,* page 322

13. Very long rods; round spores; lenticular colonies; gelatin not lique-fied; milk coagulated; non-saccharolytic.

13. *Plectridium sporospheroides,* page 323

14. Short rods; oval spores; lenticular colonies; gelatin not liquefied; milk unchanged; saccharolytic; utilizes d-aminovalerate.

14. *Plectridium aminovalericum,* page 323

B) Proteolytic:

15. Oval spores; lenticular or irregular colonies; gas formed; gelatin liquefied; coagulated serum digested; milk coagulated; H_2S formed;

indole not formed; saccharolytic; non-hemolytic; pathogenic (subcutaneous edema).

15. *Plectridium capitovalis,* page 324

16. Spherical spores; fluffy colonies; gas produced; gelatin liquefied; broth turbid; milk digested; H$_2$S formed; weakly and irregularly saccharolytic; indole not formed; non-pathogenic in pure culture; pathogenic in mixed culture.

16. *Plectridium putrificum,* page 325

17. Spherical spores; fluffy colonies; gas produced; gelatin liquefied; milk digested saccharolytic; non-pathogenic; variety of *Pl. putrificum.*

17. *Plectridium lentoputrescens,* page 326

18. Oval spores; spherical colonies; gelatin liquefied; coagulated egg-white slowly attacked; milk digested without previous clotting; saccharolytic; gas produced; non-pathogenic.

18. *Plectridium ovalaris,* page 326

19. Oval spores; irregular colonies; gas produced; gelatin liquefied; broth turbid; milk digested; fetid odor; non-pathogenic.

19. *Plectridium cadaveris,* page 327

C) Pectinolytic:

20. Oval spores; irregular colonies; gas produced; milk coagulated; nonpigmented, pectinolytic agent growing on usual media.

20. *Plectridium pectinovorum,* page 327

21. Spherical spores; greenish colonies; pectinolytic agent growing only on plant media.

21. *Plectridium virens,* page 328

D) Cellulolytic:

22. Oval spores; small, fluffy colonies; gas, indole and H$_2$S formed; gelatin liquefied; milk coagulated; becomes saccharolytic after one year's growth; cellulose attacked; non-pathogenic.

22. *Plectridium spumarum,* page 329

23. Facultatively anaerobic; oval spores; small amounts of gas; cellulolytic under anaerobic conditions; saccharolytic; milk coagulated; gelatin not liquefied; non-proteolytic; non-pathogenic.

23. *Plectridium cellulolyticum,* page 329

24. Spherical spores; no growth on usual media; thermophilic; cellulose attacked with production of ethanol and acetic acid.

24. *Plectridium sniezskoi,* page 330

25. Spherical spores; cellulose not attacked; gas produced; non-pathogenic.

25. *Plectridium omelianskii,* page 330

II. Species producing no gas:

26. Oval spores; gelatin liquefied; non-proteolytic; non-saccharolytic; milk precipitated; indole not formed; pathogenic.

    26. *Plectridium incertiem,* page 331

27. Spherical spores; irregular colonies; gelatin not liquefied; milk coagulated; non proteolytic; saccharolytic.

    27. *Plectridium sphenoides,* page 331

28. Spherical spores; fluffy or arborescent colonies; gelatin not liquefied; milk unchanged; non-proteolytic; saccharolytic; non-pathogenic.

    28. *Plectridium nonum,* page 332

29. Spherical spores; thermophilic; marked thermoresistance; non-proteolytic; saccharolytic.

    29. *Plectridium thermoaceticum,* page 332

1. *Plectridium tetani* (Nicolaier) Fischer 1895.

Synonym: Bacillus tetani Nicolaier 1894. *Clostridium tetani* (N.) Holland.

Habitat: Soil, manure, dust, feces of man and animals, especially cattle and horses, infected wounds. Extremely frequent.

Morphology: Rods with rounded ends, 0.4 to 6 μ $\times$ 3 to 4 μ; occurring singly or sometimes in pairs, seldom in filaments; swollen involution forms; spherical, terminal spore, 0.8 μ $\times$ 1.6 μ; aspect of pin; motile by means of peritrichous flagella numerous; Gram-positive.

Physiology: Strict anaerobe; microaerophilic strains may also be found. Opt. T. = 37°C. Resists 5 minutes at 100°C. Neutral red and safranin are reduced.

Cultural characters: Gas and fetid odor produced.

Deep agar: Spherical, fluffy or arborescent colonies; gas.

Broth: Diffuse turbidity; gas; disagreeable odor; H_2S, indole and NH_3 formed.

Peptone water: Diffuse turbidity; gas, H_2S, and NH_3 and volatile acids produced.

Gelatin: Slowly liquefied.

Milk: Generally not coagulated; some strains may coagulate slowly.

Coagulated serum: Not attacked.

Carbohydrates: Acid and gas from glucose, fructose, maltose, galactose, sucrose, arabinose, and lactose; however, the acids produced are neutralized by nascent NH_3 as they are formed. Some strains are non-saccharolytic.

Biochemistry: Nitrites not formed from nitrates; sulfites not reduced. Produces CO_2, H_2, ethanol, butanol, acetic and butyric acids; on the 12th day, propionic acid and propanol appear. In glucose broth, are formed in addition: phenol, acetylmethylcarbinol, methylamine, putrescin and cadaverin.

Pathogenicity, natural: Human and animal tetanus.

Pathogenicity, experimental: Fluid cultures, as well as spores, reproduce the disease in laboratory animals.

Toxin: Highly active: guinea pig killed at 1/20,000—1/200,000 ml. Produces characteristic spasms (tetanospasmin) and hemolysis (tetanolysin). Converted into toxoid.

Antitoxin: Specific; highly active.

2. *Plectridium tetanomorphum* (McIntosh and Fildes) P. 1938.

Synonym: Bacillus pseudotetanus McIntosh and Fildes 1917 or *B. tetanomorphum* McIntosh and Fildes 1919; *Clostridium tetanomorphum* (McIntosh and Fildes) Bergey.

Habitat: Soil, infected wounds, appendicular abscess. Quite frequent.

Morphology: Rods similar to *Pl. tetani;* spherical, terminal spore; motile, Gram-positive.

Physiology: Strict anaerobe. Opt. T. = 37°C. Resists 5 to 20 minutes at 100°C. Survives several years. Neutral red and safranin reduced.

Cultural characters: Gas produced.

Deep agar: Lenticular colonies; gas.

Glucose broth: Meager growth; gas and weak odor.

Gelatin: Liquefied (Hall).

Milk: Unchanged.

Coagulated serum: Blackened and partly digested.

Carbohydrates: Acid and gas from glucose and maltose; some strains ferment in addition: fructose, lactose, arabinose and xylose.

Biochemistry: Produces NH_3, acetylmethylcarbinol (traces), acetic, propionic, butyric and lactic acids.

Pathogenicity: Non-pathogenic.

3. *Plectridium hemolysans* (Markoff) P. 1938.

Synonym: Bacillus anaerobius hemolysans Markoff 1915.

Habitat: Buccal cavity, sulfurous waters from the Pyrenees.

Morphology: Rods with rounded ends, 0.5 to 0.7 $\mu \times$ 3 to 4 μ; motile; terminal spore; Gram-positive.

Physiology: Microaerophilic. Opt. T. = 37°C. Weak thermoresistance: a few minutes at 70°C. Neutral red reduced.

Cultural characters: Gas and fetid odor produced.

Deep agar: Punctiform colonies; gas. Sometimes fluffy colonies.

Glucose broth: Abundant turbidity, flaky; gas (odor of rotten eggs).

Gelatin: Liquefaction.

Milk: Coagulated in 24 hours.

Brain-medium: Not blackened; large amounts of H_2S.

Carbohydrates: Nitrites not formed from nitrates; produces NH_3, H_2S, acetic, butyric and lactic acids.

Pathogenicity, natural: Isolated from a putrid infection of the mouth and from a lung abscess in the cat.

Pathogenicity, experimental: Guinea pig, rabbit and mouse are susceptible: hemorrhagic gaseous edema.

Toxin: Active in the peritoneal route in 3 days.

Hemolysin: Very active *in vitro.*

4. *Plectridium saprogenes* (Salus) P. 1938.

Synonym: Bacillus saprogenes carnis Salus 1904.

Habitat: Putrefying meat, intestinal tract of the pig, soil. Quite frequent.

Morphology: Slightly-curved rods, 1.5 to 8.0 μ; occurring in short chains or in filaments; motile; oval, terminal spore; Gram-positive.

Physiology: Strict anaerobe. Opt. T. $= 37°C$. Resists 2 minutes at 100°C. Neutral red reduced definitively, safranin reduced temporarily.

Cultural characters: Gas and disagreeable odor produced; sometimes fetid.

Deep agar: Lenticular or spherical colonies; gas.

Glucose broth: Slowly appearing turbidity; penetrating, putrid odor.

Gelatin: Slow liquefaction.

Milk: Coagulated disagreeable odor.

Coagulated proteins: Not attacked.

Carbohydrates: Glucose, fructose, maltose, galactose, sucrose, lactose, arabinose, xylose, sorbitol, dulcitol, mannitol, glycerol and starch are fermented.

Biochemistry: Nitrites not formed from nitrates; produces NH_3, H_2S, traces of alcohol and aldehyde, volatile amines, ketones, acetic, butyric and lactic acids.

Pathogenicity, natural: Isolated in cases of war gas gangrene.

Pathogenicity, experimental: Non-pathogenic.

5. *Plectridium carnis* (Klein) P. 1938.

Synonym: Bacillus carnis Klein 1903; *Clostridium carnis* (Klein) Bergey *et al.* Must not be confused with *Cl. sextum* von Hibler which Hall and Duffet have wrongly related to *P. carnis* in spite of its subterminal spore.

Habitat: Putrefying meat, forest soil of the Ivory Coast. Quite uncommon.

Morphology: Slender rods, 0.6 μ $\times$ 1.5 to 2.5 μ; motile by means of peritrichous flagella; oval, terminal spore, 0.8 μ $\times$ 2 μ; Gram-positive.

Physiology: Strict anaerobe. Opt. T. $= 22\text{-}37°C$. Resists 15 minutes at 70°C and sometimes 1 minute at 100°C. Survives several months. Neutral red and safranin reduced.

Cultural characters: Gas and fetid odor produced.

Deep agar: Fluffy or arborescent colonies; gas.

Glucose broth: Uniform turbidity; mucoid sediment; gas. Sometimes flaky growth.

Gelatin: No liquefaction.

Milk: Unchanged.

Coagulated serum: Not attacked.

Coagulated proteins: Not attacked.

Carbohydrates: Maltose, galactose and starch very weakly fermented.

Biochemistry: Nitrites not formed from nitrates; produces NH_3 (very large amounts), H_2S, volatile amines, acetone, aldehydes, indole, cresol, actic, butyric and lactic acids.

Pathogenicity, natural: Fatal septicemia of ranch mink.

Pathogenicity, experimental: Injection of 0.1 ml. into the guinea pig produces hemorrhagic edema without gas or odor, followed rapidly by death.

6. *Plectridium indologenes* Lanthiez 1948.

Habitat: Poto-poto from the Ivory Coast.

Morphology: Straight rods, 0.6 $\mu \times$ 3 to 4 μ; occurring singly or in pairs; motile only in very young sugar-free cultures; very large, seldom seen, oval, terminal spore; Gram-positive.

Physiology: Strict anaerobe. Opt. T. $= 37°C$. Resists 3 minutes at 100°C. Survives several months. Neutral red and safranin are reduced.

Cultural characters: Small amounts of gas produced; putrid.

Glucose broth: Abundant turbidity; viscous sediment, not coherent; putrid odor.

Peptone water: Slight turbidity; indole formed.

Gelatin: No liquefaction.

Milk: Unchanged.

Coagulated proteins: Not attacked.

Carbohydrates: Glucose, lactose and galactose are fermented.

Biochemistry: Nitrites not formed from nitrates; produces NH_3, H_2S, indole (large amounts), volatile amines, ethanol, acetylmethylcarbinol, formic, butyric and lactic acids.

Pathogenicity: Non-pathogenic for the guinea pig.

7. *Plectridium fluxum* (Rodella) P. 1938.

Synonym: Bacillus III of Rodella 1902; *Plectridium gazogenes* Choukévitch 1911[1]. *Fluxum =* ephemeral.

---

[1] The strain discovered by Choukévitch in 1911 under the name *Bacillus gazogenes parvus* and which appeared in former editions of this manual under the name of *Pl. gazogenes* is identical with the species *Pl. fluxum* (Rodella). Consequently *Pl. gazogenes,* the former term, disappears from this manual.

Habitat: Stools of nurslings, large intestine of cattle, sheep and horses, soil of the Ivory Coast. Quite frequent.

Morphology: Rods measuring 0.5 μ $\times$ 5 μ, often curved; long, filamentous forms; motile; spherical, terminal spore; Gram-positive.

Physiology: Strict anaerobe. Opt. T. $= 22$-$37°$C. Resists 20 minutes at $80°$C and 1 to 5 minutes at $100°$C. Some strains short-lived, longevity quite marked for others. Neutral red reduced.

Cultural characters: Gas, but no fetid odor produced.

Deep agar: Irregular or lenticular colonies; gas.

Glucose broth: Turbid; sediment; gas, H_2S.

Gelatin: No liquefaction; fluffy colonies.

Milk: Unchanged or very slowly coagulated.

Coagulated proteins: Not attacked.

Carbohydrates: Acid and gas from glucose, fructose and maltose; galactose fermented by some strains.

Biochemistry: Produces NH_3, H_2S, volatile amines, traces of ethanol, acetic, butyric and lactic acids.

Pathogenicity, natural: Isolated by hemoculture in cases of hemolytic icterus of the new-born and from typhoid feces.

Pathogenicity, experimental: Some strains are pathogenic for the guinea pig (visceral congestion).

8. *Plectridium tertium* (Henry) P. 1938.

Synonym: Bacillus tertius Henry 1917; *Clostridium tertium* (Henry) Bergey *et al.*

Habitat: Soil, feces, mud, infected wounds, meat. Frequent.

Morphology: Slender rods, 0.4 to 0.6 μ $\times$ 4 to 8 μ; occurring singly or in pairs; curved and filamentous forms; motile by means of peritrichous flagella; oval, terminal spore; Gram-positive.

Physiology: Microaerophilic. Opt. T. $= 25$-$37°$C. Resists 10 minutes at $80°$C. Killed after 8 minutes at $97°$C. Neutral red and safranin reduced.

Cultural character: Gas produced.

Deep agar: Lenticular or arborescent colonies; gas.

Glucose broth: Abundant turbidity; gas sediment.

Blood-agar: Hemolysis.

Gelatin: No liquefaction.

Milk: Coagulated.

Coagulated proteins: Not attacked.

Carbohydrates: Acid and gas from glucose, fructose, maltose, galactose, lactose, sucrose, dextrin, aesculin, mannitol and xylose.

Biochemistry: Nitrites formed from nitrates; produces NH_3, ethanol, aldehyde, acetylemthylcarbinol, formic, propionic and lactic acids.

Pathogenicity: Non-pathogenic.

9. **Plectridium caloritolerans** (Meyer and Lang) P. 1938.

Synonym: Clostridium caloritolerans Meyer and Lang 1926.

Habitat: Isolated from old, mixed cultures of *Cl. parabotulinum* from spoiled preserves, soil from Ivory Coast. Quite uncommon.

Morphology: Rods measuring 0.5 to 0.8 μ $\times$ 8 to 10 μ; metachromatic granules; motile by means of peritrichous flagella; Gram-positive.

Physiology: Strict anaerobe. Opt. T. $= 37°$C. Resists 8½ hours at 100°C. Neutral red and safranin reduced.

Cultural characters: Gas produced.

Deep agar: Transparent, lenticular colonies with filamentous buds; gas.

Glucose broth: Abundant turbidity; gas; Indole not formed.

Gelatin: No liquefaction.

Milk: Unchanged.

Coagulated ascitic fluid: Not attacked.

Coagulated serum: Not attacked.

Casein: Abundant, gaseous growth; production of tyrosin.

Brain-medium: Greyish discoloration; gas.

Coagulated egg-white: Slightly blackened.

Carbohydrates: Acid and gas from glucose, fructose, galactose, and maltose.

Biochemistry: Nitrites formed from nitrates in the presence of mannitol; produces NH_3, volatile amines, alcohols, ketones, formic, propionic and lactic, acids.

Pathogenicity: Non-pathogenic. No toxin, nor hemolysin.

10. **Plectridium pseudo-tetanicum** (Lanz and Tavel) P. 1938.

Synonym: Bacillus pseudotetanicus Lanz and Tavel 1898. The aerobic species described by Migula in 1900 under the above name is probably a mutant of *Pl. pseudotetanicum.*

Habitat: Appendix, corpses. Quite frequent.

Morphology: Rods measuring 0.5 to 0.7 μ $\times$ 5 to 7 μ; occurring in short chains; motile by means of peritrichous flagella; oval, terminal spore; Gram-positive.

Physiology: Strict anaerobe; some strains are microaerophilic. Opt. T. $= 37°$C. Resists 2 minutes at 100°C. Facultatively anaerobic mutants frequently occur. Slight reducing power.

Cultural characters: Gas and fetid odor produced.

Deep agar: Fluffy, flaky colonies; gas.

Glucose broth: Diffuse turbidity; large amounts of gas; fetid odor; indole not formed, nor H_2S. NH_3 produced.

Peptone water: Slight turbidity; indole not formed.

Gelatin: No liquefaction.

Milk: Unchanged.

Coagulated proteins: Not attacked.

Serum: Turbid; gas and fetid odor.

Carbohydrates: Acid and gas from glucose, fructose, maltose, and galactose; arabinose, xylose and glycerol weakly fermented.

Biochemistry: Nitrites not formed from nitrates; produces NH_3, phenol, acetylmethylcarbinol, indole, ethanol, acetic and propionic acids, traces of lactic acid.

Pathogenicity: Non-pathogenic. No toxin, nor hemolysin.

11. *Plectridium cochlearium*
(Douglas, Fleming and Colebrrok) P. 1938.

Synonym: Bacillus cochlearius D., F. and C. 1920; *Clostridium cochlearium* (D., F. and C.) Bergey.

Habitat: Infected war wounds, infections, soil, preserves, intestinal tract of the horse.

Morphology: Straight rods, 0.6 to 0.8 μ $\times$ 4 to 5 μ; occurring singly or in pairs, seldom in short chains; motile by means of peritrichous flagella; oval, terminal spore; Gram-positive.

Physiology: Strict anaerobe. Opt. T. $= 37°$C; grows already at 22°C. Opt. pH $= 5.2$-8.6. Catalase-negative. Survives several years. Neutral red reduced.

Cultural characters: Small amounts of gas produced; slightly fetid odor.

Deep agar: Lenticular colonies, becoming flaky.

Agar slant: Circular colonies, translucent with crenated edges.

Glucose broth: Turbid; sediment; H_2S produced; indole not formed

Gelatin: No liquefaction.

Milk: Unchanged.

Coagulated protein: Not attacked.

Brain-medium: Blackened.

Carbohydrates: Not fermented, except glucose by some strains.

Biochemistry: Nitrites not formed from nitrates; produces NH_3, H_2S, volatile amines, traces of alcohol, aldehydes, acetic, butyric and lactic acids. Ferments glutamic acid.

Pathogenicity: Non-pathogenic.

12. *Plectridium causophilum* Lebert 1949.

Habitat: Lentil-beef preserves, Cayenne pepper and spices.

Morphology: Straight or flexuous rods with square ends, 0.7 to 0.8 μ $\times$ 5 to 7.7 μ occurring singly, in pairs or in short chains of 4-5 elements; motile by means of 7-8 flagella; oval, terminal spore, 1.2 to 1.3 μ; Gram-positive.

Physiology: Strict anaerobe. Strict thermophile: Opt. T. $= 55°$C (41-55°). Resists 30 minutes at 100°C and 10 minutes at 115°C in VF broth $+$

lentils and beef; 25 minutes at 114°C and 65 minutes at 110°C in preserves. Survives more than 3 months. Grows only in media added with beef-lentils sauce; the necessary growth factor also exists in Cayenne pepper from which it has been extracted. Neutral red, safranin and phenosafranin are reduced.

Cultural characters: Gas, but no fetid odor (tart).

Sauce-deep agar: Small, lenticular colonies with buds; gas; agar liquefied.

Sauce-glucose VF broth: Turbid; abundant gas; tart odor.

Sauce-peptone water: Turbid; gas.

Gelatin: No liquefaction.

Milk: Coagulated in 48 hours; spongy clot.

Coagulated proteins: Not attacked.

Carbohydrates sauce: Acid and gas from glucose, fructose, galactose, sucrose, lactose and maltose; glycerol and starch very slightly fermented.

Biochemistry: Nitrites not formed from nitrates; produces NH_3, ethanol, formic, butyric and lactic acids.

Pathogenicity: Non-pathogenic. No toxin, nor hemolysin.

13. *Plectridium sporospheroides* (Soriano) nov. comb.

Synonym: Clostridium sporospheroides Soriano 1948.

Habitat: Spoiled canned sardines.

Morphology: Rods measuring 0.6 to 0.7 μ $\times$ 5 to 8 μ; motile; terminal spore, 0.7 to 0.9 μ; Gram-positive.

Physiology: Anaerobic.

Cultural characters: Gas produced.

Glucose-yeast autolyzate agar: Lenticular, colonies.

Broth: Slight turbidity; no sediment.

Heart broth: Turbid; gas; viscid.

Liver broth: Turbid; gas.

Gelatin: No liquefaction.

Milk: Slow partial, coagulation; soft curd; gas.

Coagulated egg-white: Not attacked.

Brain-medium: Not blackened.

Carbohydrates: Not fermented.

Biochemistry: Nitrites not formed from nitrates; H_2S not formed, nor indole.

Pathogenicity: Non-pathogenic.

14. *Plectridium aminovalericum* (Hardman and Stadtman) nov. comb.

Synonym: Clostridium aminovalericum H. and S. 1960.

Habitat: Sewage mud.

Morphology: Rods measuring 0.4 to 0.6 μ $\times$ 0.8 to 1.2 μ; occurring singly, in pairs or in short chains; motile; oval, terminal, plectridial spore; Gram-positive in young cultures.

Physiology: Strict anaerobe. Opt. T. $= 31$-$37\,^{\circ}$C.

Cultural characters: Gas, but no fetid odor.

Deep agar: Lenticular, yellowish-white colonies, 2 to 4 mm. in diameter, with translucent edges.

Broth: Abundant turbidity.

Gelatin: No liquefaction.

Milk: Unchanged.

Carbohydrates: Acid and gas from glucose, fructose, maltose, cellobiose, arabinose, xylose, starch, dextrin and starch; sucrose and galactose weakly fermented. Lactose, inulin, glycerol, sorbitol, adonitol, dulcitol and pectin are not fermented.

Biochemistry: Nitrites not formed from nitrates; produces NH_3. May utilize d-aminovalerate as sole source of energy; from 2 moles of this salt are produced, 2 moles of NH_3, and 1 mole each of acetic, propionic and valeric acids.

Pathogenicity: Non-pathogenic. No toxin, nor hemolysin.

15. *Plectridium capitovalis* (Snyder and Hall) P. 1938.

Synonym: Bacillus capitovalis Snyder and Hall 1935; *Clostridium Capitovalis* (S. and H.) Bergey *et al.*

Habitat: Human feces, infected wounds, septicemia, dead cats.

Morphology: Rods measuring 0.5 to 0.8 $\mu \times$ 2.0 to 2.5 μ; occurring singly or in pairs; motile by means of peritrichous flagella; oval, terminal spore; Gram-positive.

Physiology: Strict anaerobe. Opt. T. $= 37\,^{\circ}$C. Resists 25 minutes at $100\,^{\circ}$C. Survives several months. Neutral red and safranin reduced.

Cultural characters: Gas produced.

Deep agar: Lenticular colonies, becoming irregular; gas.

Blood agar: Small colonies; no hemolysis.

Glucose broth: Turbid; gas; indole not formed.

Tryptone broth: Turbid; gas.

Peptone water: Turbid; gas; indole not formed.

Gelatin: Liquefaction in 2 to 5 days.

Milk: Coagulated, then slowly and partly digested.

Coagulated serum: Partly liquefied in 1 month.

Brain-medium: Browning; H_2S formed.

Carbohydrates: Acid and gas from glucose, fructose, galactose; some strains ferment in addition: maltose, sucrose, lactose, mannitol, glycerol and starch.

Biochemistry: Nitrites formed from nitrates in the presence of maltose-peptone water; produces NH_3, H_2S, volatile amines, acetone, aldehydes, acetic, butyric, valerianic and lactic acids.

Pathogenicity, experimental: Sub-cutaneous edema in the guinea pig.

Serology: Specific agglutination at 1-320.

16. *Plectridium putrificum* (Bienstick) P. 1938.

Synonym: Bacillus putrificus Bienstock 1884; *Clostridium putrificum* (B.) Reddish and Rettger 1922.

Habitat: Soil, mud, corpses, putrefying meat, buccal cavity and intestinal tract; dental caries, war wounds. Frequent.

Morphology: Rods measuring 0.4 to 0.7 μ $\times$ 7 to 9 μ; with rounded ends; often curved; filaments; occurring singly or in pairs; motile by means of peritrichous flagella; spherical, terminal spore; Gram-positive.

Physiology: Strict anaerobe. Opt. T. $=$ 37°C. Resists 15 minutes at 80°C. Survives several years. Neutral red and safranin are reduced.

Cultural characters: Gas and putrid odor formed.

Deep agar: Fluffy, hairy colonies; gas and putrid odor.

Glucose broth: Uniform turbidity of average intensity; gas and intensely putrid odor.

Gelatin: Rapid liquefaction; NH_3 and H_2S formed.

Coagulated serum: Digested in 5 days; NH_3 and H_2S formed.

Milk: Digested, without previous coagulation; H_2S formed.

Coagulated proteins (egg-white, meat, etc.): Digested; gas and putrid odor (H_2S).

Carbohydrates: Glucose weakly fermented by some strains; other strains are not saccharolytic; still others ferment very actively.

Biochemistry: Nitrites not formed from nitrates; produces NH_3, H_2S, ethanol, aldehydes, acetylmethylcarbinol (traces), acetic, butyric and lactic acids.

Pathogenicity, natural: In mixed culture, confers a putrid character to the infections.

Pathogenicity, experimental: Non-pathogenic in pure culture.

17. Varieties of *Plectridium putrificum.*

a) *Pl. lentoputrescens* (Hartsell and Rettger) P. 1938.

Synonym: Clostridium lentoputrescens Hartsell and Rettger 1934.

Habitat: Soil, feces. Quite frequent.

Morphology: Rods, often curved, 0.4 to 0.6 μ $\times$ 7 μ, with longer forms: 2 to 16 μ; occurring singly, in pairs or in short chains; motile by means of peritrichous flagella; spherical, terminal spore; Gram-positive.

Physiology: Strict anaerobe. Opt. T. $=$ 37°C.

Cultural characters: Gas and putrid odor.

Deep agar: Flaky colonies.

Glucose broth: Meager growth; indole not formed; H_2S produced.

Gelatin: Liquefaction.

Milk: Digested.

Coagulated egg-white: Digested.

Brain, coagulated serum, meat: Digested.

Carbohydrates: Glucose weakly fermented.

Pathogenicity: Non-pathogenic.

Systematics: According to Hartsell and Rettger, Reddish and Rettger, *Pl. lentoputrescens* is identical with *Pl. putrificum;* with Weinberg, Nativelle and Prévot, we prefer to believe that we are dealing with a variety of *Pl. putrificum.*

b) *Pl. paraputrificum* (Bienstock) P. 1938.

This variety does not liquefy gelatin, does not digest milk which it coagulates; it shares an antigen (agglutinogen) with *Acuformis innutritus* (Kleinscmidt), but differs from the latter by the fact that it is motile.

18. *Plectridium ovalaris* (Debono) P. 1938.

Synonym: Bacillus putrificus ovalaris Debono 1912; *Clostridium ovalaris* (D.) Bergey *et al.*

Habitat: Putrefying meat, feces, soil from Adelieland, war wounds. Quite uncommon.

Morphology: Straight or slightly-curved rods, 0.6 to 0.8 μ × 3 to 4 μ; occurring singly or in short chains of 4-8 elements; motile; oval, terminal spore; Gram-positive.

Physiology: Strict anaerobe. Opt. T. $= 22$-$37°$C. Resists 2 minutes at 100°C. Survives more than 25 years. Neutral red reduced.

Cultural characters: Gas and slightly fetid odor.

Deep agar: Spherical, punctiform colonies.

Glucose broth: Turbid; small amounts of gas.

Gelatin: Liquefaction in 3 days.

Milk: Digested without previous coagulation, or very slowly coagulated.

Coagulated egg-white: Slowly attacked, then digested.

Carbohydrates: Acid and gas from glucose and lactose; some strains ferment in addition: fructose, maltose, sucrose, galactose and starch.

Coagulated proteins: Not attacked.

Biochemistry: Nitrites not formed from nitrates; produces NH_3, H_2S, ethanol, acetone, volatile amines, acetylmethylcarbinol; formic, butyric and lactic acids.

Pathogenicity: Non-pathogenic.

19. *Plectridium cadaveris* (Klein) P. 1938.

Synonym: Bacillus cadaveris sporogenes Klein 1901.

Habitat: Large intestine of man and animals; putrefying corpses. Quite frequent.

Morphology: Rods measuring 2 to 4 μ; occurring singly, in short chains or in filaments; actively motile by means of peritrichous flagella; oval, terminal spore, 0.8 to 1.0 μ × 1.6 to 1.8 μ; Gram-positive.

Physiology: Strict anaerobe. Opt. T. $= 20$-$37°$C. Resists 1 minute at 100°C. Neutral red and safranin reduced.

Cultural characters: Gas and fetid odor produced.

Deep agar: Lenticular colonies; gas. Young colonies ar elenticular.

Glucose broth: Abundant turbidity; gas and fetid odor.

Gelatin: Rapid liquefaction; gas.

Milk: Rapid coagulation, then digested; fetid odor.

Coagulated serum: Digested; fetid odor. Other proteins partly digested.

Carbohydrates: Glucose, fructose and sucrose are fermented.

Biochemistry: Nitrites not formed from nitrates; produces NH_3, H_2S, volatile amines, indole, ethanol, butanol, acetylmethylcarbinol, acetic, butyric and lactic acids.

Pathogenicity: Non-pathogenic. No toxin, nor hemolysin.

20. *Plectridium pectinovorum* Beijerinck and van Delden.

Synonym: Granulobacter pectinovorum B. and v. D. 1906.

Habitat: Soil, surface of textile plants, especially flax. Very frequent.

Morphology: Rods measuring 0.8 μ $\times$ 10 to 15 μ; occurring singly or in pairs; motile by means of peritrichous flagella; terminal spore, 1.2 μ $\times$ 1.8 μ; Gram-positive.

Physiology: Strict anaerobe. Opt. T. $= 37°C$. Resists 5 minutes at 100°C. Opt. pH $= 7.4$. Survives more than 1 year. Neutral red slowly reduced.

Cultural characters: Gas, but no fetid odor.

Deep agar: Aggregates of lenses; gas.

Glucose VF broth: Abundant turbidity; gas; sediment.

Peptone water: Slight turbidity.

Gelatin: Slow liquefaction (12 days).

Milk: Coagulated in 24 hours; retracted clot, clear fluid.

Coagulated proteins: Not attacked.

Carbohydrates: Glucose, fructose, maltose, galactose, sucrose, lactose, glycerol and starch are fermented; pectin attacked.

Biochemistry: Nitrites not formed from nitrates; fixes free N_2; produces NH_3, H_2S (traces), aldehydes, ketones, acetylmethylcarbinol, acetic, butyric, lactic and formic (traces) acids. Some strains destroy 100% of the pectin: active agent of retting.

Pathogenicity: Non-pathogenic. No toxin, nor hemolysin.

20 bis. *Plectridium pectinovorum* var. *desulfuricans*
Seliber and Alexeev 1957.

Habitat: Retting agent adapted to alcaline pH.

Morphology: Rods measuring 0.5 μ $\times$ 4 to 5 μ; oval, terminal spore; Gram-positive.

Biochemistry: Sulfates reduced to sulfides; produces mainly butyric acid; hydrolyzes pectin.

20 ter. *Pl. pectinovorum* var. *thermophilum*
Imchenetzki and Solntzeva 1950.

Morphology: Similar to the *Plectridia,* with numerous iodophilic granules, and plectridial spore.
Physiology: Thermophilic: Opt. T. $= 56°$C.
Gelatin: No liquefaction.
Milk: Unchanged.
Carbohydrates: Glucose, fructose, maltose and arabinose are fermented.
Biochemistry: Retting of flax in 21 hours at 56°C.

20 quarto. *Pl. pectinovorum* var. *butyricum* Kaiser 1961.

Habitat: Unknown.
Morphology: Rods measuring 0.8 μ $\times$ 10 to 15 μ; terminal spore; Gram-positive.
Potato mash: Digested and broken up into mucilaginous masses.
Biochemistry: Produces acetic and butyric acids; not very pectinolytic: 50% in 7 days. Glacturonic acid attacked: 100% in 7 days. Produces small amounts of an adaptative, enzyme: endopolygalacturonidase (opt. pH $= 7.5$).
Coagulated egg-white: Attacked.

21. *Plectridium virens* Prévot 1946.

Habitat: Pond mud from Northern France.
Morphology: Straight rods, 0.6 to 0.8 μ $\times$ 3 to 4 μ; actively motile; spherical, terminal spore, 1 μ, sometimes free; Gram-positive.
Physiology: Very strict anaerobe. Opt. T. $= 26°$C (no growth at 30°C). Resists 5 minutes at 100°C. Survives 1 to 2 months. Slight reducing powers.
Cultural characters: No growth on usual media. Very slow and meager growth; gas produced.
Glucose deep agar: Fluffy, transparent colonies, appearing slowly (8 to 10 days); green pigment diffuses into the agar.
Glucose VF broth: At 26°C, slow growth taking a light-green tinge on the 10 to 15th day.
Peptone water: No growth.
Gelatin: No growth.
Milk: No growth.
Coagulated proteins: No growth.
Potato mash: Abundant, gaseous growth, highly colored in green.
Broken pea mash: Greenish growth.
Decoction of Lemma minor and of Typha angustifolia: Abundant, greenish growth.
Carbohydrates: Pectin, lactose, galactose starch, glucose, etc., actively fermented; fructose weakly fermented. Cellulose not attacked.

Biochemistry: Nitrites abundantly formed from nitrates; fermentation of *Lemma minor* decoction + galactose produces NH_3, formic and propionic acids. Pectin destroyed to the extent of 80%.

Pigment, green: soluble in water; extractible by amyl alcohol and ethyl acetate.

Pathogenicity: Non-pathogenic.

22. *Plectridium spumarum* Prévot and Pochon 1939.

Habitat: Froth from sugar refineries.

Morphology: Rods measuring 0.5 μ $\times$ 4 to 5 μ; motile; oval, terminal spore; Gram-positive.

Physiology: Strict anaerobe. Opt. T. $= 37°C$. Resists 5 minutes at 90°C. Neutral red reduced.

Cultural characters: Small amounts of gas produced.

Deep agar: Small, fluffy colonies; gas.

Glucose broth: Uniform turbidity; slight sediment; indole and H_2S formed.

Peptone water: Slight turbidity; indole and H_2S formed.

Gelatin: Liquefaction in 15 days.

Milk: Coagulated in 5 days.

Coagulated egg-white: Not attacked.

Brain-medium: Blackened.

Carbohydrates: Not fermented on isolation. After 1 year's growth on artificial media, it produces acid and gas from glucose, fructose, galactose, maltose, arabinose, xylose, sucrose, mannitol and starch.

Biochemistry: Cellulose destroyed to a great extent, without formation of pigment; produces volatile acids (acetic and butyric), ethanol (traces) and inflammable gases.

Pathogenicity: Non-pathogenic.

23. *Plectridium cellulolyticum* Pochon 1935.

Habitat: Cecum of ruminants.

Morphology: Rods measuring 0.5 μ $\times$ 3 to 4 μ; motile by means of peritrichous flagella; terminal spore, either spherical and small, 1 μ in diameter, or large and oval, 1 μ $\times$ 2 μ; Gram-positive (easily decolorized).

Physiology: Facultatively anaerobic. Opt. T. $= 40°C$ (33-48°). Opt. pH $= 8.5-9.0$. Cellulolytic only under strictly anaerobic conditions.

Cultural characters: Small amounts of gas produced.

Deep agar: Whitish, fluffy colonies with opaque center.

Glucose broth: Turbid; fragile superficial veil; slight sediment.

Peptone water: Turbid; indole not formed.

Gelatin: No liquefaction.

Coagulated proteins: Not attacked.

Milk: Coagulated under aerobic conditions; unchanged in anaerobiosis. Rumen cellulose sugar refinery-froth medium: slight turbidity, followed by opalescence; cellulose softened, then destroyed. No pigment.

Carbohydrates: Acid and gas from glucose, fructose, galactose, sucrose, arabinose, glycerol and mannitol.

Biochemistry: Nitrites not formed from nitrates; from cellulose, produces formic and acetic acids, finally propionic acid; moreover, ethanol and gas are produced. Hydrolysis of cellulose by cellulase gives glucose and cellobiose.

Pathogenicity: Non-pathogenic.

24. *Plectridium sniezskoi* (Sniezsko) P. 1940.

Synonym: Clostridium thermocellulolyticum (Siezsko) Ostertag.

Habitat: Soil.

Morphology: Rods measuring 0.6 to 0.7 μ $\times$ 3 to 5 μ; motile; spherical, terminal spore, 1.2 to 1.8 μ; Gram-positive (easily decolorized).

Physiology: Strict anaerobe. Thermophilic: Opt. T. $=$ 60-62°C.

Cultural characters: No growth on usual media, even in the presence of carbohydrates.

Milk: No growth.

Cellulose media: Cellulose attacked to the extent of 70 to 80% with production of acetic acid and ethanol; glucose also fermented.

Pathogenicity: Non-pathogenic.

25. *Plectridium omelianskii* (Henneberg) Spray 1948.

Synonym: Bacillus omelianskii Henneberg 1922, emend. Clausen 1931.

Habitat: Soil, cheese, intestinal tract of man, horse and cattle.

Morphology: Straight or slightly-curved rods, 0.5 to 0.7 μ $\times$ 5 to 15 μ; occurring singly, in pairs or in masses of parallel rods; motile before spore formation; spherical, terminal spore, 1.0 to 1.5 μ, swelling the rod; Gram-positive, becoming Gram-negative at sporulation; young cells are stained wine-red by iodine.

Physiology: Strict anaerobe, tolerating an oxygen pressure of 25-30 mm. Hg. Opt. T. $=$ 37-42°C. Resists 40 minutes at 100°C. Opt. pH $=$ 7.0-7.4.

Asparagin agar slant (in vacuo): Delicate, barely visible, transparent colonies.

Asparagin deep agar: Delicate, fluffy, greyish-white colonies with fine projections.

Cellulose liver-broth: Gaseous growth, not turbid.

Asparagin-gelatin: Liquefaction in 6 to 10 days.

Milk: Soft curd in 24 hours; yellowish-red to orange sediment.

Carbohydrates: Not fermented. Cellulose weakly attacked.

Biochemistry: Nitrites not formed from nitrates; indole not formed; H_2S (traces) produced. Fermentation of cellulose produces CH_2 and H_2, prevents pigment formation. Methane not produced. This latter product was formed by a contaminant in Clausen's cultures; it is described in this Manual under the name of *Terminosporus omelianskii.*

Pathogenicity: Non-pathogenic.

26. *Plectridium incertum* (McIntosh) P. 1938.

Synonym: Bacillus III C McIntosh 1917.

Habitat: Infected war wounds, gangrene of the mandibule, brain abscess. Quite uncommon.

Morphology: Slender rods, 0.4 to 0.5 μ $\times$ 2 to 3 μ; weakly motile; oval, terminal spore, 1.0 μ $\times$ 1.25 μ; Gram-positive.

Physiology: Strict anaerobe. Opt. T. $=37°$C. Resists 5 minutes at 100°C. Survives several years. Neutral red reduced.

Cultural characters: No gas produced.

Deep agar: Lenticular colonies.

Glucose broth: Marked turbidity; indole not formed.

Gelatin: Liquefaction.

Milk: Casein precipitated without digestion.

Coagulated proteins: Not attacked.

Carbohydrates: Not fermented.

Biochemistry: Nitrites formed from nitrates; produces NH_3, volatile amines, aldehydes, ketones, acetylmethylcarbinol, formic, butyric and lactic acids.

Pathogenicity, experimental: Injection of 1 ml. into the guinea pig produces an abscess.

Serology: Specific agglutination at 1-2,000.

27. *Plectridium sphenoides* (Douglas, Fleming and Colebrook) P. 1938.

Synonym: Bacillus sphenoides D., F. and C. 1920; *Clostridium sphernoides* (D., F. and C.) Bergey.

Habitat: Infected wounds.

Morphology: Rods with pointed ends; occurring in pairs; motile; spherical, terminal spore; Gram-positive.

Physiology: Strict anaerobe. Opt. T. $=30$-$35°$C.

Cultural characters: No gas produced.

Deep agar: Spherical or irregular colonies.

Glucose broth: Turbid.

Gelatin: No liquefaction; fluffy colonies with black halo.

Milk: Coagulated.

Carbohydrates: Glucose, lactose, mannitol, sucrose, dextrin, starch and salicin are fermented.

Pathogenicity: Unknown.

28. *Plectridium nonum* (von Hibler) P. 1938.

Synonym: Bacillus IX von Hibler 1908.

Habitat: Unknown.

Morphology: Rods with granular cytoplasm; motile by means of peritrichous flagella; spherical, terminal spore; Gram-positive.

Physiology: Very strict anaerobe. Opt. T. $= 37°$C. Resists 10 minutes at 80°C. Survives several years. Isolated only with the help of yeast autolyzate. Neutral red and safranin reduced.

Cultural characters: No gas produced; tart odor.

Deep agar: Fluffy, arborescent, sometimes lenticular, colonies.

Glucose broth: Turbid; acidified.

Gelatin: No liquefaction.

Milk: Casein precipitated.

Coagulated proteins: Not attacked.

Carbohydrates: Acid, but no gas, from glucose, fructose, maltose, galactose, lactose, sucrose, starch and glycerol.

Biochemistry: Nitrites not formed from nitrates; produces NH_3, volatile amines, aldehydes, ketones, phenol, H_2S, ethanol, acetic, valerianic and traces of butyric and lactic acids.

Pathogenicity: Non-pathogenic. Some strains may kill the guinea pig.

29. *Plectridium thermoaceticum.*

(Fontaine, Peterson, McCoy, Johnson and Ritter) P. 1948.

Synonym: Clostridium thermoaceticum F., P., M., J. and R. 1942.

Habitat: Horse dung, where it participates in cellulolysis.

Morphology: Rods measuring 0.4 μ $\times$ 2.8 μ; motile by means of peritrichous flagella; spherical, terminal spore; Gram-positive.

Physiology: Strict anaerobe. Thermophilic: Opt. T. $= 55$-$60°$C (45-64). Resists 8 hours at 100°C and 15 minutes at 120°C.

Cultural characters: No gas, or fetid odor produced.

Agar surface (*in vacuo*): Circular, opaque, smooth colonies.

Glucose-tryptone medium (*buffered and added with liver extract*): Abundant growth.

Gelatin: Not attacked.

Milk: Unchanged.

Coagulated proteins: Not attacked.

Carbohydrates: Acid, but no gas, from glucose, fructose, galactose, mannose, d-xylose, d-arabinose, aesculin, d-lactic acid and gluconic acid.

Biochemistry: Nitrites formed from nitrates; fermentation of glucose produces acetic acid and traces of ethanol.

Pathogenicity: Non-pathogenic.

APPENDIX

In spite of the uncertainties concerning some of the characters of the 2 following species, they may be classed provisionally with the *Plectridia*.

Plectridium aceticum Wieringa nov. comb.

Synonym: Clostridium aceticum Wieringa 1936.
Habitat: Mud. Uncommon.
Morphology: Rods; motile; terminal spore.
Physiology: Strict anaerobe. Opt. pH $= 8\text{-}9$ $(7.5\text{-}10.5)$.

Cultural characters: Growth only on mineral media containing: sodium bicarbonate, sodium sulfate, potassium monophosphate, ammonium chloride, magnesium chloride, magnesium sulfate and iron sulfate, in an atmosphere containing CO_2 and H_2, and in the presence of a growth factor isolated from mud.

Biochemistry: Synthetizes acetic acid from CO_2 and H_2 according to the equation:

$$4H_2 + 2CO_2 + CH_3COOH + 2H_2O.$$

In an organic medium containing malt extract, bicarbonate and mud extract, the equation becomes:

$$3NaHCO_3 + 4H_2 + CH_3COONa + Na_2CO_3 + 4H_2O.$$

The malt extract may be replaced by yeast extract or casein hydrolyzate; the necessary growth factors then are: biotin, pyridoxamin and pantothenic acid.

Pathogenicity: Non-pathogenic.

Systematics: Its position will be determined only when the reaction to the Gram stain is known.

Plectridium glycolicum (Gaston and Stadtman) nov. comb.

Synonym: Clostridium glycolicum Gaston and Stadtman 1963.
Habitat: Stagnant pond mud.

Morphology: Rods measuring $0.5\ \mu \times 5\ \mu$; occurring singly or in short chains; motile by means of peritrichous flagella; oval, terminal spore; Gram-positive.

Physiology: Strict anaerobe. Opt. T. $= 22\text{-}37°C$. Reducing powers.

Cultural characters: Gas, but no fetid odor produced.

Agar slant (in vacuo): Flat, circular colonies with smooth border and old-ivory tint.

Blood-deep agar: Gas produced.

Gelatin: No liquefaction.

Thioglycollate broth: Turbid.

Milk: Slightly acidified, but not coagulated.

Coagulated proteins: Not attacked.

Coagulated egg-white: Slightly attacked.

Carbohydrates: Acid and gas from glucose, fructose, sorbitol, dulcitol and cellulose; xylose and maltose weakly fermented.

Biochemistry: Nitrites not formed from nitrates; produces H_2S, ethanol, 7% acetic and 93% propionic acids. Utilizes ethyleneglycol as source of carbon and energy. Requires 15 amino acids, biotin and pantothenate for optimum growth on ethlyeneglycol.

GENUS II: *ACUFORMIS* Prévot 1940.

Definition.—Non-motile *Plectridiaceae.*

This genus comprises actually 14 species, of which here is the key to their determination:

A) Species producing gas:

1. Lenticular colonies; gas produced; gelatin liquefied; milk coagulated; indole not formed; pathogenic.
   1. *Acuformis spermoides,* page 335

2. Spores of large size; dendritic colonies; gas produced; gelatin not liquefied; milk unchanged; but digested; saccharolytic; indole not formed; non-pathogenic.
   2. *Acuformis macrosporus,* page 335

3. Microaerophilic; isolated in normal dog liver; gas produced; proteolytic and saccharolytic; non-pathogenic.
   3. *Acuformis caninus,* page 336

4. Fluffy colonies; gas produced; gelatin liquefied; coagulated egg-white digested; milk digested; glucose fermented; non-pathogenic.
   4. *Acuformis filamentosus,* page 336

5. Lenticular colonies; gas produced; gelatin liquefied; milk precipitated; indole formed; saccharolytic; non-pathogenic.
   5. *Acuformis alcaligenes,* page 337

6. Irregular colonies; saccharolytic; acidophilic; thermophilic; nitrates reduced; non-pathogenic.
   6. *Acuformis thermoacidophilus,* page 337

7. Thermophilic; oval spores; circular colonies; gelatin not liquefied; meat digested; gas produced; saccharolytic; nitrates not reduced; indole not formed; H_2S produced; non-pathogenic.
   7. *Acuformis thermoputrificus,* page 337

8. Circular colonies; small amounts of gas; gelatin not liquefied; milk acidified; non-pathogenic.
   8. *Acuformis dubitatus,* page 338

9. Spherical spores; punctiform, filamentous colonies; gelatin liquefied; putrid odor; milk digested; H₂S formed; glucose fermented.
   9. *Acuformis putrefaciens,* page 338

10. Lenticular colonies; oval spores; gelatin not liquefied; milk coagulated; non-proteolytic; saccharolytic; non-pathogenic.
    10. *Acuformis perennis,* page 338

11. Large angular colonies, very small, spherical spores; gelatin liquefied; milk coagulated; saccharolytic; non-pathogenic.
    11. *Acuformis angulosus,* page 339

B) Species producing no gas:

12. Gelatin not liquefied; milk unchanged; saccharolytic; non-pathogenic.
    12. *Acuformis innutritus,* page 339

13. Oval spores; ramified colonies; gelatin liquefied; casein attacked; coagulated egg-white digested; putrid odor; non-saccharolytic; non-pathogenic.
    13. *Acuformis immobilis,* page 340

14. Gelatin not liquefied; milk slowly coagulated; saccharolytic; pathogenic for man.
    14. *Acuformis innocuus,* page 340

1. *Acuformis spermoides* (Ninni) P. 1940.

Synonym: Bacillus spermoides Ninni 1920.

Habitat: Soil from high mountains.

Morphology: Slender, slightly-curved rods, 4 to 10 μ; non-motile; oval, elongated, terminal spore; Gram-positive.

Physiology: Strict anaerobe. Opt. T. = 37°C.

Cultural characters: Gas produced.

Deep agar: Lenticular colonies.

Glucose broth: Uniform turbidity; gas; sediment; indole not formed.

Gelatin: Liquefaction; gas; punctiform colonies.

Liver broth: Markedly acidified; gas.

Milk: Coagulated in 24 hours; gas.

Pathogenicity, experimental: Guinea pig dies from progressive wasting in 12 days after the injection of 0.2 ml.

Systematics: Bergey has wrongly identified this species with *Plectridium tertium* (Henry); the latter is motile, while *A. spermoides* is non-motile.

2. *Acuformis macrosporus* (Adamson and Cutler) P. 1940.

Habitat: Septic and gangrenous wounds. Quite uncommon.

Morphology: Rods measuring 1 to 2 μ × 6 to 7 μ; occurring singly, in pairs or in short chains of 4-6 elements; non-motile; terminal spore of large size; Gram-positive.

Physiology: Strict anaerobe. Opt. T. $= 37°$C.
Cultural characters: Small amounts of gas produced.
Deep agar: Dendritic colonies; small amounts of gas.
Glucose broth: Turbid; gas; indole not formed.
Gelatin: No liquefaction.
Milk: Acidified and slightly peptonized.
Carbohydrates: Glucose, maltose and lactose are fermented.
Pathogenicity: Non-pathogenic.

3. *Acuformis caninus* (Wolback and Saiki) P. 1940.

Habitat: Liver of normal dog. Quite frequent.

Morphology: Rods measuring 1 μ $\times$ 8 to 9 μ; occurring singly, in pairs or in short chains; filamentous and club-shaped involution forms; chromaffinic granules; non-motile; terminal spore, 1.0 μ 1.5 μ; Gram-positive.

Physiology: Microaerophilic. Opt. T. $= 37°$C.

Cultural characters: Gas produced. Growth only in media containing fresh organs of dog or guinea pig, especially aqueous extract of dog liver.

Dog liver-media: Turbid; abundant gas (CO_2); medium becomes red; H_2S formed.

Coagulated proteins: Attacked.

Carbohydrates: Fermented.

Pathogenicity: Non-pathogenic. Probable role in the aseptic autolysis of liver.

4. *Acuformis filamentosus* (Distaso) P. 1940.

Synonym: Bacillus putrificus filamentosus Distaso 1911; *Clostridium filamentosum* (D.) Bergey.

Habitat: Slender rods with rounded ends, 0.4 μ $\times$ 2.8 μ; occurring singly, in short chains or in filaments; non-motile;[1] terminal spore; Gram-positive.

Physiology: Strict anaerobe. Opt. T. $= 37°$C. Resists 1 minute at 100°C. Neutral red and safranin reduced.

Cultural characters: Small amounts of gas and fetid odor produced.

Deep agar: Cotton-wool tufts; small amounts of gas.

Glucose broth: Odor of scatole; trace of indole formed.

Gelatin: Liquefaction.

Milk: Casein precipitated, then digested.

Coagulated egg-white: Becomes transparent, then digested.

Carbohydrates: Maltose fermented; glucose weakly fermented.

Biochemistry: Produces NH_3, H_2S, alcohols, aldehydes, acetic, butyric and lactic acids.

Pathogenicity: Non-pathogenic.

---

[1] Cited by Bergey as motile.

5. *Acuformis alcaligenes* (Debono) P. 1940.

Synonym: Bacillus anaerobicus alcaligenes Debono 1912; *Clostridium alcaligenes* (D.) Bergey.

Habitat: Human feces. Uncommon.

Morphology: Slender rods with rounded ends; occurring singly or in short chains; non-motile; terminal spore; Gram-positive.

Cultural characters: Small amounts of gas formed.

Deep agar: Granular, lenticular colonies, 2 to 3 mm. in diameter; small amounts of gas.

Glucose broth: Uniform turbidity; disagreeable odor; indole formed.

Gelatin: Liquefaction.[2]

Milk: Precipitated and alcalinized.

Carbohydrates: Glucose and lactose are fermented.

Pathogenicity: Non-pathogenic.

6. *Acuformis thermoacidophilus* (Damon and Feirer) P. 1940.

Synonym: Clostridium thermoacidophilum Damon and Feirer 1925.

Habitat: Horse dung. Uncommon.

Morphology: Rods measuring 1.2 μ $\times$ 10 μ; non-motile; oval, terminal spore; Gram-positive.

Physiology: Strict anaerobe. Thermophilic: Opt. T. = 37-55°C.

Cultural characters: Gas produced. Acidophilic.

Deep agar: Irregular colonies.

Carbohydrates: Abundant gas and acid from: sucrose, mannitol, inulin, glycerol and starch.

Biochemistry: Nitrites formed from nitrates.

Pathogenicity: Non-pathogenic.

7. *Acuformis thermoputrificus* (Damon and Feirer) P. 1940.

Synonym: Clostridium thermoputrificum Damon and Feirer 1925.

Habitat: Horse dung.

Morphology: Rods with rounded ends and homogeneous cytoplasm, 0.5 μ $\times$ 2 to 5 μ; non-motile; oval, terminal spore; Gram-positive.

Physiology: Strict anaerobe. Thermophilic: Opt. T. = 37-55°C.

Cultural characters: Gas produced.

Deep agar: Circular colonies.

Broth: Turbid; abundant gas; indole and H_2S formed.

Gelatin: No liquefaction.

Meat: Digested.

Carbohydrates: Acid and gas from glucose, lactose, starch, maltose, glycerol, sucrose, mannitol and inulin.

---

[2] No liquefaction, according to Bergey.

Biochemistry: Nitrites not formed from nitrates.
Pathogenicity: Non-pathogenic.

8. *Acuformis dubitatus* (Rodella) P. 1940.

Habitat: Milk, soils of France and Africa. Quite frequent.

Morphology: Slender rods, 0.5 $\mu \times$ 4 μ; may form very long filaments; non-motile; small, spherical terminal spore; Gram-positive.

Physiology: Strict anaerobe. Opt. T. $= 37°$C. Resists 1 to 10 minutes at 100°C. Survives several years. Neutral red and safranin reduced.

Cultural characters: Gas produced.

Deep agar: Circular, fluffy colonies, seldom lenticular.

Glucose broth: Turbid; gas; slightly fetid odor.

Gelatin: Fluffy colonies; no liquefaction.

Milk: Acidified, not coagulated, but peptonized.

Coagulated proteins: Not attacked.

Carbohydrates: Glucose, maltose, fructose and galactose more or less fermented; glycerol and starch very weakly fermented.

Biochemistry: Nitrites not formed from nitrates; produces NH_3, H_2S, ethanol (traces), acetic and butyric acids, traces of lactic acid.

Pathogenicity: Non-pathogenic.

Systematics: This species is certainly not a variety of *Cl. lactopropyl-butylicum* Tissier and Gashing, as has been supposed, since its spore is terminal; moreover, its cultural characters are also different.

9. *Acuformis putrefaciens* (McBryde) P. 1940.

Synonym: Bacillus putrefaciens McBryde 1911; *Clostridium putrefaciens* (McBryde) Sturges and Drakes 1927.

Habitat: Slaughtered pork meat.

Morphology: Rods with rounded ends, 0.5 to 0.7 $\mu \times$ 3 to 15 μ; occurring singly, in short chains or as long filaments; non-motile; spherical, terminal spore; Gram-positive.

Physiology: Strict anaerobe. Opt. T. $= 18$-25°C. No growth at 37°C.

Cultural characters: Gas produced.

Deep agar: Small, filamentous colonies.

Glucose vroth: Moderate turbidity; sediment; putrid odor.

Gelatin: Liquefaction in 3 to 5 days.

Milk: Coagulated, then digested; indole not formed; small amounts of H_2S produced.

Carbohydrates: Acid and gas from glucose.

Biochemistry: Nitrites not formed from nitrates.

Pathogenicity: Non-pathogenic.

10. *Acuformis perennis* Prévot 1940.

Habitat: Intestinal tract of man and pig.

Morphology: Straight rods with rounded ends, 0.3 to 0.4 μ × 1.6 to 3.0 μ; occurring singly, in pairs or in short chains; non-motile; oval, terminal spore; sporangia measure 0.5 μ × 3 to 5 μ; Gram-positive.

Physiology: Strict anaerobe. Opt. T. = 37°C. (26-39). Resists 2 minutes at 100°C. Opt. pH = 7.0. Survives more than 20 years. Neutral red definitively reduced, safranin temporarily reduced.

Cultural characters: Gas produced.

Deep agar: Lenticular colonies; agar broken up by gas.

Glucose VF broth: Rapid and abundant turbidity and gas; acidified.

Peptone water: Meager growth; no gas.

Gelatin: No liquefaction.

Milk: Acidified, coagulated; retraction of the clot.

Coagulated proteins: Not attacked.

Carbohydrates: Acid and gas from glucose, fructose, maltose, galactose, sucrose, arabinose and lactose.

Biochemistry: Nitrites not formed from nitrates; produces NH_3, volatile amines, acetylmethylcarbinol, propionic and valerianic acids, traces of lactic acid.

Pathogenicity, natural: Acute appendicitis.

Pathogenicity, experimental: Non-pathogenic for mouse and guinea pig.

11. *Acuformis angulosus* (Distaso) P. 1957.

Synonym: Bacillus angulosus Distaso 1912; *Clostridium angulosum* (Distaso) Hauduroy.

Habitat: Intestinal tract of man.

Morphology: Short, thick rods with rounded ends; occurring singly or in pairs; sometimes long forms forming acute angles; encapsulated; non-motile; very small, spherical terminal spore slightly swelling the rod; Gram-positive.

Cultural characters: Gas, but no fetid odor produced.

Deep agar: Opaque, yellowish, angular colonies of large size; gas.

Glucose broth: Turbid.

Glucose gelatin: Liquefaction; cloudy turbidity.

Milk: Coagulated in 14 days.

Coagulated egg-white: Not attacked.

Carbohydrates: Acid and gas from glucose, lactose and sucrose.

Biochemistry: Produces indole, and butyric acid.

12. *Acuformis innutritus* (Kleinschmidt) P. 1940.

Synonym: Bacillus innutritus Kleinschmidt 1934.

Habitat: Feces of nurslings, appendix. Uncommon.

Morphology: Slender, short rods; occurring in short chains or as filaments; non-motile; terminal spore; Gram-positive.

Physiology: Strict anaerobe. Opt. T. = 37°C. Resists 2 minutes at

100°C. Killed after 15 minutes at 100°C.

Cultural characters: No gas formed.

Deep agar: Circular colonies.

Broth: Abundant turbidity; no gas.

Gelatin: No liquefaction.

Milk: Coagulated.

Brain-medium: Not blackened.

Carbohydrates: Glucose, galactose, fructose, sucrose, lactose, maltose and salicin are fermented.

Pathogenicity: Non-pathogenic. No toxin, or hemolysin.

Serology: The 2 strains of Kleinschmidt were agglutinated by the *anti-putrificus* serum of Hall and Ridgway and *vice versa,* so that these authors concluded that these two species were identical. But then *A. innutritus* is non-motile, while *Pl. paraputrificum* is motile; at the most, one can think of a common agglutinogen.

13. *Acuformis immobilis* (Distaso) P. 1940.

Synonym: Bacillus putrificus immobilis Distaso 1909.

Habitat: Soil. Uncommon.

Morphology: Slender rods with rounded ends; occurring in pairs or in short chains; non-motile; oval, terminal spore; Gram-positive.

Physiology: Strict anaerobe. Opt. T. = 37°C.

Cultural characters: Gas not produced.

Deep agar: Ramified colonies; no gas.

Glucose broth: Turbid; no gas, but putrid odor.

Gelatin: Liquefaction in 24 hours.

Milk: Precipitated, then digested.

Coagulated egg-white: Digested; putrid odor.

Carbohydrates: Not fermented.

Pathogenicity: Non-pathogenic.

14. *Acuformis innocuus* (Smith and King) nov. comb.

Synonym: Clostridium innocuum Smith and King 1962.

Habitat: Very probably natural cavities of man, in particular digestive tract.

Morphology: Rods measuring 0.4 to 1.0 μ × 2 to 4 μ; non-motile; oval, terminal spore swelling the rod; Gram-positive.

Physiology: Strict anaerobe. Opt. T. = 35°C. Thermoresistance unknown.

Cultural characters: Very small amounts of gas formed, but not fetid.

Agar Slant (in vacuo): White, glistening, elevated colonies, 1.5 to 2.5 mm. in diameter, with neat border. No hemolysis on blood agar.

Gelatin: No liquefaction.

Milk: Slowly coagulated by some strains.

Coagulated proteins: Not attacked.

Cabohydrates: Acid but no gas from glucose, sucrose, salicin and mannitol; maltose weakly and irregularly fermented.

Biochemistry: Nitrites not formed from nitrates. Indole not formed.

Pathogenicity, natural: Purulent pleurisy, infarcts of the brain, appendicular abscess, sub-diaphragmatic abscess, abdominal exsudate in intestinal occlusion, infected wound, abscess of abdominal wall, compound fracture.

Pathogenicity, experimental: Non-pathogenic. No toxin, or hemolysin.

Chapter 8

ORDER III: SPOROVIBRIONALES Prévot 1940.

After more than 70 years' research on the sulfate-reducing *Vibrios,* it is evident that their classification is far from satisfactory for the majority of bacteriologists. If it is still doubtful whether the species *desulfuricans* and its varieties are really sporeformers, the main reason for including them in the *Desulfovibrio* of this edition, it is nonetheless certain that the species *ferroxydans* and *orientis* are sporeformers: we have had the occasion to photograph their spore and determine their thermoresistance, which is of the order of 5 to 10 minutes at 70°C for the species *orientis,* and 20 minutes at 75°C for the species *ferroxydans* which, moreover, does not reduce the sulfates but reduces the nitrates and oxidizes $Fe++$ to $Fe+++$ It is therefore absolutely certain that *Sporovibrio* Starkey exist, and we place them here while awaiting more complete information permitting to determine their definitive systematic position.

FAMILY I: *SPOROVIBRIONACEAE* P. 1940.

Definition.—Sporeforming, Gram-negative vibrios. This family actually comprises one single genus.

GENUS I: *SPOROVIBRIO* Starkey 1938.

Definition.—Typical vibrios (crescent-shaped or comma-shaped bacteria), motile, sporeforming, Gram-negative. The spore is spherical, centrally-located, highly refringent and swells the bacterial body. The 2 species known presently are strict anaerobes. Here is the key to their determination:

A) Sulfate-reducers; chemo-autotrophic:
  1. Central or eccentric spore; motile by means of 1-2 polar or para-polar flagella; resists 5 minutes at 70°C; reduces sulfates to sulfides in the presence of lactate, thiolactate or pyruvate.
     1. *Sporovibrio orientis* (Adams and Postgate) nov. comb., page 343

B) Sulfates not reduced; chemo-autotrophic:

2. Vibrios of large size; very small and seldom seen spore; mono-trichous; weak thermoresistance; reduces nitrates to nitrites and oxydizes Fe to Fe; utilizes lactate, pyruvate and glucose.

2. *Sporovibrio ferroxydans*, page 343

1. *Sporovibrio orientis* (Adams and Postgate) nov. comb.

Synonym: Desulfovibrio orientis Adams and Postgate 1959.

Morphology: Slightly-curved rods, 1.5 μ $\times$ 4.8 μ; occurring in pairs or in short chains; motile by means of 1-2 polar or parapolar flagella; central or eccentric spore, seldom seen; Gram-negative.

Physiology: Strict anaerobe. Opt. T. $= 30$-$37°C$. Resists, 5 minutes at $80°C$. Contains a cytochrome pigment, but no desulfoviridin. No hydrogenase present.

Cultural characters: Slow growth, requiring special media containing lactate $+$ sulfate $+$ thiolacetate; may utilizie pyruvate instead of lactate, but not butyrate, propionate nor acetate.

Lactate-sulfate-iron-deep agar: Black colonies.

Gelatin: No liquefaction.

Biochemistry: Nitrites not formed from nitrates; sulfates reduced to sulfides (dissimilation reaction) according to the reaction:

$$2CH_3CHOHCOOH + Na_2SO_4 = Na_2S + CH_3COOH + CO_2 + H_2O$$

2. *Sporovibrio ferroxydans* Pochon and Barjac 1954.

Habitat: Soil.

Morphology: Vibrios measuring 1 μ $\times$ 4 to 6 μ; motile by means of one polar flagellum; small spore, seldom seen; Gram-negative.

Physiology: Strict anaerobe. Resists 20 minutes at $75°C$. No growth on usual media.

Cultural characters: Gas, but no fetid odor produced.

Nitrate-iron-saline agar: Circular, irregular, rust-colored colonies.

Biochemistry: Nitrites formed from nitrates; sulfites and sulfites not reduced to sulfides; oxydizes ferrous salts to ferric hydroxyde utilizes lactates, pyruvates and glucose. Grows on saline media containing ammonia or nitrates as source of N_2.

Chapter 9

CLASS OF ACTINOMYCETALES
Buchanan emend.

Definition.—Short, elongated or filamentous rods; true pseudo-branching; swollen, club-shaped forms; free or sessile spheroids; no true endospores, but possibility of differentiating the extremities as conidia; pigmented or nonpigmented. Definite affinity with the lower fungi.

One order which comprises anaerobic species.

ORDER I: *ACTINOBACTERIAES* Prévot.

Actinomycetales which are generally non-acid-fast. Usually non-motile, Gram-positive. One single family.

FAMILY: *ACTINOMYCETACEAE* Buchanan emend.

Definition.—Gram-positive Actinobacteriales.

The experimental study of several hundred strains of Actinomycetaceae and of the infections to which they give rise has obliged us to review our conception of 1940 on the structure of this family. We now recognize only 2 genera: *Corynebacterium* and *Actinobacterium,* closely related furthermore, quite difficult to distinguish and differing from each other only by biometric characters; each has a sub-genus: *Propionibacterium,* sub-genus of *Corynebacterium; Bifidobacterium,* sub-genus of *Actinobacterium.*

Nonetheless, a very important character has been revealed during the course of recent research work concerning the pathogenicity of these genera, and it helps to distinguish between them: the anaerobic coryne-bacterioses differ neatly by their constitution, pathological anatomy, their evolution, their prognosis and treatment from the anaerobic actino-bacterioses. As far as the sub-genera are concerned, the *Propionibacterium* are completely devoid of any pathogenicity, while *Bidifobacterium* has a single pathogenic species, causing a benign infection which has nothing in common with the corynebacterioses and the actinobacterioses. Thus, the new conception regarding these bacteria, as we now propose it, is in the nature of facilitating greatly their determination.

Here are the definitions and the keys to the determination of these genera and sub-genera:

However, we will place provisionnally after these 2 genera a taxonomic unit which could be assimilated to a genus or to a sub-genus: *Micromonospora*.

1. Non-sporeforming rods, non-motile, Gram-positive, showing swellings, metachromatic granules and branching; less than 3.5 μ in length; salmon-pink colonies; catalase-positive; produce acetic acid; pathogenic.

   1. *Corynebacterium*, page 345

1 bis. Non-sporeforming rods, non-motile, Gram-positive, showing swellings; occur as chains of cocci; microaerophilic; less than 3.5 μ in length; produce propionic acid; non-pathogenic.

   1 bis. *Propionibacterium*, page 355

2. Non-sporeforming rods, non-motile, Gram-positive, filamentous; showing in cultures branching and club-shaped swellings and in pathological specimens radiate masses of ramified and club-shaped forms; more than 3.5 μ in length; white colonies; catalase-negative; produce acetic acid; pathogenic.

   2. *Actinobacterium*, page 357

2 bis. Non-sporeforming rods, non-motile, Gram-positive, with bifid or doubly bifid extremities; club-shaped swellings; produce acetic and lactic acids; generally non-pathogenic.

   2. bis. *Sub-genus Bifidobacterium*, page 360

3. In waiting position: Filamentous rods with ramifications perpendicular to the axis of the main filament, and bearing conidia or pre-conidia on conidiophores.

   3. *Micromonospora*, page 364

GENUS I: *CORYNEBACTERIUM* Lehmann and Neumann 1896.

Definition.—Non-sporeforming rods, Gram-positive, showing branching, swellings and metachromatic granules. This genus comprises actually 12 strictly anaerobic or microaerophilic species less than 3.5 μ in length, salmon-pink colored, catalase-positive and forming propionic acid as the main fermentation product. Most species are pathogenic and produce anaerobic corynebacterioses, involving mainly the reticulo-endothelial system.

Here is the key to the determination of the anaerobic *Corynebacteria:*

A) Species producing no gas:

1. Type species. Average size; strict anaerobic, becoming microaerophilic; catalase-positive; lenticular colonies becoming salmon-pink; gelatin not lequefied; milk coagulated; highly pathogenic.

   1. *Corynebacterium anaerobium*, page 346

2. Small size: circular salmon-pink colonies; gelatin not liquefied; milk unchanged; saccharolytic; pathogenic.
   2. *Corynebacterium granulosum,* page 347

3. Small size; pleomorphic; circular, salmon-pink colonies; gelatin liquefied; milk coagulated; weakly saccharolytic.
   3. *Corynebacterium liquefaciens,* page 348

4. Serophilic; spontaneously microaerophilic; gelatin not liquefied; milk unchanged; non-proteolytic; pathogenic.
   4. *Corynebacterium pyogenes,* page 349

5. Small size; acidophilic; polyhedral colonies; saccharolytic; gelatin not liquefied; milk unchanged; non-pathogenic.
   5. *Corynebacterium lymphophilum,* page 350

6. Small size; spontaneously microaerophilic; gelatin not liquefied; milk unchanged; saccharolytic; non-pathogenic.
   6. *Corynebacterium hepatodystrophicans,* page 350

7. Small size; lenticular colonies; non-proteolytic; non-saccharolytic; non-pathogenic.
   7. *Corynebacterium adamsoni,* page 351

B) Species producing gas:

8. Small size; microaerophilic; gelatin not liquefied; milk slowly coagulated; saccharolytic; highly pathogenic.
   8. *Corynebacterium parvum,* page 351

9. Large size; gelatin liquefied; milk coagulated and partly digested; H$_2$S formed; saccharolytic; pathogenic.
   9. *Corynebacterium avidum,* page 352

10. Average size; strict anaerobe; gelatin not liquefied; milk unchanged; saccharolytic; indole formed; pathogenic.
    10. *Corynebacterium diphtheroides,* page 353

11. Small size; microaerophilic; acidophilic; non-pathogenic.
    11. *Corynebacterium renale cuniculi,* page 354

12. Microaerophilic; gelatin slowly or not liquefied; milk slowly or not coagulated; pathogenic (acné).
    12. *Corynebacterium acnes,* page 354

1. *Corynebacterium anaerobium* (Massini) P. 1938.

Synonym: Bacillus anaerobius diphteroides Massini 1913.

Habitat: Natural cavities of man and, probably, of animals. Very frequent.

Morphology: Rods similar to C. *diphteriae,* 0.4 μ × 1.5 to 3.0 μ; non-motile; no endospores; metachromatic granules; Gram-positive.

Physiology: Strict anaerobe; catalase-negative on isolation; most strains remain strict anaerobes, some become catalase-positive and microaerophilic. Opt. T. $= 37°C$. Survives 2 to 3 months. Neutral red and phenosafranin not reduced.

Cultural characters: No gas, or fetid odor produced.

Deep agar: Punctiform colonies, becoming lenticular (simple or complex) or irregular and salmon-pink.

Glucose VF broth: Abundant turbidity, sometimes clotty; sediment. No gas, or odor; some strains grow as granular flakes.

Peptone water: Slight turbidity.

Gelatin: No liquefaction; sometimes very slowly liquefied.

Milk: Slowly coagulated; fermented cheese odor.

Coagulated proteins: Not attacked.

Carbohydrates: Glucose, lacutose, maltose, galactose, lactose sucrose, starch and glycerol are fermented.

Biochemistry: Nitrites formed from nitrates by most strains; produces NH_3, volatile amines, aldehydes, ketones, indole (traces or none), propionic, acetic and lactic acids.

Pathogenicity, natural: Isolated very frequently: ganagrenous pulpitis, otitis, mastoiditis, brain abscess, pulmonary abscess, purulent pleurisy, purulent arthritis, osteitis, mastitis, pseudoactinomycosis, cellulitis; positive anaerobic hemoculture in: malignant endocarditis, rhumatismal cariopathy, recurring or continuous septicemia preceding or accompanying malignant hemo pathies, such as: Hodgkin's disease, leukosis, malignant reticulosis, cryptic cancer. Also found in chick embryos, endocrine implants, lesions and lymph glands in whipple's disease.

Pathogenicity, experimental: Either rapidly fatal, acute corynebacteriosis by intramuscular injection of pathological specimens or of cultures into the guinea pig; or rapidly fatal, acute corynebacteriosis with verrucous endocarditis by intravenous injection of the bacteria into the rabbit; finally, slow autosterilization of the latter, with hypergic phenomena and occurrence of an acute, diffuse, plasmodial reticulosis, followed by death in 8 to 10 weeks.

Serology: Common antigen shared with *C. diphteroides, C. parvum* and *C. avidum.*

2. *Corynebacterium granulosum* (Jungano) P. 1938.

Synonym: Bacille granuleux Jungano 1909.

Habitat: Intestinal tract of the rat; natural cavities of man. Frequent.

Morphology: Rods similar to *C. diphteriae;* average size; pointed ends; non-motile; no endospores; metachromatic granules; Gram-positive.

Physiology: Strict anaerobe. Opt. T. $= 37°C$. Resists a few minutes at $60°C$. Survives 15 days. Generally catalase-negative. Neutral red not reduced.

Cultural characters: No gas, or fetid odor produced.

Deep agar: Circular colonies; no gas; sometimes lenticular colonies, becoming salmon-pink.

Glucose broth: Turbid; no gas.

Gelatin: No liquefaction.

Milk: Unchanged.

Coagulated egg-white: Not attacked.

Carbohydrates: Glucose and galactose are fermented; fructose, maltose, sucrose, glycerol and starch fermented in addition by a few strains.

Biochemitsry: Nitrites generally not formed from nitrates; produces NH_3, volatile amines, ketones, indole, scatole (traces), acetic, propionmic and lactic acids.

Pathogenicity, natural: Isolated from pyorrheic pulpitis, pseudo-actinomycosis, acne and furunculosis, brain abscess, endocarditis, arthritis, meningitis, septicemia occurring in malignant hemopathies.

Pathogenicity, experimental: Non-pathogenic or feebly pathogenic for laboratory animals.

3. *Corynebacterium liquefactiens* (Jungano) P. 1938.

Synonym: Bacillusparvus liquefaciens Jungano 1908.

Habitat: Natural cavities of man, pond mud. Frequent.

Morphology: Small, pleomorphic rods, 0.4 μ $\times$ 1.5 to 2.5 μ, with central or terminal swelling; bifid extremities, seldom branched; non-motile; no endospores; Gram-positive (irregular staining, granular forms resembling streptococci).

Physiology: Strict anaerobe. Resists 3 minutes at 60°C. Catalase-negative; may become positive and microaerophilic. Survives several months. Neutral red and phenosafranin not reduced.

Cultural characters: No gas, or fetid odor produced; sometimes slightly disagreeable odor.

Deep agar: Lenticular colonies (small, average, and large), sometimes irregular; white at first, become salmon-pink with ageing.

Glucose VF broth: Uniform turbidity; acidified; indole formed.

Peptone water: Slight turbidity; indole formed.

Gelatin: Liquefied in 1 to 2 days, sometimes more slowly.

Milk: Coagulated and sometimes partly digested.

Coagulated proteins: Generally not attacked; some strains attack coagulated serum and fibrin (partly digested).

Carbohydrates: Glucose, fructose, maltose and lactose are fermented; some strains ferment in addition: galactose, sucrose and glycerol.

Biochemistry: Nitrites formed from nitrates by most strains; produces NH_3, H_2S (irregularly), volatile amines, aldehydes, ketones, indole, acetoin (irregularly), and propionic (always present), acetic or formic and sometimes lactic acids.

Pathogenicity, natural: Frequently isolated in: pulmonary gangrene, pyorrhea alveolaris, dental, sub-maxillary and cervival abscesses, suppurative arthritis, amlignant endocarditis, meningitis, septicemia preceding or following malignant lymphogranulomatosis, lekemia, rhumatic cardiopathies, hepatitis.

Pathogenicity, experimental: Intramuscular injection into the guinea pig produces rapidly fatal acute corynebacteriosis. Intravenous injection into the rabbit produces rapidly fatal acute corynebacteriosis with verrucous endocarditis; may occur also, auto-sterillization of the latter with hypergic phenonema and appearance of a diffuse plasmodial acute retirulosis fatal in 8 to 10 weeks.

Serology: Anti-*liquefaciens* serum agglutinates in general the homologous as well as the heterologous strains, but does not react with any other anaerobic species of *Corynebacterium.*

4. *Corynebacterium pyogenes* (Roux) P. 1938.

Synonym: Bacillus pyogenes bovis Roux 1905.

Habitat: Suppurative processes in cattle, natural cavities of man. Quite frequent.

Morphology: Short, slender rods, 0.5 μ $\times$ 1.0 to 1.5 μ; occurring singly, in masses, as V-forms, in palissades and short filaments; swellings, Y-forms; metachromatic granules; non-motile; no endospores; Grampositive.

Physiology: Microaerophilic. Opt. T. $= 37°C$. Not thermoresistant. Generally catalse-negative. Serophilic. Survives more than 1 month. Neutral red and phenosafranin not reduced.

Cultural characters: No gas, or fetid odor produced.

Deep agar: Small, punctiform colonies, seldom lenticular.

Serum-agar: Small, punctiform colonies.

Glucose broth: Turbid.

Gelatin: No liquefaction.

Milk: Unchanged.

Coagulated proteins: Not attacked.

Carbohydrates: Clucose, fructose, maltose, galactose, sucrose, starch and glycerol are fermented.

Biochemistry: Nitrites generally not formed from nitrates; produces NH_3, volatile amines, aldehydes, acetic, propionic and lactic acids, (sometimes formic acid instead of acetic).

Pathogenicity, nautral: Suppurative processes of cattle; in man; suppurative adenitis, purulent arthritis, cystitis, etc.

Pathogenicity, experimental: In the rabbit, fluctuating odorless subcutaneous abscess; in the guinea pig, the same lesions.

Systematics: This species is closely related to the pyogenic *Corynebacteria* of Lucet.

5. *Corynebacterium lymphophilum* (Torrey) Bergey *et al.*

Synonym: Bacillus lymphophilus Torrey 1916.

Habitat: Lymph glands of man. Frequent.

Morphology: Pleomorphic rods, 0.3 μ $\times$ 0.4 to 0.8 μ; occurring singly or in pairs; no granules; non-motile; no endospores; Gram-positive.

Physiology: Strict anaerobe. Opt. T. $= 37°$C (30-41). Acidophilic. No reducing activity. Catalase-positive.

Cultural characters: No gas, or fetid odor produced.

Acid glucose-deep agar: Polyhedral, pyramidal colonies, 2 mm. thick; tart odor.

Glucose broth: Slight cloudiness in the deeper layers.

Gelatin: No liquefaction.

Milk: Unchanged.

Coagulated serum: Not attacked.

Carbohydrates: Glucose, fructose, maltose and starch are actively fermented; sucrose, galactose and glycerol are feebly fermented.

Biochemistry: Nitrites formed from nitrates; produces NH_3, acetic and propionic acids.

Pathogenicity, natural: Isolated from lymph glands in malignant lymphogranulomatosis and in urinary infections.

Pathogenicity, experimental: Non-pathogenic for guinea pig and rabbit.

Serology: Specific agglutination at 1-500 to 1-1,000.

6. *Corynebacterium hepatodysytrophicans* (Kuczinski) P. 1938.

Synonym: Bacillus hepatodystrophicans Kuczinski 1929.

Habitat: Organs of monkey infected by yellow fever virus. Quite frequent.

Morphology: Thin, irregular rods, 0.3 to 0.7 μ $\times$ 2 to 3 μ; coccoid corms; club-shaped, degenerated forms; ramified Y-forms; occurring in short chains; non-motile; no endospores; Gram-positive.

Physiology: Microaerophilic. Opt. T. $= 26$-$37°$C. Killed at 55°C. Acidophilic (Opt. pH $= 6.4$).

Cultural characters: No gas produced.

Acid-glucose deep agar (pH $= 6.0$): Colonies of undetermined from.

Glucose broth: Abundant turbidity; sediment; disagreeable odor; terminal pH $= 5.2$.

Gelatin: No liquefaction.

Milk: Unchanged.

Carbohydrates: Acid but no gas from glucose, glactose and glycerol.

Pathogenicity: Non-pathogenic.

Serology: Specific agglutination at 1-100; cross-reaction with *C. renale cuniculi.* However, these two species are not identical, since the former produces gas and the latter does not. At any rate, *C. hepatodystrophicans* has nothing to do with yellow fever.

7. *Corynebacterium adamsoni* (Adamson) P. 1938.

Synonym: Bacillus D Adamson.

Habitat: Infected war wounds. Uncomon.

Morphology: Small, straight, diphteroid rods; non-motile; Gram-positive.

Cultural characters: No gas produced.

Deep agar: Lenticular colonies.

Glucose broth: Abundant turbidity; indole not formed.

Coagulated proteins: Not attacked.

Carbohydrates: Not fermented.

Pathogenicity, experimental: Non-pathogenic.

8. *Corynebacterium parvum* Mayer 1926.

Synonym: Corynebacterium parvum infectiosum Mayer 1926.

Habitat: Natural cavities of man, especially mouth and genital tract. Very frequent.

Morphology: Very small rods, 0.3 μ $\times$ 1.4 μ; poles swollen; pseudo-branching; non-motile; no endospores; Gram-positive (sometimes bipolar staining).

Physiology: Strict anaerobe. Catalase-negative on isolation; several strains eventually become catalase-positive and microaerophilic, more rarely facultatively anaerobic. Opt. T. $= 37°$C. Not thermoresistant. Survives more than 1 month. Some strains reduce neutral red, very few reduce Janus-green.

Cultural characters: Very small amounts of gas produced. No fetid odor.

Deep agar: Punctiform colonies, becoming motsly lenticular (simple or compound), some irregular; no gas.

Glucose VF broth: Uniform turbidity and sediment; gas production is seldom spontaneous, and so very slight that is appears only after tapping the tube.

Peptone water: Slight turbidity; no gas.

Gelatin: No liquefaction.

Milk: Generally slow coagulation.

Coagulated proteins: Not attacked.

Carbohydrates: Glucose, fructose, maltose, lactose, galactose, sucrose and starch generally are fermented; glycerol is fermented by a few strains.

Biochemistry: Nitrites formed from nitrates by some strains; produces NH_3, volatile amines, H_2S (more or less large amounts), indole (traces), aldehydes, ketones, propionic (main acid), acetic or formic (secondary acid) and lactic (by some strains) acids.

Pathogenicity, natural: Very frequently isolated by anaerobic hemo-culture in malignant endocarditis and hemopathies: Hodgkin's disease, splenomegaly, leucosis, myeloblastosis, reticuloses; in puerperal septicemia (especially postabortum), suppurative adenopathies, suppurative arthritis, cervival pseudo-actinomycosis, lung abscess, genital infections (leuhorrhea, adnexitis) and purulent cystitis.

Pathogenicity, experimental: Either rapidly fatal acute corynebacteriosis by intramuscular injection of pathological specimens or of pure cultures into the guinea pig; or rapidly fatal acute corynebacteriosis with verrucous endocarditis by intravenous injection of the bacteria into the rabbit; finally, slow autosterilisation of the latter with hypergic phenomena and occurrence of an acute, diffuse, plasmodial reticulosis, followed by death in 8 to 10 weeks.

9. *Corynebacterium avidum* (Eggerth) P. 1938.

Synonym: Bacteroides avidus Eggerth 1935.

Habitat: Natural cavities of man and animals, mud from drinking troughs, preserved fish (North Africa). Frequent.

Morphology: Rods with pointed, rounded, bifurcate or clubbed ends, 0.4 to 0.5 $\mu \times$ 1.5 to 3 μ; metachromatic granules; non-motile; no endospores; Gram-positive.

Physiology: Strict anaerobe. Opt. T. $= 37°C$. Not thermoresistant. Catalase-negative on isolation, becoming catalase-positive and facultatively anaerobic. Survives more than 1 year. Neutral red and phenosafranin not reduced.

Cultural characters: Gas, but no fetid odor produced.

Deep agar: Lenticular colonies, 1 to 3 mm. in diameter, whitish at first, then becoming progressively salmon-pink and ocre. No gas.

Glucose VF broth: Turbid; acidified; gas (H_2S); little or no indole.

Peptone water: Slight turbidity.

Gelatin: Slow liquefaction.

Milk: Coagulated; partly digested by some strains.

Coagulated serum: Partly digested by some strains.

Fibrin: Partly digested by some strains.

Other coagulated proteins: Slightly attacked not attacked.

Carbohydrates: Glucose, fructose, glactose, maltose, lactose, and sucrose are fermented by practically all strains; dextrin, glycerol and starch are fermented by some strains.

Biochemistry: Nitrites formed from nitrates by several strains; produces NH_3, H_2S, volatiles amines, aldehydes, ketones, indole, propionic (main acid), acetic or formic (escondary acid) and butyric (seldom) acids; lactic acid produced by a few strains.

Pathogenicity, natural: Isolated by hemoculture in recurring septicemia, malignant endocarditis and malignant hemopathies (Hodgkin's disease, lymphosarcoma of the spleen, acute leukosis, adenosplenomegaly).

Pathogenicity, experimental: Either rapidly fatal acute corynebacteriosis by injection of pathological specimens or of pure cultures into the guinea pig; or, rapidly fatal, acute corynebacteriosis with verrucous endocarditis by intravenous injection of the bacteria into the rabbit; finally, slow auto-sterilization of the latter with hypergic phenomena and appearance of an acute, diffuse, plasmodial reticulosis, followed by death in 8 to 10 weeks.

Serology: Shares a common antigen with *C. diphteroides, C. parvum* and *C. anarobium.*

10. *Corynebacterium diphteroides* (Jungano) P. 1938.

Synonym: Bacille diphtéroide Jungano 1909.

Habitat: Intestinal tract of the white rat, natural cavities of man. Quite frequent.

Morphology: Rods similar to C. diphteriae, 0.5 to 0.6 $\mu \times$ 2 to 3 μ, with polar swelling, pseudo-branching; occurring singly, in pairs, in packets and acute angle forms; metachromatic granules; non-motile; no endospores; Gram-positive.

Physiology: Strict anaerobe. Opt. T. $= 37°$C. Not thermoresistant. Survives 1 to several months. Catalase-negative; some strains may become catalase-positive and give facultatively anaerobic mutants. Neutral red reduced by most strains.

Cultural characters: Gas, but no fetid odor produced.

Deep agar: Punctiform colonies; some may become irregular, lenticular or fluffy; gas.

Glucose VF broth: Abundant turbidity; gas.

Peptone water: Slight turbidity.

Gelatin: No liquefaction.

Milk: Unchanged.

Coagulated proteins: Not attacked.

Carbohydrates: Glucose, fructose, maltose, sucrose and galactose are fermented by most strains.

Biochemistry: Nitrites not formed from nitrates; produces NH_3, H_2S, volatile amines, aldehydes, ketones, indole, acetic and propionic acids, with sometimes a third acid (iso-butyric). Some strains produce lactic acid.

Pathogenicity, natural: Isolated in fibrous osteitis, purulent arthritis, septicemia, purulent pleurisy and alveolar pyorrhea.

Pathogenicity, experimental: Inoculation of pathological specimens into the rabbit and guinea pig produces a fatal corynebacteriosis. Pure cultures may lose their virulence. Intravenous injection of the bacteria into the rabbit may produce either rapidly fatal corynebacteriosis with verrucous endocarditis, or a diffuse giganto-cellular reticulosis appearing late and producing death in 8 to 10 weeks.

Serology: No antigen shared by other species of anaerobic *Coryne-bacteria;* this species constitutes by itself serotype II.

11. *Corynebacterium renale-cuniculi*
(Manteufel and Herzberg) P. 1938.

Synonym: Bacterium renale cuniculi M. and H. 1930.

Habitat: Normal kidney of rabbit, monkey and guinea pig. Quite frequent.

Morphology: Short, slender rods, 0.5 to 0.6 μ occuring in masses; diphteroid aspect; non-motile; no endospores; Gram-positive (bipolar staining with unstained spots).

Physiology: Microaerophilic. Opt. T. $= 37°$C. Not thermoresistant. Acidophilic. Survives 1 to 3 months. Obligate serophile. Neutral red reduced.

Cultural characters: Gas produced. Isolation in Smith-Noguchi medium with pieces of fresh rabbit kidney, or in media added with fresh inactivated serum. No fetid odor.

Deep agar: Lenticular colonies.

Glucose broth: Slow growth (8 days); gas.

Peptone water: Slight turbidity; gas.

Brain-medium: Rapid growth with tart odor.

Blood-agar: No growth.

Gelatin: No liquefaction.

Milk: Unchanged.

Proteins: Not attacked.

Carbohydrates: Not fermented.

Biochemistry: Nitrites not formed from nitrates; produces NH_3, H_2S, volatile amines, indole, scatole (traces), acetic acid and a second acid, probably iso-butyric, and lactic acid.

Pathogenicity, natural: Isolated from a brain abscess.

Pathogenicity, experimental: Intravenous injection of the bacteria into the rabbit produce a fatal general infection; among the lesions, a fibrinous endocarditis is found. No toxin, or hemolysin.

Serology: Specific agglutination at 1-400 to 1-8,000; cross-reaction with *C. hepatodystrophicans*.

12. *Corynebacterium acnes* (Gilchrist) Eberson.

Synonym: Bacillus acnes G. 1901; *Actinomyces acnes* (Gilchrist) Eberson 1918; *Fusiformis acnes* Holland 1920; *Propionicbacterium acnes* Douglas and Gunter 1946.

Habitat: Sebaceous glands, hair follicles, pustules of acne.

Morphology: Small rods, 0.5 μ $\times$ 1.5 to 2 μ, sometimes club-shaped, sometimes with alternating zones of stained and unstained material; non-motile; no endospores; Gram-positive.

Physiology: Microaerophilic to facultatively anaerobic. Opt. T. $= 35°$ to $37°$C. Catalase-positive.

Cultural characters: Slow and meager growth; no gas, or fetid odor produced.

Agar slant: Very small, circular, transparent colonies, becoming pink.

Slightly acid glucose-deep agar: More abundant growth; circular colonies.

Glucose broth: Remains clear; clotty growth which settles.

Gelatin: Generally no liquefaction; some strains liquefy very slowly.

Milk: Slowly coagulated; soft curd. Some strains do not coagulate.

Potato: No growth in aerobiosis; under anaerobic conditions, red streaks.

Blood-Loeffler's serum: Small, greyish colonies, becoming pink.

Carbohydrates: Glucose, fructose, sucrose, lactose, galactose, maltose and inulin are fermented.

Biochemistry: Nitrites formed from nitrates; produces NH_3, indole (sometimes), acetic and propionic acids, sometimes lactic acid.

Pathogenicity, natural: Acne.

Pathogenicity, experimental: Acneiform lesions in the mouse.

SUB-GENUS I bis: *PROPIONIBACTERIUM* Orla-Jensen.

Non-motile, non-sporeforming rods, resembling the corynebacteria in anaerobic neutral media, and sometimes the streptococci; under aerobic conditions, appear as elongated, irregular, swollen and ramified rods. Metachromatic granules; produce propionic acid.

This sub-genus comprises 6 species which are preferably anaerobic:

1. Ferments pentoses.
   1. *Propionibacterium pentosaceum,* page 356

2. Milk unchanged; ferments arabinose.
   2. *Propionibacterium arabinosum,* page 356

3. Milk coagulated; ferments dextrin, glycogen and starch.
   3. *Propionibacterium technicum,* page 356

4. Catalase-positive; ferments cellobiose and salicin.
   4. *Propionibacterium raffinosaceum,* page 356

5. Milk coagulated; catalase-positive; nitrites not formed from nitrates; lactose fermented.
   5. *Propionibacterium shermani,* page 356

6. Milk unchanged; catalase-positive; nitrites not formed from nitrates; disaccharides not fermented.
   6. *Propionibacterium freudenreichi,* page 356

1. *Propionibacterium pentosaceum*
(von Freudenreich and Orla-Jensen) van Niel.

Synonym: Bacillus acidi-propionici van Freudehreich and Orla-Jensen 1906.

Habitat: Dairy products, Emmenthaler cheese, soil.

Morphology: Ramified, swollen rods, 3 to 4 μ in length; in neutral media, spheroids, 0.8 μ in diameter; non-motile; no endospores; metachromatic granules; Gram-positive.

Physiology: Microaerophilic. Opt. T. $= 30°C$. Not thermoresistant. Feebly catalase-positive.

Cultural characters: Small amounts of odorless gas.

Deep agar: Punctiform colonies 1 to 2 mm. below the surface of the agar; little or no gas.

Broth: Slight turbidity; small amounts of gas.

Yeast-gelatin: No liquefaction.

Milk: Acidified, coagulated.

Coagulated proteins: Not attacked.

Carbohydrates: Acid and gas from glucose, fructose, galactose, mannose, lactose, maltose, sucrose, raffinose, mannitol, sorbitol, glycerol, arabinose, xylose, and rhamnose. Acid, but no gas, from adonitol, arabitol, erythritol, aesculin, inositol, salicin and trhalose.

Biochemistry: Nitrites and N_2 formed from nitrates; produces CO_2, acetic and propionic acids. Lactic and pyruvic acids are fermented as well as dyhydroxyacetone.

Pathogenicity: Non-pathogenic.

Species very closely related to the preceding:

2. *Propionibacterium arabinosum* Hitchner 1932.
Differs by the absence of coagulation of milk, and non fermentation of xylose and rhamnose.

3. *Propionibacterium technicum* van Niel 1928.
Coagulates milk; ferments dextrin, glycogen and starch.

4. *Propionibacterium raffinosaceum* Werkman and Ludall 1931.
Catalase-positive; ferments cellobiose and salicin.

5. *Propionibacterium shermani* (Sherman) van Niel.
Coagulates milk; catalase-positive; nitrites not formed from nitrates; ferments lactose.

6. *Propionibacterium freudenreichi* (von Freudenreich and Orla-Jensen) van Niel.
Milk unchanged; catalase-positive; nitrites not formed from nitrates; disaccharides not fermented.

GENUS II: *ACTINOBACTERIUM* Haass 1960 (1).

Synonym: Cohnistreptothrix Pinoy 1913.

Non-motile, non-sporeforming, sometimes filamentous, Gram-positive rods, showing in culture, swellings and branching, in pathological specimens, radiate masses of club-shaped forms; no aerial mycelium; white colonies; catalase-negative; produce acetic acid.

This genus comprises actually 4 anaerobic species:

A) Species producing no gas:

1. Lenticular coloniles; no gas; clotty growth in broth; gelatin not liquefied; milk unchanged; non-proteolytic; feebly saccharolytic; hemolytic; pathogenic (anaerobic actinobacterioses).
   1. *Actinobacterium israeli,* page 357

2. Obligate serophile; circular colonies; no gas; ascitic broth turbid; pathogenic for man.
   2. *Actinobacterium meyeri,* page 358

3. Irregular colonies; clotty growth in broth; gelatin not liquefied; milk coagulated; non-proteolytic; weakly pathogenic.
   3. *Actinobacterium abscessum,* page 359

B) Species producing gas:

4. Microaerophilic; clotty growth; gelatin not liquefied; milk unchanged.
   4. *Actinobacterium cellulitis,* page 360

1. **Actinobacterium israeli** (Wolff and Israel) Sampietro 1908.

Synonym: Actinomyces israeli W. and I. 1891; *Streptothrix isreali* Kruse 1896; *Discomyces israeli* Gedoelst 1902; *Cohnistreptothrix isreali* Pinoy 1913; *Brevistreptothrix israeli* Lignieres 1924; *Proactinomyces israeli* Jensen 1931; *Corynebacterium israeli* Lentze 1938. Not to be confused with *Actinomyces bovis* Harz which is aerobic.

Habitat: Natural cavities of man, especially mouth. Frequent.

Morphology: Pleomorphic, swollen rods, 0.8 to 1.0 μ $\times$ 4 to 6 μ; show branching; slightly-curved or filamentous; occurring singly or in masses; non-motile; no endospores; Gram-positive.

Physiology: At first, strict anaerobe; then microaerophilic. Opt. T. $=$ 37°C. Killed after 20 minutes at 56°C. Survives 3 months with repeated transfers. Catalase-negative. Neutral red and phenosafranin not reduced.

Cultural characters: No gas, or fetid odor produced. Growth promoted by serum.

Deep agar: Coherent, lenticular colonies; no pigment.

Glucose broth: Whitish, curdled growth; fluid clear.

Gelatin: No growth at 26°C. No liquefaction at 37°C.

Milk: Unchanged.

Coagulated proteins: Not attacked.

Blood media: Hemolysis (with human blood only).

Carbohydrates: Acid, but no gas from glucose, lactose, maltose, marnitol, sucrose; slow fermentation.

Biochemistry: Nitrites not formed from nitrates; produces NH_3, ethanol (traces) acetylmethylcarbinol, acetic and lactic acids; some strains produce formic acid.

Pathogenicity, natural: Essentially human actinobacterioses, with the mouth (tooth or tonsil) as starting point; several forms: cervicofacial, jugal, thoracic, visceral, etc. In the white or yellow grains of the pus, other germs may also be found, mostly fusiforms. May also be isolated from lesions other than characteristic actinobacteriosis: purulent pleurisy, tonsillar phlegmon, brain abscess. May also be met in animal actinobacteriosis, but less often (guinea pig, cattle, etc.).

Pathogenicity, experimental: In laboratory cultures, virulence is rapidly lost. To revitalize the pathogenicity, nonspecific agents must alter the host's tissues: agar, mucin, adrenalin, saliva; thus, a fatal disease may be set up in the guinea pig or the rabbit with the same characteristics as those of the human disease: viscid pus with white grains which show the radiate masses of club-shaped forms.

1. bis. Variety *indo-sinensis* Reynes 1947.

Characteristics: Microaerophilic; non-serophilic; curdled growth.

2. *Actinobacterium meyeri* (Kurt Meyer) P. 1938.

Synonym: Cohnistreptothrix of K. Meyer 1911.

Habitat: Natural cavities of man, especially mouth, organism of certain aniamls (guinea pig, cattle). Frequent.

Morphology: Rods measuring 0.4 to 0.5 $\mu \times$ 3 to 5 μ; occurring often as long segmented filaments; terminal swellings; primary and secondary branching; the swellings and clubs contain large amounts of deoxyribonucleic acid which can be detected with special staining procedures (Piekarski; Robinow); non-motile; no endospores; Gram-positive.

Physiology: Strict anaerobe. Opt. T. = 37°C. Obligate serophile; ascitic fluid may replace serum. Survives several months. Neutral red reduced by some strains.

Cultural characters: No gas, nor fetid odor produced.

Serum-deep agar: Lenticular colonies (simple, compound or irregular).

Serum-glucose VF broth: Diffuse turbidity; powdery sediment.

Serum-peptone water: Slight turbidity.

Serum-gelatin: No liquefaction.

Serum-milk: No coagulation.

Coagulated proteins: Not attacked.

Carbohydrates: Glucose, fructose, maltose, galactose and sucrose are fermented generally.

Biochemistry: Nitrites not formed from nitrates; produces NH_3, volatile amines, aldehydes and ketones irregularly; indole formed by some strains. Acetic acid produced by practically all strains with a second acid which may be: formic, propionic or butyric. catalase never produced.

Pathogenicity, natural: Isolated mainly from human, less often from animal actinobacteriosis. In association, may participate in other infections, such as alveolar pyorrhea, sinusitis, lung abscess, purulent pleurisy, acute appendicitis, peritonitis, salpingitis.

Pathogenicity, experimental: Some strains may produce without any adjuvant a purulent infection in the guinea pig, rapidly fatal by intraperitoneal route, slowly wasting by intramuscular route. With adjuvants (musin, adrenalin, filtered saliva), a typical actinobacteriosis with white or yellow grains is reproduced; it is more or less rapidly fatal according to the route of injection. The intratesticular injection is most favorable.

3. *Actinobacterium abscessum* (Neschezadimenko) P. 1938.

Synonym: Cohnistreptothrix anaérobie N. 1908.

Habitat: Human body, especially buccal cavity. Quite frequent.

Morphology: Filamentous rods, sometimes ramified; swellings, but no terminal clubs; 0.75 to 1.0 μ $\times$ 5 to 60 μ; non-motile; no endospores; Gram-positive.

Physiology: Strict anaerobe. Opt. T. $= 36$-$37°C$ .Non-thermoresistant. Short-lived. No catalase produced. Neutral red and phenosafranin not reduced.

Cultural characters: No gas produced.

Deep agar: Rare, irregular colonies with delicate projections.

Glucose broth: Flakes; clear fluid.

Coagulated proteins: Not attacked.

Gelatin: No liquefaction; growth with black sediment.

Milk: Coagulated in 3 to 4 days.

Carbohydrates: Glucose, fructose, maltose, lactose, sucrose, galactose, sorbitol and starch are fermented.

Biochemistry: Nitrites formed from nitrates; produces NH_3, H_2S, volatile amines, aldehydes, ketones, acetylmethylcarbinol; acetic and lactic acids.

Pathogenicity, natural: Isolated from abscesses and phlegmons of the floor of the mouth, dental abscesses, dental granuloma, cervicofacial and broncho-pulmonary actinobacterioses, maxillary sinusitis and osteophlegmon of the maxillary bone.

Pathogenicity, experimental: Same as the preceding species.

4. *Actinobacterium cellulitis* Linhard 1949.

Habitat: Buccal cavity of man. Quite frequent.

Morphology: Highly pleomorphic rods, extensively ramified, with club-shaped ends; single cells measure 0.6 μ $\times$ 5 to 7 μ; clubs measure 1.2 to 1.8 μ; non-motile; no endospores; Gram-positive.

Physiology: Microaerophilic. Serophilic on isolation, but becomes adapted little by little to growth without serum. Resists 1 minute at 60°C. Survives more than 5 weeks. Neutral red, safranin and phenosafranin are not reduced.

Cultural characters: Gas, but no fetid odor produced.

Deep agar: Squat, lenticular colonies of cuneiform type; no gas.

Glucose VF broth: Abundant growth which sediments rapidly to leave a clear fluid; slight gas production becomes evident upon tapping.

Peptone water: Very slight, curdled growth.

Gelatin: No liquefaction.

Milk: Unchanged.

Coagulated proteins: Not attacked.

Carbohydrates: Glucose, fructose, maltose, galactose and sucrose are fermented.

Biochemistry: Nitrites formed from nitrates in 5 days, in peptone water added with either fructose, maltose or galactose; produces NH_3, volatile amines, aldehydes, ketones, formic and propionic acids.

Pathogenicity, natural: Jugal actinobacteriosis of dental origin.

Pathogenicity, experimental: Non-pathogenic for the guinea pig without adjuvants.

SUB-GENUS II bis: *BIFIDOBACTERIUM* Orla-Jensen 1924.

Definition.—Non-motile, non-sporeforming. Gram-positive rods showing club-shaped swellings and bifid or doubly-bifid ends.

Although closely related to the preceding genus, *Bifidobacteria* are nonetheless quite distinct. This genus comprises actually 6 anaerobic species which are more or less pathogenic, but never causing actinobacteriosis.

A) Species producing no gas:

1. Lenticular colonies; viscid zoogloea in glucose broth; gelatin not liquefied; milk coagulated; no gas produced; non-proteolytic; saccharolytic (especially lactose); produces lactic and acetic acids; indole not formed; non-pathogenic; tendency to become facultatively anaerobic.

   1. *Bifidobacterium bifidum,* page 361

2. Rods of large size; lenticular colonies surrounded by a nebulous halo; viscid zoogloea in mannitol broth; indole not formed; gelatin not liquefied; milk slowly coagulated; saccharolytic; produces acetic acid; feebly pathogenic.

    2. *Bifidobacterium appendicitis,* page 362

3. Highly pleomorphic rods; lenticular colonies surrounded by a constellation of small colonies; microaerophilic; gelatin not liquefied; milk unchanged; saccharolytic (except lactose); non-pathogenic.

    3. *Bifidobacterium constellatum,* page 362

4. Pleomorphic rods of small size; microaerophilic; lenticular colonies; milk unchanged.

    4. *Bifidobacterium intestinalis,* page 363

5. Irregular rods; gelatin not liquefied; milk unchanged; saccharolytic; non-pathogenic.

    5. *Bifidobacterium cornutum,* page 363

B) Species producing gas:

6. Large rods; irregular, arborescent colonies; gelatin not liquefied; milk unchanged.

    6. *Bifidobacterium bifurcatum,* page 364

1. *Bifidobacterium bifidum* (Tissier) Orla-Jensen.

Synonym: Bacillus bifidus communis Tissier 1899; *Bacteroides bifidus* C. and C. 1919; *Lactobacillus bifidus* (Tissier) Kulp and Rettger 1924.

Habitat: Intestinal tract of the nursling and, secondarily, of adults; acessorily, mouth, vagina and intestinal tract of animals. Very frequent.

Morphology: Pleomorphic rods, 0.5 to 0.7 $\mu \times$ 2.0 to 5.0 μ; with pointed and bifurcate ends; sometimes club-shaped or doubly-bifid; non-motile; no endospores; Gram-positive.

Physiology: Strict anaerobe; some strains are microaerophilic, still others may become facultatively anaerobic. Opt. T. $= 22$-$37°$C. Killed at $60°$C. Survives 3 to 4 weeks.

Cultural characters: No gas produced.

Deep agar: Lenticular colonies, 2 to 3 mm. in diameter; no gas.

Glucose broth: Turbid in 2to 3 days; cloudy sediment; no gas.

Gelatin: No liquefaction.

Milk: Rapid and complete coagulation; markedly acidified; no gas.

Coagulated proteins: Not attacked.

Peptone water: Good growth; indole not formed, nor phenol.

Carbohydrates: Acid but no gas from glucose, lactose, sucrose, fructose, galactose and inulin; dextrin, starch, maltose, raffinose and trehalose are fermented by some strains.

Biochemistry: Produces lactic and acetic acids in the ratio 3:1. Urea hydrolyzed according to Tissier, but none of our strains do so.

Pathogenicity: Non-pathogenic. It is even an *in vivo* and *in vitro* antagonist of the pathogenic enteric bacteria. However, it has been found in certain urinary infections where it may set up an irritation by means of the acidity which it produces.

Pathogenicity, experimental: Non-pathogenic.

2. *Bifidobacterium appendicitis* (Lotti) P. 1938.

Synonym: Bacillus Lotti 1909.

Habitat: Intestinal tract of man; appendix. Uncommon.

Morphology: Rods of large size, 1 μ $\times$ 6 to 8 μ, straight or slightly-curved with rounded ends; occurring singly or in short chains; numerous bifurcate or candlelight-shaped forms; non-motile; no endospores; Gram-positive.

Physiology: Strict anaerobe. Opt. T. = 37°C. Killed at 70°C. Survives 10 days. Neutral red not reduced.

Cultural characters: No gas produced. Requires glucose for growth.

Deep agar: Lenticular colonies surrounded by a halo 3 to 4 mm. in diameter. No gas produced.

Glucose broth: Turbid in 24 hours; acetic odor; no gas; indole not formed.

Gelatin: No liquefaction.

Milk: Acidified in 3 to 4 days; coagulated in 15 days.

Coagulated proteins: Not attacked.

Carbohydrates: Glucose, fructose, maltose, sucrose, galactose, lactose, sorbitol and starch are fermented.

Biochemistry: Nitrites not formed from nitrates: produces NH_3, H_2S, volatile amines, aldehydes, ketones, acetylmethylcarbinol, formic, butyric and lactic acids. Some strains produce only lactic acid.

Pathogenicity, natural: Isolated from appendix and jugal abscess, gaseous colitis.

Pathogenicity, experimental: Injection into the guinea pig causes death by wasting in a few days.

3. *Bifidobacterium constellatum* (White) P. 1938.

Synonym: Bacillus constellatus White 1921.

Habitat: Digestive tract of the bee. Frequent.

Morphology: Straight or slightly-curved rods, 0.3 to 0.8 μ $\times$ 2.5 to 4 μ; pleomorphic; forked ends; club-shaped swollen forms; fusiform elements; occurring singly or in short chains; radiate aspect; non-motile; no endospores; Gram-positive.

Physiology: Very strict anaerobe; some microaerophilic strains may become facultatively anaerobic.

Deep agar: Lenticular colonies surrounded by a constellation of smaller colonies; growth in the form of a disk in the upper layers.

Glucose broth animal charcoal: Curdled growth.

Gelatin: No liquefaction.

Milk: No growth.

Carbohydrates: Glucose and maltose are fermented.

Pathogenicity: Non-pathogenic.

4. *Bifidobacterium intestinalis* (Jacobson) P. 1938.

Synonym: Bacillus intestinalis tuberculiformis Jacobson 1908.

Habitat: Intestinal tract of the child. Quite uncommon.

Morphology: Delicate, highly pleomorphic rods; short forms and filamentous elements; S- or V-forms; terminal branching; forked ends; non-motile; no endospores; Gram-positive.

Physiology: Strict anaerobe. Opt. T. $= 37°$C. Survives 2 to 3 weeks.

Cultural characters: No gas produced.

Deep agar: Lenticular colonies.

Glucose broth: Turbid; curdled sediment; very markedly acidified; tart odor; indole not formed.

Gelatin: No growth.

Milk: No growth.

Pathogenicity: Non-pathogenic.

5. *Bifidobacterium cornutum* (Distaso) P. 1938.

Synonym: Bacillus cornutus Distaso 1912.

Habitat: Mouth and intestinal tract of man, organism of the horse. Quite frequent.

Morphology: Irregular rods, 0.3 $\mu \times$ 2 to 3 μ; occurring singly or in pairs; swollen and forked ends, horn-like or doubly bifid like stag horns; spheroids in old cultures; non-motile; no endospores; Gram-positive.

Physiology: Strict anaerobe. Not thermoresistant. Short-lived. Requires growth factor from fresh serum or brain extract. Neutral red and safranin are reduced.

Cultural characters: No gas produced; slightly fetid odor.

Deep agar: Circular colonies in 48 hours.

Gelatin: No liquefaction.

Milk: Unchanged.

Carbohydrates: Acid but no gas from glucose, fructose, galactose and maltose.

Biochemistry: Nitrites not formed from nitrates; produces NH_3, H_2S, ketones, acetic and lactic acids.

Pathogenicity, natural: Isolated from a case of ulcerous sore in the horse.

Pathogenicity, experimental: Non-pathogenic for rabbit, guinea pig and mouse.

6. *Bifidobacterium bifurcatum* (Choukévitch) P. 1938.

Synonym: Bacillus bifurcatus gazogenes Choukévitch 1911.

Habitat: Intestinal tract of the horse. Quite uncommon.

Morphology: Large rods, 1 to 2 μ $\times$ 6 to 15 μ; occurring singly, in pairs, in short chains, sometimes in long filaments; forked ends; non-motile; no endospores; Gram-positive.

Physiology: Strict anaerobe. Opt. T. $= 37°$C.

Cultural characters: Gas produced.

Deep agar: Irregular colonies, 5 mm. in diameter; sometimes arborescent; large amounts of gas formed; acidfied.

Glucose broth: Slight turbidity; sediment; gas.

Gelatin: No liquefaction.

Milk: Unchanged.

Pathogenicity: Non-pathogenic.

GENUS III: *MICROMONOSPORA* Orskov 1923.

Definition.—Pleomorphic, filamentous, ramified rods; the primary and secondary ramifications are perpendicular to the main filament; no aerial mycelium; multiplication by conidia located at the end of short conidiophores; Gram-positive; non-acid-fast; aerobic and strict anaerobes; saprophytic in the soil and intestinal tract of certain insects.

This genus actually comprises 2 strictly anaerobic species of which here is the key:

1. *Micromonospora propionici* Hungate 1946.

Habitat: Intestinal tract of the termite.

Isolation: On cellulose-deep agar.

Morphology: Ramified rods, bearing spheroids of 0.8 μ on the end of short branches; filaments; non-motile; no endospores; Gram-positive (in young cultures).

Physiology: Strict anaerobe. Opt. T. $= 30$-$40°$C. Very slow growth.

Cultural characters: Gas produced very slowly.

Cellulose-deep agar: Spherical, white colonies, 0.5 mm. in diameter, surrounded by a clear space of digested cellulose.

Liquid media: Requires an organic compound, such as liver extract, yeast extract, dry grass; growth is then more abundant.

Biochemistry: Cellulose digested with production of CO_2, acetic and propionic acids; but no H_2, nor neutral volatile products.

2. *Micromonospora acetoformici* Sébald and Prévot 1962.

Habitat: Posterior region of the intestinal tract of *Reticulitermes lucifugus* var. *saintonnensis.*

Isolation: On saline media containing cellulose (anaerobic conditions—Pochon).

Morphology: Filamentous, abundantly branched rods (primary and secondary ramifications are perpendicular to the axis of the main filament); filaments measure 0.4 to 0.6 μ $\times$ 10 to 100 μ; corpuscules isolated or grouped by 2 or 4, less often in masses often on the stem or extremity of short ramifications; preconidia and conidia born on conidiophores, 0.8 to 1.2 μ; non-motile; Gram-positive.

Physiology: Strict anaerobe, growing only on Pochon medium, first de-aerated, then sealed under vacuum. Opt. T. $= 37°C.$ (20-37°C). Non-thermophilic. Resists 15 minutes at 100°C.

Cultural characters: No growth on peptone water, broth and VF agar, or coagulated proteins. On Pochon medium, growth in 48 hours; large, circular, cottony, white colonies adhering on filter-paper, to the walls of the tube, to glass slides immersed in the medium. Shaking will remove then. Fragment of brain added to the culture will become ochre-colored.

Bryant's liquid medium: Ochre colonies.

Bryant's agar medium: Numerous, cottony, ochre colonies. No digestion of the cellulose.

Plain gelatin: Meager and inconstant growth. Slow liquefaction (2 months).

Cohn's gelatin with animal charcoal: Rapid liquefaction (a few hours).

Milk: Precipitated, then digested in 7 to 10 days; sometimes coagulated prior to digestion.

Carbohydrates: Glucose, fructose, maltose and starch are fermented; cellulose not attacked.

Biochemistry: Nitrites formed from nitrates in 24 hours; produces indole, formic, acetic and lactic acids. Essential source of C is CO_3Ca in Pochon's medium.

Pathogenicity: Non-pathogenic.

Chapter 10

CLASS ALGOBACTERIA.

The *Algobacteria* comprise 2 classes:
1. *Siderobacteriales* or iron bacteria, aerobic;
2. *Thiobacteriales* or sulfur bacteria, of which many are anaerobic.

CLASS II: *THIOBACTERIALES* Buchanan emend.
(Sulfur bacteria).

The taxonomy of the *Thiobacteriales* is in full evolution. The existence of anaerobic species in this class is now unanimously admitted. They are not, however, sufficiently described, as far as their physiology and biochemical characters are concerned, to permit delineation of natural groups permitting an easy determination as found in the preceding classes. Description of the few forms which have been cultivated in anaerobiosis and sufficiently studied to appear in this Manual are borrowed in part from van Niel, Bergey *et al.,* and Bourrelly.

We shall describe them in the taxonomical order proposed by Bourrelly in 1954 who, very reasonably, separates the red sulfur bacteria or *Rhodobacteriales* from the green sulfur bacteria or *Chlorobacteriales*.

ORDER I: *RHODOBACTERIALES* Pringsheim emend.

Sulfur bacteria growing in sulhydric surroundings; bacteriochlorophyll and carotenoid pigment usually give them a red color. Colorless, unicellular and flagellated forms.

FAMILY I: *THIORHODACEAE* Molisch 1907.

Unicellular micro-organisms, often living as aggregates; spherical, ovoid, cylindrical, vibrioid, spirilloid, filaments. Grow in media rich in sulfides and require sunlight or infrared rays. Produce pigment: purple or brown (bacteriochlorophyll carotenoids). Anaerobic or microaerophilic. Photosynthetic; presence of sulfur globules inside the bacterial body.

This family comprises 3 anaerobic species belonging to 3 different genera:

366

1. *Thiosarcina rosea* (Schroeter) Winogradsky.

Habitat: Mud and stagnant waters rich in H_2S and exposed to sunlight. Sulfur springs. Very frequent.

Morphology: Sarcina, 2 to 3 μ in diameter, occurring in cubic packets of 8-64 cells. Slightly motile. Pink pigment becoming practically black.

Physiology: Strict anaerobe. Photosynthetic, requiring H_2S or sulfide.

2. *Thiopedia rosea* Winogradsky.

Habitat: Same as for the preceeding species. Frequent.

Morphology: Cocci, 1 to 2 μ, sometimes elongated, growing in considerable masses, light red to black in color.

Physiology: Strict anaerobe. Photosynthetic, requiring H_2S or sulfides.

3. *Chromatium okeni* (Ehrenberg) Perty.

Habitat: Sulfurated stagnant waters. Quite frequent.

Morphology: Large cells, 5 to 6 $\mu \times$ 8 to 15 μ, containing 1 or several granules of sulfur; actively motile; purple-red.

Physiology: Strict anaerobe; requires H_2S and sunlight; infrared rays are favourable; may tolerate a small quantity of air.

Cultural characters: On Bavendamm's mineral medium: NH_3, CO_2 or CO_3R, and Ca to neutralize SO_4H_2 produced; or on van Niel's medium: Na_2S, NH_4Cl, K_2SO_4, $MgCl_2$, $NaHCO_3$, agar, pH $= 8.0$-8.5.

FAMILY II: *THIOBACTERIACEAE* Skuja 1948.

Colorless, unicellular, flagellated forms; no pigment. This family comprises 4 genera, two of which contain anaerobic species:

GENUS I: *MACROMONAS* Utermohl and Koppe 1923.

Cylindrical, colorless bacteria; actively motile by means of a polar flagellum. Contains $CaCO_3$ and sulfur granules.

1. *Macromonas mobilis* (Lauterborn) U. and K.

Habitat: Soft waters containing sulfite and calcium.

Morphology: Large cells, 8 to 14 $\mu \times$ 12 to 30 μ; actively motile by a polar flagellum; contains sulfur and calcium carbonate.

Physiology: Microaerophilic; requires H_2S.

2. *Macromonas bipunctata* (Gicklhorn) U. and K.

Habitat: Fresh waters containing calcium.

Morphology: Cells measuring 10 to 15 μ, containing calcium carbonate.

Physiology: Microaerophilic.

GENUS II: *THIOVULUM* Hinze 1913.

Spherical or ovoid cells; cytoplasm concentrated at one end, a vacuole occupying the remainder; reproduction by constriction; actively motile (rotation); globule of sulfur in the cytoplasm. One anaerobic species:

1. *Thiovulum majus* Hinze 1913.

Habitat: Sulfite waters; decomposing algae; soft and marine waters.
Morphology: That of the genus. Size: 5 to 20 μ in diameter; contains a globule of sulfur.
Physiology: Microaerophilic; requires H_2S.

FAMILY III: *ATHIORHODACEAE* Molisch.

Purple and brown photosynthetic bacteria which do not contain globules of sulfur, but require an organic growth factor; pleomorphic; motile; Gram-negative.
Three genera:

GENUS I: *RHODOPSEUDOMONAS* Kluyver and van Niel.

Red or yellowish-brown bacteria; photosynthetic.
This genus comprises actually 3 anaerobic species:

1. *Rhodopseudomonas palustris* (Molisch) van Niel.

Habitat: Mud and stagnant waters. Frequent.
Morphology: Short rods, sometimes slightly-curved, 0.6 to 0.8 μ $\times$ 1.2 to 2 μ; In old cultures are seen long forms (10 μ), irregular, swollen, sometimes ramified; motile by means of a polar flagellum; Gram-negative.
Physiology: Microaerophilic; may grow under strictly anaerobic conditions if sunlight is present (photosynthetic); Opt. T. $= 37°C$. Opt. pH $=$ 6-8.5. May produce facultatively anaerobic mutants.
Cultural characters: No fetid odor. Grows abundantly and rapidly on thiosulfate glutarate and ethanol.
Gelatin: No liquefaction.
Carbohydrates: Not fermented.
Biochemistry: Utilizes leucin; pigment is pink in media added with glycerol, malonate or thiosulfate; reddish-brown in media containing fatty acids (bacteriochlorophyll carotenoids).

2. *Rhodospeudomonas gelatinosa* (Molisch) van Niel.

Differs from the preceding species by: its strictly anaerobic character, liquefaction of gelatin, utilization of alanin, asparagin, aspartic and glutamic acids; fermentation of glucose, fructose, mannose, glycerol, mannitol, sorbitol, citrates and tartrates.

3. *Rhodopseudomonas capsulata* (Molisch) van Niel.

Synonym: Rhodonostoc capsulatum Molisch 1907.

Habitat: Stagnant waters and mud. Very frequent.

Morphology: According to the pH of the medium, cells may be spherical or rod-shaped; often non-motile, but when motile, it is by means of a polar flagellum; at pH $= 7.0$, occurs in short chains of spherical cells; above pH $= 7.0$, elongated cells measuring 0.5 to 1.0 $\mu \times$ 1.0 to 1.6 μ; Gram-negative.

Physiology: Photosynthetic anaerobe. Opt. T. $= 25°$C. Opt. pH $=$ 6-8.5. Growth is not inhibited by 02.

Cultural characters: Grows only in the presence of fatty acids and side-chained acids; abundant growth on propionate, 2-1,000.

Gelatin: No liquefaction.

Carbohydrates: Growth stimulated by 2-1,000 of glucose and levulose.

Biochemistry: May oxidize H_2. Utilizes alanin and glutamic acid. Thiamin is necessary growth factor; some strains require biotin and nicotinic acid. Brown or yellowish-brown pigment, due to bacteriochlorophyll and carotenoids, turns red in the presence of O_2; does not diffuse.

GENUS II: *RHODOSPIRILLUM* (Molisch) van Niel emend.

Spiral-shaped, motile bacteria; Gram-negative; red or brown pigment. This genus comprises actually 4 anaerobic species.

1. *Rhodospirillum rubrum* (Esmarch) Molisch.

Habitat: Mud and stagnant waters. Frequent.

Morphology: Spirals measuring 0.5 to 1.5 $\mu \times$ 2 to 4 μ, with very long forms (50 μ); swollen forms; motile by means of a polar flagellum; red pigment (bacteriochlorophyll carotenoids); Gram-negative.

Physiology: Microaerophilic. Opt. T. $= 30\text{-}37°$C. Opt. pH $= 6\text{-}8.5$. May tolerate a partial pressure of O_2.

Cultural chacters: Fetid odor. Photosynthetic under anaerobic conditions if illuminated.

Gelatin: No liquefaction.

Biochemistry: Utilizes alanin, aspartic and glutamic acids, fatty acids, ethanol.

2. *Rhodospirillum fulvum* (Molisch and Buder) van Niel.

Habitat: Waters, mud.

Morphology: Spirals measuring 0.5 $\mu \times$ 2.5 μ; amplitude 1.0 to 1.5 μ; swollen forms; motile; red or orange-brown.

Physiology: Strict anaerobe. Opt. T. $= 30°$C. May become microaerophilic.

Cultural characters: Photosynthetic under anaerobic conditions if sunlight is present.

Yeast water-deep agar: Growth in anarobic layers only.

Gelatin: No liquefaction.

Biochemistry: May utilize fatty acids and C_4 di-acids; glutamic acid is not utilized; ethanol may be utilized either alone or in combination with glucose; other carbohydrates and poly-alcohols are not utilized; aspartic acid may be utilized, but not thiosulfate.

3. *Rhodospirillum molischianum* Giesberg 1947.

Habitat: Stagnant waters and mud, hay extract under anaerobic conditions. Very frequent.

Morphology: Spirals measuring 0.7 to 0.9 μ $\times$ 5 to 10 μ, with 1 to 2 complete spirals; amplitude 1.3 to 2 μ $\times$ 4 to 6 μ.

Physiology: Photosynthetic anaerobe.

Cultural characters: Grows only in media containing ethanol, fatty acids or hydroxy-acids; citrate may be utilized.

Gelatin: No liquefaction.

Biochemistry: Reddish-brown pigment, due to bacteriochlorophyll carotenoids, has 2 absorption bands, one at 520, the other at 485.

Systematics: Closely related to *Rhodospirillum rubrum, Rh. fulvum* and *Rh. photometricum.*

4. *Rhodospirillum photometricum* Molisch 1907.

Habitat: Stagnant waters and mud. Very frequent.

Morphology: Large spirally-wound cells, with 1 to 2 complete spirals; amplitude 4 to 6 μ $\times$ 7 to 10 μ; actively motile by means of a single flagellum.

Physiology: Photosynthetic anaerobe.

Cultural characters: Grows only on media containing ethanol, fatty acids or hydroxy-acids.

Gelatin: No liquefaction.

Biochemistry: May utilize citrate. Reddish-brown pigment, due to bacteriochlorophyll carotenoids, has 2 absorption bands, one at 520, the other at 485.

Systematics: Closely related to *Rh. rubrum* and *Rh. fulvum.*

GENUS III: *RHODOMICROBIUM* Duchow and Douglas 1949.

Spherical or oval cells, attached by means of a delicate, branched filament; reproduction begins by budding in a young filament, from the polar region of a mature or immature cell, or from any point on the filament between two cells; the end of the filament swells to forms a spherical cell which increases in size to take an oval shape; non-motile; no endospores; Gram-negative.

Contains bacteriochlorophyll which permits a photosynthetic metabolism depending upon outside oxidizable compounds and not accompanied by the production of oxygen.

Also contains carotenoid pigments which give a salmon-pink or deep orange-red color to the cultures, depending upon the intensity of the growth.

Type species: *R. vannieli.*

1. *Rhodomicrobium vannieli* Duchow and Douglas 1949.

Habitat: Stagnant waters, mud.

Morphology: The mature ovoid cell measures 1.2 μ $\times$ 2.8 μ; filaments measure 0.3 μ; reproduction as described for the genus.

Physiology: Catalase-positive.

Cultural characters: Grows only under anaerobic conditions and with sunlight; depends upon organic hydrogen donors. Fluid cultures flocculate. Pigment is salmon-pink to deep orange-red.

Agar: Somber-red, irregular colonies with rough surface.

Biochemistry: Sulfides, thiosulfates and carbohydrates not utilized; organic growth factors are not necessary.

ORDER II: *CHLOROBACTERIALES* Skuja 1948.

Photosynthetic, green sulfur bacteria growing in H_2S-containing media. Two families:

FAMILY I: *CHLOROBACTERIACEAE* Geitler and Pascher.

Photosynthetic, green bacteria growing only in the presence of large amounts of H_2S; no intracellular sulfur granule, but sulfur deposited outside the bacterial body; green chlorophyll-like pigment (different from plant chlorophyll and bacteriochlorophyll); does not liberate O_2.

Out of the 6 genera which make up this family, only 1 comprises anaerobic species.

GENUS I: *CHLOROBIUM* Nadson 1912.

Green sulfur bacteria, occurring singly or in short chains, of variable size, spherical or elongated, sometimes spirally-wound; no endospores. Two anaerobic species:

1. *Chlorobium limicola* Nadson 1912.

Habitat: Mud and stagnant waters rich in H_2S and exposed to sunlight; more rarely, sulfur springs.

Morphology: Spherical or ovoid cells, 0.5 to 1.0 μ in diameter, often united in chains like streptococci; elongated forms measure 0.7 $\mu \times$ 2.5 μ; produces mucus which agglomerates the individual cells into irregular packets; greenish-yellow pigment; nonmotile; abnormal forms of 5 to 6 μ, vacuolar or swollen rods, or spiral forms.

Physiology: Strict anaerobe. Grows only in the presence of H_2S and sunlight. No growth in the presence of organic matter.

2. *Chlorobium thiosulfatophilum* Larsen 1952.

Differs from the preceding species in that it utilizes H_2S, sulfides S, H_2, S_2O_3 and S_4O_6 and reducing agents or hydrogen donors.

FAMILY II: *CHLOROCHROMATIACEAE* Skuja 1948.

Small, green bacteria, adhering to another organism, *Bacterium* or *Flagellate.*

Three genera, one of which contains anaerobic species.

GENUS I: *CHLOROCHROMATIUM* Lanuterborn 1906.

Ovoid or cylindrical, green sulfur bacteria, occurring in aggregates; motile by a polar flagellum; chlorophyll-like pigment; photosynthetic.

Only one species: *Chlorochromatium aggregatum* Lauterborn 1906.

Habitat: Similar to the preceding species.

Morphology: Cells measuring 1 to 2.5 $\mu \times$ 0.5 to 1.0 μ, occurring in aggregates of 8-16 cells around a central *bacterium;* the ensemble measures 2.5 to 5.0 $\mu \times$ 7 to 12 μ.

Physiology: Photosynthetic anaerobe; requires H_2S and sunlight.

ORDER III: *BEGGIATOALES* Buchanan 1955.
SINGLE FAMILY: *BEGGIATOACEAE* Migula.

Colorless forms; intracellular reserve fulfur.

Seven genera, one of which comprises 2 anaerobic species.

GENUS *ACHROMATIUM* Schewiakoff 1893.

Ellipsoidal or spherical cells, occurring singly; motile without flagella. Two microaerophilic species:

1. *Achromatium oxaliferum* Schewiakoff 1893.

Habitat: Running water containing H_2S and Ca salts.

Morphology: Spherical or ovoid cells measuring 7 μ, with filaments up to 35 to 100 μ; motile; contains a globule of sulfur and cristals of $CaCO_3$ (highly refringent spherules).

Physiology: Microaerophilic. Requires H_2S.

2. *Achromatium volutans* (Hinze) Bergey *et al.*

Habitat: Marine mud containing H_2S, decomposing marine algae.

Morphology: Smaller than the preceding species: 5 μ, with filaments up to 40 μ; motile without flagella; contains a globule of sulfur and $CaCO_3$.

Physiology: Microaerophilic. Requires H_2S.

Chapter 11

CLASS OF SPIROCHAETALES
Buchanan emend.

Spirally-curved, flexuous cells, motile but without flagella.

The *Spirochaetales* comprise strictly anaerobic species.

Their taxonomy has known a great deal of progress when Robinson and Heist-Clise separated the large free marine and aquatic forms constituting the family of *Spirochaetaceae* Swellengrebel, all aerobic or facultative, from the short and average-sized parasitic forms for which Schaudinn had proposed already in 1905 an autonomous family of which the type species is *Treponema*. We must deplore nonetheless the unfortunate construction of the name which Bergey *et al.* use for this family; we shall therefore substitute the more logical and euphonic name of *Treponemataceae* which at any rate has priority since it dates from 1905. This family comprises numerous anaerobic species distributed among 2 genera.

FAMILY: *TREPONEMATACEAE* Schaudinn emend.

Helicoidal cells, measuring 4 to 16 μ in length; longer forms occur when daughter-cells do not separate; spirals are regular or not, are more or less flexuous; terminal filament; parasites of *Vertebrae,* and often pathogenic.

This family comprises 3 genera, two of which contain anaerobic species. Here is the key to the determination of the latter:

1. Stained with difficulty by the usual staining methods, but staining well with Giemsa and silver impregnation techniques.
   1. *Treponema,* page 374
2. Easily stained by the usual aniline derivatives.
   2. *Borrelia,* page 354

GENUS I: *TREPONEMA* Schaudinn.

Spirally-wound cells of 4 to 16 μ; ends sometimes prolonged by a terminal filament; winding is tight, permanent; stained by Giemsa or silver impregnation after mordancing; amplitude, about 1 μ; motile by reptation and rotation: in wet preparations, visible only on dark field. This genus comprises 20 anaerobic species, which have been grown only on special media such as: Noguchi, Kritchewski and Séguin, Vinzent and Daufresne. They are all obligate serophiles. Many are pathogenic. Here is the key to their determination:

A) Group of the genital organs species:
1. Agent of syphilis.
   1. *Treponema pallidum,* page 376
2. Agent of framboesia or yaws.
   2. *Treponema pertenue,* page 376
3. Agent of caraté or pinta.
   3. *Treponema carateum,* page 377
4. Agent of treponematosis in the rabbit.
   4. *Treponema cuniculi,* page 377
5. Similar to *Tr. pallidum* and often found with it in gential syphilitic lesions, but non-pathogenic.
   5. *Treponema reiteri,* page 377
6. Highly refringent; found in necrotic and muco-membranous, genital lesions of man.
   6. *Treponema refringens,* page 377

B) Group of commensals in man and animals, often associated with the *Fusiforms* in the fuso-treponemal symbiosis.
7. Opaque colonies surrounded by a halo; gelatin liquefied; proteolytic; putrid; H_2S formed in large amounts; neutral red reduced.
   7. *Treponema microdentium,* page 378
8. Cloudy colonies; non-proteolytic; gelatin not liquefied; putrid; H_2S formed in lesser amounts; neutral red reduced.
   8. *Treponema ambigua,* page 379
9. Longer and thicker than the preceding; actively motile; gelatin not liquefied; non-proteolytic; putrid odor.
   9. *Treponema comandoni,* page 379
10. Non-proteolytic; not putrid; H_2S not formed; neutral red not reduced.
    10. *Treponema skoliodonta,* page 380
11. Definitely leptospiroidal; hazy colonies; gelatin not liquefied; non-proteolytic; no odor; H_2S not formed; neutral red partly reduced.
    11. *Treponema trimerodonta,* page 380
12. Large size; haloed colonies; weak odor; gelatin slowly liquefied; slightly proteolytic; neutral red reduced.
    12. *Treponema macrodentium,* page 381
13. Similar to *Tr. microdentium;* produces mucus.
    13. *Treponema mucosum,* page 381

14. Non-pathogenic; found in smegma; stained purple-red by Giemsa.
    14. *Treponema calligyrum,* page 381

15. Non-pathogenic; not putrid.
    15. *Treponema minutum,* page 382

16. Non-proteolytic; putrid odor; lenticular colonies; non-pathogenic in pure culture; pathogenic in mixed culture (footrot of sheep).
    16. *Treponema penortha,* page 382

17. Non-proteolytic; non-putrid; bullous colonies; non-pathogenic.
    17. *Treponema enterogyrata,* page 383

18. Long, swollen forms; stained red by Giemsa; agent of phagedenic ulcer.
    18. *Treponema phagedenis,* page 383

19. Difficult to grow; characteristics not well-known; often associated with *F. fusiformis* in Vincent's angina.
    19. *Treponema vincenti,* page 383

20. Free forms from soft-water mud, with enormous spheroids; saccharolytic.
    20. *Treponema zuelzerae,* page 384

1. *Treponema pallidum* (Schaudinn and Hoffmann) Schaudinn.

Synonym: Spirochaeta pallidum Schaudinn and Hoffmann 1905.

Habitat: Active lesions of syphilis. Very frequent.

Morphology: Slender spirochete, 0.25 to 0.3 μ $\times$ 6 to 14 μ, with pointed ends; amplitude, 1 μ; thickness 0.5 to 1.0 μ; one or more undulations; spirally-wound terminal filament; no flagella; tranverse division; stained by Giemsa.

Physiology: Completely lyzed by bile salts or saponin, 10% solution. Resists tryptic digestion. Strict anaerobe. Opt. T. $=35\,^{\circ}$C.

Cultural characters: Growth at 35° in dilute serum containing fresh tissue and under strictly anaerobic conditions; slight turbidity.

Pathogenicity: Cause of syphilis. Laboratory cultures are non-pathogenic.

Serology: Reagin producing numerous serological reactions.

2. *Treponema pertenue* Castellani 1905.

Synonym: Spirochaeta pertenus Castellani 1905; Spirochaeta or Treponema pallidula.

Habitat: Active lesions of yaws or framboesia.

Morphology: Resembles *Tr. pallidum;* spirally-wound cells measuring 0.25 to 0.3 μ $\times$ 18 to 20 μ.

Physiology: Strict anaerobe.

Cultural characters: Grows only in serum containing fresh tissue and under strictly anaerobic conditions: slight turbidity.

Pathogenicity: Cause of yaws.

Serology: Cross-reaction with *Tr. pallidum.*

3. *Treponema carateum* Brumpt.

Synonym: Tr. herrejoni; Tr. pictor; Tr. pintae; Tr. americanum.

Morphology: Similar to *Tr. pallidum* and *Tr. pertenue.*

Physiology: Not yet studied.

Pathogenicity: Cause of caraté or pinta.

4. *Treponema cuniculi* (Arzt and Kerl 1914) Noguchi.

Morphology: Similar to the preceding species, but longer.

Physiology: Not well-known; has not been cultiviated.

Pathogenicity: Cause of treponematosis in the rabbit.

5. *Treponema reiteri* (Reiter) nov. comb.

Synonym: Reiter's *Treponema* 1924.

Habitat: Genital organs of man. Quite frequent.

Morphology: Similar to *Tr. pallidum,* but larger; two phases in its reproduction: 1. by transverse division; 2. by terminal swelling giving birth to several daughter cells.

Physiology: Strict anaerobe. Facultatively serophilic. Marked longevity.

Cultural characters: Good growth on glucose-yeast extract-trypticase medium.

Chick embryo: Good growth.

Pillot's modification of Brewer's medium: Medium of choice for maximum populations.

Minimal medium (glucose-yeast extract-trypticase): arginine, acetate, a sulfhydryl compound and serum albumin are necessary; essential growth factors are: pantothenic acid, glutamine and 1-phenylethylamine.

Biochemistry: May de-aminate: l-glutamate, l-histidine, l-cystein, l-arginin and l-thionin. From glutamate, produces NH_3, CO_2 and succinic acid.

Pathogenicity: Non-pathogenic.

Serology: An antigen will fix complement with syphilitic serum.

6. *Treponema refringens* (Schaudinn and Hoffmann) 1905; *Borrelia refringens* (S. and H.) Bergey *et al.*

Habitat: Necrotic and muco-membranous genital lesions of man.

Morphology: Treponema measuring 0.5 to 0.75 μ × 6 to 20 μ, with pointed ends terminated by a very fine filament; highly refringent; reproduction by transverse division or by means of a sessile spheroid containing a large number of spirochetogenous granules; very fragile undulating membrane which may break to liberate fibrils simulating peritrichous flagella; actively motile.

Physiology: Strict anaerobe. Obligate serophile.

Cultural characters: Grows only in dilute serum added with a fragment of fresh tissue.

7. *Treponema microdentium* Noguchi 1912.

Synonym: Spirochaeta microdentium.

Habitat: Buccal cavity; dental sediment, lung, intestinal tract. Very frequent.

Morphology: Cells, 4 to 7 μ in length with 6 to 12 spiral turns; actively motile; rotation upon the axis and weak movement of flexion; rigid appearance; occurring singly or grouped in asteroids; spiral turns are thin and regular, less than 1 μ; stained black by Giemsa; after division, the cells are united together by a terminal undulating filament; in old cultures, abnormal forms, numerous and highly varied; presence of free granules, bearing an undulating filament.

Physiology: Strict anaerobe. Opt. T. $= 35°$C. Not thermoresistant. Survives several months if conditions are avourable.

Cultural characters: No gas formed, but putrid odor.

I. Media containing fresh kidney (Noguchi, Kritchewsky and Séguin):

1. *Fresh kidney horse serum:* Rapid and abundant growth; slight turbidity around the kidney, topped by moiré rings; massive coagulation on the 8th day, then digestion of the curd; fetid odor; blackening; large amounts of H_2S; no gas formed.

2. *Semi-solid fresh kidney serum-agar:* Hazy colonies; coagulation followed by digestion and formation of a black sediment; H_2S formed.

3. *Semi-solid serum rabbit kidney:* Transparent, hazy colonies, with opaque center, surrounded by a clear halo; no gas; H_2S.

II. Autoclaved kidney media: Slower growth.

Neutral red reduced.

Malachite green becomes sulfur-yellow.

III. Media without kidney:

Serum-broth (in vacuo): Slow growth, appearing around the 15th day; serum digested.

Na pyruvate and Ca sulfide stimulate growth.

Agar-serum: Formless colonies, confluent, developing very slowly.

IV. Partly digested media:

Trypsin digest of serum: Abundant growth.

Gelatin: Liquefied.

Coagulated egg-white: Digested.

Carbohydrates: Not fermented.

Biochemistry: Fermentation of pork kidney produces NH_3, H_2S, indole and acetic acid.

Pathogenicity, natural: Isolated from numerous pathological processes of the mouth and respiratory tract in which it participates actively as a putrid pyogenic agent. In symbiosis with the fusiforms, it causes alveolar pyorrhea, gingivitis, stomatitis, noma, Vincent's angina and tonsillitis, pulmonary gangrene, appendicitis.

Pathogenicity, experimental: In pure culture, weakly or not pathogenic. In association with: 1. *Fusiformis fusiformis,* it produces a fatal putrid abscess from which the *Treponema* is retrieved; 2. *Sphaerophorus necrophorus,* it causes a rapidly fatal putrid gangrene from which the *Treponema* are equally retrieved.

Serology: Specific agglutination at 1-1,000.

8. *Treponema ambigua* Seguin and Vinzent 1936.

Synonym: Spirochaeta ambigua S. and V. 1936.

Habitat: Buccal cavity, lung, Quite frequent.

Morphology: Very similar to *Tr. microdentium* in pathological specimens; slightly longer in laboratory cultures: 7 to 12 μ, with 12 to 16 spiral turns; also slightly thicker and less rigid.

Physiology: Strict anaerobe. Opt. T. $= 30$-$35°C$. Killed at $56°C$. Short-lived.

Cultural characters: No gas produced. Obiligate serophile.

Serum-agar: Hazy colonies.

Serum-broth: Slight turbidity; serum is coagulated, but not digested. Putrid, tart odor.

Gelatin: No liquefaction.

Coagulated proteins: Not attacked.

Lead-serum-agar: Not blackened.

Malachite Gree: Feebly reduced.

Neutral red: Feebly reduced.

Biochemistry: Produces NH_3, H_2S, indole and acetic acid.

Pathogenicity, natural: Isolated from fetid suppurations of the mouth and lungs (generally in symbiosis with the fusiforms).

Pathogenicity, experimental: Non-pathogenic in pure culture. Associated with *F. fusiformis,* causes fatal putrid abscess in the guinea pig.

Serology: Not agglutinated by anti-*microdentium* serum.

9. *Treponema comandoni* Seguin and Vinzent 1936.

Synonym: Spirochaeta comandoni S. and V. 1936.

Habitat: Buccal cavity. Quite frequent.

Morphology: Longer and thicker than *Tr. ambigua.* Actively motile. Amplitude: 2 μ.

Physiology: Strict anaerobe. Opt. T. = 30-35°C. Killed at 56°C short-lived.

Cultural characters: No gas produced. Obligate serophile.

Serum-agar: Hazy colonies.

Serum-broth: Cloudy turbidity; serum is coagulated, but not digested tart, putrid odor.

Gelatin: No liquefaction.

Coagulated serum: Not attacked.

Biochemistry: Produces NH_3, H_2S, indole, acetic, propionic and lacti acids.

Pathogenicity, natural: Isolated in association with *F. shaminei* i infectious incidents concerning wisdom teeth.

Serology: Agglutination; no cross-reaction with *Tr. microdentium.*

10. *Treponema skoliodonta* Hoffman 1920.

Synonym: Spirochaeta skoliodonta H. 1920; *Spirochaeta acut* Krtichewsky and Séguin.

Habitat: Buccal cavity. Frequent.

Morphology: Spirochetes measuring 8 μ in length, with 9 spiral turns flexible; spiral turns may be open or tight; vermicular movement.

Physiology: Strict anaerobe. Opt. T. = 33°C. Killed at 55°C. Short lived.

Cultural characters: No gas produced. Obligate serophile.

Serum-agar: Hazy colonies.

Serum-broth: Meager growth; no odor.

Coagulated serum: Not attacked.

Lead-serum agar: Not blackened.

Neutral red: Partly reduced.

Pathogenicity: Isolated in association with fusiforms in bronchopleuro pulmonary infections of man: bronchiectasis, putrid pleurisy, etc.

11. *Treponema trimerodonta* Hoffmann 1920.

Synonym: Spirochaeta trimerodonta Hoffmann 1920.

Habitat: Buccal cavity. Quite frequent.

Morphology: Spirochetes with definite leptospiroidal aspect; 6 μ ir length; amplitude: 0.6 μ; terminal hooks with twirling movement; helicoida structure.

Physiology: Strict anaerobe. Opt. T. = 30-35°C. Killed at 56°C Short-lived.

Cultural characters: No gas produced. Obligate serophile.

Serum-agar: Hazy colonies, localized around a piece of kidney.

Serum-broth: Meager growth; no odor.

Coagulated serum: Not attacked.

Lead agar: Slowly blackened.

Neutral red: Partly reduced.

Pathogenicity, natural: Isolated from putrid broncho-pleuropulmonary infections.

Systematics: This species represents a transition between the *Treponema* and the *Leptospira*.

12. *Treponema macrodentium* Noguchi 1912.

Synonym: Spirochaeta macrodentium (Noguchi) S. and V.; *Spirochaeta tenuis* Gerber.

Habitat: Buccal cavity. Frequent.

Morphology: Spirochetes of large size, 12 μ in length, with 6 spiral turns; amplitude: 2 μ; the terminal spirals are often uncoiled and larger; active movements of rotation and flexion.

Physiology: Strict anaerobe. Opt. T. $= 35°$C. Killed at 55°C. Short-lived.

Cultural characters: No gas produced. Obilgate serophile.

Serum-agar: Hazy colonies, with slight transparent halo.

Serum-broth: Slight turbidity; weak odor.

Gelatin: Slow liquefaction.

Coagulated serum: Slightly attacked.

Lead agar: Blackened.

Neutral red: Reduced.

Malachite green: Reduced.

Pathogenicity, natural: Isolated in the same putrid infections as the preceding species, but more often in pyorrhea alveolaris and Vincent's angina.

Pathogenicity, experimental: An artificial combination of *Tr. macrodentium* with the fusiforms will permit the reproduction in the guinea pig of putrid infections.

13. *Treponema mucosum* Noguchi 1913.

Synonym: Spirochaeta mucosum Noguchi.

Habitat: Buccal cavity.

Morphology: Quite similar to *Tr. microdentium;* stained red by Giemsa.

Physiology: Strict anaerobe. Differs from *Tr. microdentium* only by its production of mucus in laboratory cultures. Putrid odor.

Pathogenicity, natural: Isolated in alveolar pyorrhea, where it plays the part of a putrid agent.

14. *Treponema calligyrum* Noguchi 1918.

Synonym: Spirochaeta calligyrum Noguchi.

Habitat: Humna smegma.

Morphology: Spirochetes measuring 0.3 to 0.4 μ $\times$ 6 to 14 μ; spiral turns are regular, 1.0 to 1.5 μ $\times$ 1.6 μ; pointed ends; stained purple-red by Giemsa.

Physiology: Strict anaerobe. Obligate serophile.

Cultural characters: Grows only on serum added with fragments of fresh tissue and under strictly anaerobic conditions.

Pathogenicity: Non-pathogenic.

15. *Treponema minutum* Noguchi 1913.

Synonym: Spirochaeta minutum Noguchi 1913; *Treponema genitalis* Noguchi 1918.

Habitat: Human genital organs.

Morphology: Spirochetes measuring 0.25 to 0.3 μ $\times$ 3 to 14 μ; spiral turns measure 0.2 to 0.5 μ $\times$ 0.9 to 1.0 μ; each end is terminated by a short lateral hook.

Physiology: Strict anaerobe. Obligate serophile. Neutral red and safranin are reduced.

Cultural characters: Grows only on serum added with fragments of fresh tissue and under strictly anaerobic conditions. No gas produced.

Gelatin: No liquefaction.

Milk: Unchanged.

Coagulated serum: Not attacked.

Carbohydrates: Not fermented.

Biochemistry: Produces NH_3, indole, ketones, volatile amines (traces), propionic and lactic acids.

Pathogenicity: Non-pathogenic.

16. *Treponema penortha* (Beveridge) P. 1948.

Synonym: Spirochaeta penortha Beveridge 1936.[1]

Habitat: Foot-rot of sheep.

Morphology: Filamentous and spirally-wound bacteria measuring 0.25 to 0.3 μ $\times$ 6 to 10 μ; irregularly bearing spheroids meaguring 0.5 to 2.5 μ; motile by spiral undulations (no flagella nor terminal filament); no endospores; Gram-negative.

Physiology: Strict anaerobe. Opt. T. $= 37°$C. Killed at 55°C. Requires 10% CO_2. Survives 8 months.

Isolation: Very difficult, in VF agar horse serum.

Cultural characters: Gas and putrid odor produced.

Blood-VF deep agar: Translucent, lenticular colonies.

Blood-agar slant: Convex, whitish colonies with greenish or pink sheen.

Semi-solid VF agar slice of fresh potato: Gaseous growth.

VF broth: No growth.

---

[1] It is probable that this species is identical with *Tr. podovis* described by Blaizot in 1928; but the description of the latter is not sufficient to place this assertion beyond argument.

Milk: Coagulated.

VF broth fresh potato: Flaky growth.

Pathogenicity: Non-pathogenic in pure culture; in association with *Rist. nodosa* and *F. pedipedis,* produces foot-rot of sheep. No hemolysin.

Serology: Agglutination at 1-2,400.

17. *Treponema enterogyrata* (Vinzent and Séguin) P. 1957.

Synonym: Spirochaeta enterogyrata Vinzent and Séguin 1939.

Habitat: Intestinal tract of man, to the exclusion of other natural cavities.

Morphology: Very supple spirochete measuring 0.6 μ $\times$ 12 μ, with 3 to 15 spiral turns. Actively motile.

Physiology: Strict anaerobe. Rapidly produces involution forms in culture. Survives 1 month.

Cultural characters: Obligate serophile; easily adapted to media without serum.

Kidney-serum-agar: Abundant growth. Colonies occur in the shape of large bubbles.

Gelatin: No liquefaction.

Coagulated serum: Not digested.

Biochemistry: H_2S not produced.

Pathogenicity: Isolated from human feces of patients parasitized by *Lamblia* or by *Trichomomas.*

18. *Treponema phagedenis* (Noguchi) Topley and Wilson.

Synonym: Spirochaeta phagedenis Noguchi; *Borrelia phagedenis* (N).

Habitat: Phagedenic ulcer.

Morphology: Spirally-wound bacteria, 0.7 to 0.8 μ $\times$ 10 to 51 μ, with 1 to 2 spiral turns, and pointed ends; the long forms show a central swelling; no flagella, nor terminal filament; stained red by Giemsa.

Physiology: Strict anaerobe. Obligate serophile.

Cultural characters: Grows only on Noguchi's medium or on Vinzent's medium.

Biochemistry: Produces NH_3, H_2S, indole (traces) and acetic acid.

Pathogenicity, natural: In association with the fusiforms, causes phagedenic ulcer.

Pathogenicity, experimental: Rabbit and monkey are susceptible.

19. *Treponema vincenti* Brumpt 1922.

Synonym: Spirochaeta vincenti Blanchard 1906; *Borrelia vincenti* (B.) Bergey *et al.* Many authors refuse to consider this species as valid; they maintain that it represents a number of mixed strains. It therefore appears here with all necessary reserve.[1]

Morphology: Spirochetes measuring 0.5 to 0.75 μ $\times$ 8 to 12 μ, with shallow, irregular spirals and delicate terminal filament; stained by aniline dyes; actively motile with a vibratory movement.

Physiology: Strict anaerobe. Obligate serophile.

Cultural characters: Grows only on Noguchi-type media.

Pathogenicity, natural: Found in association with *F. fusiformis* and the other fusiforms in putrid infections of the mouth and respiratory tract.

Pathogenicity, experimental: In pure culture, non-pathogenic. In association, pathogenic for laboratory animals.

20. *Treponema zuelzerae* Veldkamp 1960.

Habitat: Mud from soft waters containing H_2S.

Morphology: Flexible cells, measuring 0.2 to 0.35 μ $\times$ 8 to 16 μ; with shallow, irregular undulations; amplitude: 1 μ; in old cultures, filamentous forms measuring 80 μ result from incomplete division; the structure of the cells is rougher and more irregular than that of the other *Treponema;* spheriods appear during the stationary phase, more often on the ends; motile by undulating motion; invisible under direct lighting; deeply stained by basic fuchsin, carbol-fuchsin and carbol-erythrosin.

Physiology: Strict anaerobe. Opt. T. $=$ 37-40°C. Grows at 20°C. Opt. pH $=$ 7-8.

Cultural characters: Requires CO_2.

Deep agar: Lenticular or spherical colonies, greyish, extensive, translucent.

Glucose-yeast extract: Good growth.

Tryptone-casitone-peptone water: Good growth.

Carbohydrates: Glucose, mannose, galactose, xylose, trehalose, cellobiose, maltose and starch are fermented.

Biochemistry: Produces NH_3, CO_2, H_2, acetic, lactic and succinic acids. $NaNO_3$ cannot be utilized as sole source of N. Ca SO_4 not reduced.

Pathogenicity: Non-pathogenic.

Serology: Proteic antigen giving a positive complement-fixation reaction with syphilitic serum.

GENUS II: *BORRELIA* Swellengrebel 1907.

Spirally-wound cells measuring 8 to 10 μ in length, with rough, irregular, shallow, angular spiral turns; ends generally pointed with delicate filaments; easily stained by aniline dyes; refraction index close to that of the *Eubacteria;* parasitic of numerous animal species and man.

---

[1] The terms *Treponema buccale, Treponema eurigyrata, Treponema bronchialis,* etc. do not correspond to pure and cultivable species. They are not included here, therefore.

This genus comprises 6 species which have grown under anaerobic ɔnditions. (The species *phagedenis, vincenti* and *refringens* which Bergey *t al.* place in this genus are in reality *Treponema* and are placed with the receding genus).

1. Agent of avian spirochetosis transmitted by ticks.
   1. *Borrelia anserina,* page 385
2. Agent of human relapsing fever of European type, transmitted by lice.
   2. *Borrelia recurrentis,* page 385
3. Agent of human relapsing fever of African type (central and southern), transmitted by ticks.
   3. *Borrelia duttoni,* page 386
4. Agent of human relapsing fever of African type (eastern).
   4. *Borrelia kochi,* page 386
5. Agent of human relapsing fever of American type.
   5. *Borrelia novyi,* page 386
6. Blood and lesions of pigs suffering from hog cholera; non-pathogenic.
   6. *Borrelia hyos,* page 386

1. *Borrelia anserina* (Sakharoff) Bergey *et al.*

Synonym: Spirochaeta anserina Sakharoff 1891; *Spirille des poules* ʃarchoux and Salimbeni; *Spirochaeta gallinarum* (Blanchard 1905) C. ɲd C. 1913; *Borrelia gallinarum* Swellengrebel.

Habitat: Fowl suffering from spirochetosis.

Morphology: Spirally-wound organisms, 0.25 to 0.3 $\mu \times$ 8 to 16 μ; ɪmplitude: 1.8 μ; terminal granule, and hooked filament; actively motile; ɪsible without staining; easily stained by aniline dyes.

Physiology: Strict anaerobe. Obligate serophile.

Culture characters: Grows only on Smith-Noguchi medium. No odor.

Pathogenicity: Septicemia of fowls, transmitted by ticks (*Argas ɐrsicus, Ornithodorus moubata*); geese and ducks are also susceptible.

2. *Borrelia recurrentis* (Lebert) Bergey *et al.*

Synonym: Spirochaeta obermeieri Cohn 1875; *Spirochaeta recurrentis* ɔ. and N. 1907.

Morphology: Spirally-wound organisms, 8 to 16 μ in length, with 4 ɔ 12 flexuous spirals, shallow, irregular, with pointed ends; actively motile ʳith no flagella; visible under direct lighting; easily stained by Giemsa and ɲiline dyes; Gram-negative.

Physiology: Strict anaerobe. Obligate serophile.

Cultural characters: Grows only on ascitic fluid added with fragments of fresh kidney (Galloway's medium), Marchoux and Chorine's medium, Li Yan Po's medium). Completely lyzed by 10% bile or saponin.

Pathogenicity, natural: Relapsing fever human of European type, transmitted by lice.

Pathogenicity, experimental: The monkey is susceptible.

3. *Borrelia duttoni* (Novy and Knapp) Bergey *et al.*

Synonym: Spirochaeta duttoni Todd 1906; *Treponema duttoni* Topley and Wilson.

Habitat: Organs of the tick, *Ornithodorus moubata.*

Morphology: Spirally-wound organisms, 0.2 to 0.25 μ $\times$ 14 to 17 μ, irregularly-curved, with delicate filament at each end.

Physiology: Strict anaerobe.

Cultural characters: Grows only in dilute serum added with fresh tissue and under strictly anaerobic conditions.

Pathogenicity, natural: Relapsing fever of African type (central and southern) transmitted by ticks.

Germ reservoir: Wild burrowing rodents. Many authors feel that this species is simply a variety of the preceding species.

4. *Borrelia kochi* (Novy) Bergey *et al.*

Synonym: Spirochaeta kochi Novy 1907.

Habitat: East Africa (rodents?).

Morphology: Similar to *B. recurrentis.*

Physiology, Cultural characters: Similar to those of the preceding species.

Pathogenicity, natural: Relapsing fever of East Africa.

Pathogenicity, experimental: Rat and mouse are susceptible.

Serology: No cross-reactions with *B. recurrentis* and *B. duttoni.*

5. *Borrelia novyi* (Schellak) Bergey *et al.*

Synonym: Spirochaeta novyi Schellak 1907.

Habitat: America.

Morphology: Similar to *B. recurrentis.*

Cultural characters: Similar to those of *B. recurrentis.*

Pathogenicity, natural: American relapsing fever.

Pathogenicity, experimental: Monkey, rat and mouse are susceptible.

Serology: No cross-reactions with *B. recurrentis, B. duttoni* and *B. kochi.*

6. *Borrelia hyos* Bergey *et al.*

Synonym: Spirochaeta hyos King and Drake 1915.

Habitat: Blood, intestinal tract and lesions of pigs suffering from hog cholera.

Morphology: Short, thick, spirally-wound organisms, $1\mu \times 5$ to $7\ \mu$; actively motile.

Physiology: Strict anaerobe.

Cultural characters: Grows only on media containing blood or ascitic fluid, added with fragments of fresh tissue.

Pathogenicity: Probably associated with hog cholera.

Chapter 12

GROUP OF UNCERTAIN TAXONOMIC POSITION

DURING the first decade of the present century several investigators working together or separately discovered the agents of pleuro-pneumonia, (Nocard and Roux; Borrel, Dujardin-Beaumetz, Jeantet and Jouna), contagious agalaxia (Bridré and Donatién) and gave them the generic name of *Asterococcus* (Borrel *et al.*). This was only the beginning of a long series of discoveries, and at the present time this genus comprises 15 species. The taxonomy and systematical position of this genus have suffered a great number of unjustified disruptions which are still going on. Thus, have we seen *Asterococcus* become successively *Coccobacillus, Micromyces, Mycoplasma, Asteromyces, Anulomyces, Borrelomyces, Bovimyces, Pleuropneumonia.*

For reasons difficult to understand, Freundt has elected to choose *Mycoplasma,* family of *Mycoplasmataceae,* order of *Mycoplasmatales,* constituting the 10th order in the class of *Schizomycetes* in Bergey's 7th edition.

After having studied the problem throughly, we cannot help but come to the conclusion that we are dealing here with an important and interesting group of bacteria, but their systematical position is still somewhat uncertain and their nomenclature has not been definitively decided upon. For these reasons, we keep the generic name of *Asterococcus* Borrel to include 2 anaerobic or microaerophilic species of which here is the key for their determination:

Genus *Asterococcus* Borrel *et al* 1910.

Synonym: If this name must be abandoned because it was used in 1908 by Scherffel for a unicellular algae, the law of priority requires that we replace it with *Asteromyces* Wroblewski 1931. All the other synonyms are posterior to the latter and valueless.

Definition: Highly pleomorphic micro-organisms. In fluid or solid culture media, elementary corpuscles produce one or several filaments which branch out to form a pseudomycelium. At a later stage, condensation of material occurs to give birth to rings and spheroids which become free and some of which give rise to giant forms. These, finally, become granular and produce elementary bodies of 125 to 250 mμ, which filter through candles; stain with difficulty by aniline dyes; easily stained by Giemsa; non-motile; Gram-negative.

Thirteen aerobic forms and two species which are preferentially anaerobic. Growth on agar media produces very small, opaque, granular colonies with dark center and transparent edges. Parasites of man and animals. One saprophytic species.

1. Smooth growth at the bottom of semi-solid media; glucose not fermented.

    1. *Asterococcus salivarius,* page 389

2. Glucose fermented.

    2. *Asterococcus fermentans,* page 389

1. *Asterococcus salivarius* (Edward) nov. comb.

Synonym: Mycoplasma salivarium Edward 1955.

Habitat: Human saliva.

Morphology: Elementary bodies giving rise to filaments, ramifications and a mycelioid structure; filaments divided by septa; spheroids; present L-cycle; size 125 to 250 mμ; non-motile; Gram-negative.

Physiology: Strict anaerobe on isolation; anaerobic by predilection. Slowly reduces methylene blue.

Serum-agar: Spotted film.

Blood agar: No hemolysis.

Rabbit blood agar: Good growth, stimulated by the addition of ribonucleic acid.

Pathogenicity: Unknown.

Carbohydrates: Not fermented.

2. *Asterococcus fermentans* (Edward) nov. comb.

Synonym: Mycoplasma fermentans Edward 1955.

Habitat: Ulcerated genital lesions, in association with *Fusiformis* and *Treponema.*

Morphology: Mycelioid, stable structure with filaments measuring 10 to 30 μ; Gram-negative.

Physiology: Strict anaerobe or microaerophilic. Methylene blue is reduced. Growth is stimulated by ribonucleic acid under anaerobic conditions at pH $= 7$-8.

Serum-agar: Film and spots.

Blood agar: No hemolysis.

Broth: Opacified.

Semi-solid media: Smooth growth.

Carbohydrates: Glucose, fructose, galactose, maltose, glycogen, dextrin and starch are fermented.

Pathogenicity: Injection into the mouse produces abscesses.
Systematics: Closely related, but different serologically from
A. salivarium.

REFERENCES

ADAMS and POSTGATE: J. Gen. Microb., 1959, *20*, 252.
ALADAME: Ann. I.P., 1951, *81*, 339.
ANDRE: Thèse de Médecine, Paris 1948.

BAALSRUD: Arch. f. Mikrob., 1954, *201*, 34.
BABA: J. Agr. Chem. Soc. Jap., 1943, *19*, 207.
BARKER: Ant. v. Leeuw. 1947, *12*, 114.
BARKER and BECK: J.B.C., 1941, *141*, 3.
BARKER and HAAS: J. Bact., 1944, *47*, 301.
BARKER and PEDERSON: J. Bact., 1944, *47*, 307.
BARKER and TAHA: J. Bact., 1942, *43*, 347.
BEERENS and ALADAME: Ann. I.P., 1949, *76*, 476.
BEERENS and DEMOUCHY: C. r. Soc. Biol., 1948, *142*, 1107.
BEERENS and GAUMONT: Ann. I.P. Lille, 1953, 5, 113.
BEERENS and GOUDAERT: Ann. I.P. Lille, 1953, 5, 119.
BEESCH and LEGG: U.S. Letters Pat., 1947, no. 2, 420, 998.
BEESCH: U.S. Letters Pat., 1948, no. 2, 439, 791.
BEEUWKES and ALADAME: Ann. I.P., 1948, *75*, 390.
BENNEJANT: Thèse de Médecine, Paris, 1955.
BERGEY: Manual of Determinative Bacteriology, 5th ed., Williams & Wilkins,
　　Co., Baltimore, 1939.
BEVERIDGE: Council Sc. Ind. Res., 1941, *140*.
BEZJAK: Ann. I.P., 1952, *82*, 98.
BILLY: Ann. I.P., 1965, *109*, 147.
BLAT and BARKER: J. Bact., 1947, *54*, 381.
BOKKENHEUSER: Ann. I.P., 1951, *80*, 548.
BOSWORTH: J. Comp. Path. Therap., 1943, *53*, 245.
BOURRELY: Rev. algologique, 1954, *1*, 29.
BRISOU and PREVOT: Ann. I.P., 1954, *86*, 722.
BRISOU: Ann. I.P., 1957.
BRUNEAU: Rev. med. Fr. extr.-Or., 1941, 1118.
BRYANT *et al:* J. Bact., 1958, *76*, 15.
BRYANT, SMALL, ROUMA and ROBINSON: J. Bact., 1958, *76*, 529.
BRYGOO: Ann. I.P., 1950, *78*, 795.
BRYGOO and ALADAME: Ann. I.P., 1953, *84*, 640.
BUCHANAN: J. Bact., 1916, *1*, 591, 1917, *2*, 155; 1917, *2*, 347; 1917, *2*, 603;
　　1918, *3*, 27; 1918, *3*, 175, 403; 461 and 541.

CALAME: Ann. I.P., 1951, *80*, 438; 1952, *82*, 377.
CAMPBELL: J. Bact., 1957, *73*, 220 and 225.
CARBONE: Prog. Ind. Tess., 1917.
CARDON: Proc. Soc. Exp. Biol. Med., 1942, *51*, 267.
CARDON and BARKER: J. Bact., 1946, *52*, 629.

COHEN and RAYNAUD: Ann. I.P., 1947, *73*, 95.
COOPER, KELLER and JOHNSON: Amer. J. Dis. Child., 1934, *47*, 388 and 596.
COULOMBIER: "Les Listerioses humaines," Thèse de Médecine, Paris, 1955.

DELAPORTE: "Recherches cytologiques sur les Bactéries et les Cyanophycées," Thèse de sciences, Paris, 1939.
DOETSCH, HOWARD, MANN and OXFORD: J. Gen. Microb., 1957, 16, 156.
DUCHOW and DOUGLAS: J. Bact., 1949, *58*.

EDWARD: Brit. J. Ven. Dis., 1953, *29*, 148; J. Gen. Microb., 1951, *5*, 566.
EIKEN: Acta Path. Microb. Skand., 1958, *43*, 404.
ENEBO: Physiol. Plantarum, 1951, *4*, 653.

FELLERS: Abstr. Bact., 1923, *7*, 351.
FLORENT: C. r. Soc. Biol., Belge, 1953.
FOUBERT and DOUGLAS: J. Bact., 1948, *56*, 25 and 35.

GASTON and STADTMAN: J. Bact., 1963, *85*, 386.
GERMAN: Thèse de sciences, Paris, 1953.
GIESBERGER: J. Microb. Serol., 1947, *13*, 137.
GUNNISON, CUMMINS and MEYER: Proc. Soc. Exp. Biol. Med., 1936, *35*, 278.
GUILLAUMIE, KREGUER and FABRE: C. r. Soc. Biol., 1946, *140*, 436; Ann. I.P., 1946, *72*, 814.
GUTTIEREZ, DAVIS, LINDHAL and WARMICK: Appl. Microb., 1959, *7*, 304.

HALL: J. Gen. Microb., 1952, *7*, 350.
HAMLIN and HUNGATE: J. Bact., 1956, *72*, 548.
HARDMAN and STADTMAN: J. Bact., 1960, *79*, 544.
HARRISON and HANSON: Ant. v. Leeuw. 1963, *29*, . .22.
HUET: Ann I. P., 1952, *82*, 238.
HUET and ALADAME: Ann. I.P., 1952, *82*, 766.
HUNGATE: Bact. Rev., 1950, *14*, 1; J. bact., 1963, *86*, 848.

ISEKI, FURUKAWA and YAMAMOTO: Proc. Jap. Acad., 1959, *35*, 620.

JOHNS: J. Gen. Microb., 1951, *5*, 317 and 326.

KAISER: Thèse de sciences, Paris, 1961.
KAMEN and VERNON: J. Bact., 1954, *67*, 617.
KIMURA and LIAO: Proc. Jap. Acad., 1953, *29*, 132.
KIRCHHEINER: Ann. I.P., 1940, 64.
KOERBER and PATOCKA: Ann. I.P., 1948, *74*, 254.

LAHELLE and THJOTTA: Acta Path. Microb. Scand., 1945, *22*, 319.
LANGFORD, FABER and PELCZAR: J. Bact., 1950, *59*, 349.
LARSDEN: J. Bact., 1952, *64*, 187.
LEBERT: Ann. I.P., 1948, *74*, 256; 1949, *76*, 548.
LEGALL: J. Bact., 1963, *86*, 1120.
LESSEL and BREED: Bact., Rev., 1954, *18*, 165.
LINHARD: Ann. I.P., 1949, *76*, 478.
LOTH: C. r. Soc. Biol., 1942, *136*, 162.

MAGARA, GO, SO and AKIMA: Jap. Med. J., 1948, *1*, 289.
MAGROU and PREVOT: C. r. Acad. Sc., 1948, *226*, 1229.
MAGROU and PREVOT: Ann. I.P., 1948, *75*, 99.
MANDIN: Thèse de médecine, Montpellier, 1956.
MARTRES, BRYGOO and THOUVENOT: Ann. I.P., 1952, *83*, 139.

MAZUREK, BAZIN and KARSENTI: Ann. I.P., 1952, *82*, 631.
MCBEE: J. Bact., 1948, *56*, 653.
MCCLUNG and MCCOY: U.S. Letters Pat., 1940, no. 2, 195, 629.
MCCOY: U.S. Letters Pat., 1946, no. 2, 398, 837.
MERCER and VAUGHN: J. Bact., 1951, *62*, 27and 38.
MEYER, MALGRAS and ALADAME: Ann. I.P., 1952, *82*, 240.
MOLLER and SCHEIBEL: Acta Path. Microb. Scand., 1960, *48*, 80.
MORCOS: J. Bact., 1932, *23*, 449.
MOUREAU: Ann. I.P., 1955, *88*, 231.
MOUREAU and ALADAME: Ann. I.P., 1951, *81*, 337; 1955, *89*, 127.
MOUREAU and GIUNTINI: Ann. I.P., 1956, *90*, 728.

NAKAHADA and HARADA: J. Agr. Chem. Soc. Jap., 1949, *23*, 178.
NECTOUX and SUCHET: An. Oculist., 1953, *186*, 538.

OSTERTAG: Z. f. Hyg. u. Inf., 1952, *133*, 489.

PATOCKA and PREVOT: Soc. fr. Microb., 1947, 3 avril.
PATOCKA and REYNES: Soc. fr. Microb., 1947, 9 Janvier.
PATOCKA and SEBEK: Bull. Internat. Ac. Tch. Sc., 1951, *52*, 307; *61*, 1.
PISU and ALADAME: Ann. I.P., 1952, *82*, 379.
POCHON: Ann. I.P., 1949, *77*, 419.
POCHON: Ann. I.P., 1941, *66*, 57; 1942, *68*, 353 and 467.
POCHON and BARJAC: C. r. Ac. Sc., 1954, *238*, 627.
PREVOT: Ann. Sc. nat., 1933, 23-260.
PREVOT: Ann. I.P., 1938, *60*, 285; *61*, 72.
PREVOT: Trav. Station zool. Wimereux, 1938, *13*, 597.
PREVOTS IIIe Congres Internat. Microb., New York, 1939.
PREVOT: Ann. I.P., 1940, *64*.
PREVOT: C. r. Soc. Biol., 1940, *133*, 246, 384 and 574; *134*, 350 and 353.
PREVOT: Ann. Ferm., 1940, *5*, 467.
PREVOT: C. r. Soc. Biol., 1941, *135*, 103 and 105.
PREVOT: Ann. I.P., 1941, *67*, 87 and 471.
PREVOT: Ann. I.P., 1945, *71*, 317.
PREVOT: Ann. I.P., 1946, *72*, 2and 662.
PREVOT: C. r. Acad. Sc., 1946, *222*, 246; *223*, 1035.
PREVOT: Ann. I.P., 1948, *74*, 157; *75*, 387 and 571.
PREVOT: Le Soufre, 1948, p. 145.
PREVOT: Acta path. microb. scand., 1948, *25*, 564.
PREVOT: Ann. I.P., 1949, *76*, 492; *77*, 400.
PREVOT: Rev. stomat., 1949, *50*, 539.
PREVOT: Ann. I.P., 1950, *79*, 1.
PREVOT: La Nature, 1952, *3205*, 147.
PREVOT: "Biologie des Maladies dues aux Anaerobies," Flammarion, 1955, 580 p.
PREVOT: Bull. Acad. nat. med., 1955, *139*, 355.
PREVOT: Rev. fr. ex. clin. biol., 1956, *1*, 201.
PREVOT: Path et Biol., 1956, *32*, 755.
PREVOT: Ann. I.P., 1956, *91*, 766.
PREVOT: "Traite de Systematique bactérienne," Dunod, 2 vols., Paris, 1961, 1200 p.
PREVOT, BEALAND and TARDIEUX: Ann. I.P., 1950, *79*, 763.
PREVOT, BEERENS and ZIMMES: Ann. I.P., 1947, *73*, 390.

PREVOT, BESSE and DEFAGONDE: Ann. I.P., 1950, *79*, 903.
PREVOT and BILLY: Ann. I. P., 1961, *100*, 475.
PREVOT and BRISOU: Ann. I. P., 1954, *86*, 722.
PREVOT and BRYGOO: Ann. I. P., 1950, *78*, 274; *79*, 1.
PREVOT and CAPPONI: Ann. I. P., 1949, *77*, 722.
PREVOT, COHEN and NISMAN: Soc. fr. Microb., 1947, 3 avril
PREVOT, COHEN and RAYNAUD: C. r. Soc. Biol., 1946, *140*, 350.
PREVOT and COLLAB.: Ann. I.P., 1949, *50*, 539.
PREVOT and COLLAB.: Ann. I. P., 1950, *79*, 763.
PREVOT and COLLAB.: Ann. I. P., 1951, *81*, 85.
PREVOT and COLLAB.: Ann. I. P., 1955, *89*, 352.
PREVOT and COLLAB.: Bull. Acad. nat. Méd., 1955, *139*, 355.
PREVOT and COLLAB.: Ann. I. P., 1956, *91*, 766.
PREVOT and COLLAB.: Ann. I. P., 1958, *95*, 16.
PREVOT and COLLAB.: Ann. I. P., 1958, *95*, 369.
PREVOT and COLLAB.: C. r. Acad. Sc., 1963, *256*, 329; *257*, 13.
PREVOT and CORDIER: C. r. Soc. Biol., 1941, *135*, 992.
PREVOT and CORDIER: Ann. I. P., 1941, *67*, 473.
PREVOT and CORDURIER: Ann. I. P., 1949, *76*, 232.
PREVOT, DE CADORE and THOUVENOT: Ann. I.P., 1959, *97*, 860.
PREVOT, DEZEST and LEVATIDI: C. r. Acad. Sc., 1954, *238*, 1937.
PREVOT, DIGEON and ENESCU: C. r. Soc. Biol., 1946, 140, *5*, and 76.
PREVOT, DIGEON, PEYRE, PANTALEON and SENEZ: Ann. I. P., 1947, *73*, 409.
PREVOT and ENESCU: C. r. Soc. Biol., 1946, *140*, 76.
PREVOT and HUET: Ann. I.P., 1951, *80*, 94.
PREVOT, GIUNTINI and THOUVENOT: Ann. I. P., 1954, *86*, 774.
PREVOT and HUET: Bull. Acad. nat. Méd., 1951, *135*, 432.
PREVOT, HUET and THEVENARD: Bull. Acad. nat. Méd., 1952, *136*, 323.
PREVOT, JANOT and TAM: C. r. Acad. Sc., 1963, *256*, 3785.
PREVOT and KIRCHHEINER: C. r. Soc. Biol., 1938, *128*, 840 and 963; *129*, 158.
PREVOT and KIRCHHEINER: C. r. Acad. Sc., 1939, *209*, 182.
PREVOT and LAPLANCHE: Soc. fr. Microb., 1947, 6 fev. and 3 avril.
PREVOT, LEVATIDI, TARDIEUX and NAZIMOFF: Ann. I. P., 1955, *88*, 537.
PREVOT and LOTH: C. r. Soc. Biol., 1941, *135*, 457 and 609.
PREVOT and LOTH: Ann. Ferm., 1941, 6, 76.
PREVOT and LOTH: Ann. I. P., 1941, *67*, 244.
PREVOT and MALGRAS: Ann. I. P., 1950, *78*, 133.
PREVOT and MAZUREK: Ann. I. P., 1953, *84*, 879; *85*, 125.
PREVOT, MAZUREK and TARDIEUX: Ann. I. P., 1951, *81*, 173; *83*, 186.
PREVOT and MOREL: Bull. Acad. nat. Méd., 1964, *148*, 540.
PREVOT and MOUREAU: Ann. I. P., 1952, *82*, 13.
PREVOT and PEYRE: C. r. Soc. Biol., 1946, *140*, 77.
PREVOT, PIECHAUD and THOUVENOT: Ann. I. P., 1954, *86*, 778.
PREVOT and POCHON: Ann. I. P., 1951, *80*, 672.
PREVOT, POULIQUEN and TARDIEUX: Bull. Acad. nat. Méd., 1954, *138*, 308.
PREVOT and RAYNAUD: Ann. I. P., 1943, *69*, 378; *70*, 50, 182 and 185.
PREVOT and RAYNAUD: C. r. Acad. Sc., 1944, *218*, 126; *222*, 1531.
PREVOT and RAYNAUD: Ann. I. P., 1947, *73*, 65 and 67.
PREVOT and RAYNAUD: Ann. I. P., 1955, *88*, 229.
PREVOT, RAYNAUD and DIGEON: Soc. fr. Microb., 1946, 7 nov.
PREVOT, RAYNAUD and TATAKI: Ann. I. P., 1951, *80*, 553.
PREVOT and REINERT: C. r. Soc. Biol., 1942, *136*, 288.
PREVOT and ROSSI: Bull. Acad. vet., 1948, *21*, 387 and 391.

PREVOT and SAISSAC: Ann. I. P., 1950, *79*, 763.
PREVOT and SANSONNENS: Soc. fr. Microb., 1947, 5 juin.
PREVOT and SARRAF: Ann. I. P., 1961, *99* 629.
PREVOT, SILLIOC and QUENTIN: Bull. Acad. vét., 1953, *26*, 73.
PREVOT and TAFFANEL: Ann. I. P., 1942, *68*, 259, 363 and 420.
PREVOT and TAFFANEL: Ann. Ferm., 1942, *7*, 65.
PREVOT and TAFFANEL: C. r. Soc. Biol., 1942, *136*, 384, 415, 451 and 480; *138*, 401.
PREVOT and TAFFANEL: Ann. I. P., 1942, *68*, 559; *71*, 152.
PREVOT and TAFFANEL: C. r. Acad. Sc., 1943, *216*, 94.
PREVOT and TARDIEUX: Ann. I. P., 1953, *84*, 879.
PREVOT, TARDIEUX and ROSANSKY: Ann. I. P., 1955, *88*, 124.
PREVOT and THOUVENOT: Ann. I. P., 1954, *87*, 716; *86*, 667.
PREVOT and THOUVENOT: Ann. I. P., 1959, *97*, 234.
PREVOT and THOUVENOT: Ann. I. P., 1962, *103*, 925.
PREVOT, THOUVENOT and KAISER: Ann. I. P., 1957, *93*, 429 and 766.
PREVOT, THOUVENOT, PETRIGALLA and SILLIOC: Ann. I. P., 1956, *91*, 929.
PREVOT, THOUVENOT, PITRE and BRESSOU: Ann. I. P., 1954, *86*, 776.
PREVOT and VEILLON: C. r. Soc. Biol., 1938, *128*, 451; *129*, 931; *132*, 239; *133*, 249.
PREVOT and VINZENT: Ann. I. P., 1949, *76*, 74.
PREVOT and WEISLITZ: Ann. I. P., 1946, *72*, 144.
PREVOT and ZIMMES: C. r. Soc. Biol., 1946, *140*, 110.
PREVOT and ZIMMES: Soc. fr. Microb., 1947, 9 janv.
PREVOT, ZIMMES, PEYRE and LANTHIEZ: Ann. I. P., 1947, *73*, 222.
PRINGSHEIM: Nature, 1953, p. 172.

RAYNAUD: Thèse de sciences, Paris, 1946.
RAYNAUD: Ann. I. P., 1949, *77*, 434.
RAYNAUD, ROBIN and LAJUDIE: Ann. I. P., 1948, *74*, 333.
REYNES: Arch. I. P., Indochine, 1940.
REYNES: Soc. fr. Microb., 1947, 9 janvier.
ROBIN: Ann. I. P., 1948, *74*, 258.

SAISSAC and ANDRE: Soc. fr. Microb., 1947, 5 juin.
SAISSAC, BRUGIERES and RAYNAUD: Ann. I.P., 1952, *82*, 356.
SARTORY and MEYER: C. r. Acad. Sc., 1941, *212*, 817.
SARTORY and MEYER: Bull. Acad. Med., 1940, *123*, 98.
SCHNELLEN: Onderzoekingen over de methaangisting, these Delft, 1947.
SCHWABACHER, LUCAS and RIMIGTON: J. Gen. Miroc., 1947, *1*, 109.
SEBALD: Thèse de sciences, Paris, 1962.
SEBALD and PREVOT: Ann. I. P., 1962, *102*, 189.
SEDAILLAN, BERTOYE and CARRAZ: J. med. Lyon, 1948, *30*, 589.
SEDAILLAN, MOINECOURT and MARAL: Bull. Soc. méd. Hop. Paris, 1948, p.346.
SEGUIN: Ann. Dermat. Syph., 1939, *10*, 833.
SEGUIN and VINZENT: Ann. I. P., 1938, *61*, 255; *67*, 37.
SELIBER and ALEXEEV: Mikrobiologuija, 1957, *26*, 99.
SHIMWELL: J. Inv. Brewing, 1937, *43*, 507; 1950, *56*, 179.
SIJPESTEJN: Ant. v. Leeuw., 1949, *15*, 49.
SMITH and KING: J. Bact., 1962, *83*, 938.
SOMPOLINSKY: Ann. I. P., 1950, *79*, 204.
SORIANO: Rev. asoc. argent. Dietol., 1948, *6*, 36.
SPRAY: J. Bact., 1948, *55*, 841.

STADTMAN and BARKER: J. Bact., 1951, *61*, 81; *62*, 3 and 269.
STADTMAN and McCLUNG: J. Bact., 1957, *73*, 218.
STANIER: "Some singular features of bacteria as dynamic systems", Monograph E. Backer, Acad. Press, New York, 1956.
STELLMACH-HELWIG: Arch. Mikrob., 1961, *38*, 50.
SZULMAJSTER and KAISER: Ann. I. P., 1960, *98*, 774.

TANNER: Ann. I. P., 1949, *76*, 541.
TARDIEUX: Ann. I. P., 1951, *80*, 275.
TARDIEUX: Ann. I. P., 1955, *89*, 686.
TARDIEUX and BEERENS: Ann. I. P., 1951, *81*, 97.
TARDIEUX, HUET and BJORKLUND: Ann. I. P., 1952, *82*, 763.
TARDIEUX and NARBONNE: Ann. I.P., 1949, *76*, 181.
TARDIEUX and NISMAN: Ann. I. P., 1952, *82*, 458.
TARDIEUX and SEGOND: Ann. I. P., 1949, *76*, 543.
TATAKI: Thèse de médecine, Athènes, 1954.
TATAKI and HUET: Ann. I. P., 1953, *84*, 890.
TCHAN, POCHON and PREVOT: Ann. I. P., 1948, *74*, 394.
THEILADE and GILMOUR: J. Bact., 1961, *81*, 661.
THJOTTA, HARTMANN and BOE: Avh. utg. av Det Nortske Videnskaps Akademie I Oslo I Mat.-Naturv. Kl., 1939, no. 5.
THOUVENOT and FLORENT: Ann. I. P., 1954, *86*, 237.

VAN BEYNUM and PETTE: Z. f. Bakt., II., 1935, *93*, 208.
VAN NIEL: Bact. Rev., 1944, *8*, 1.
VELDKAMP: Ant. v. Leeuw., 1960, *26*, 103.
VINZENT and LINHARD: Ann. I. P., 1949, *76*, 545.
VINZENT and REYNES: Soc. fr. Microb., 1947, 9 janvier.
VINZENT and SEGUIN: Bull. Acad. nat. Méd., 1939, *121*, 407.
VINZENT and TATAKI: Ann. I. P., 1951, *81*, 92.

WACHSMAN and BARKER: J. Bact., 1954, *68*, 400.
WALKER: Austr. J. Agric. Res., 1961, *12*, 171.
WEINBERG, NATIVELLE and PREVOT: "Les Microbes anaérobies", 1937, Masson et Cie., Paris, 1100 p.
WHITELEY: J. Bact., 1952, *63*, 163.
WHITELEY and DOUGLAS: J. Bact., 1951, *61*, 605.
WHITMORE and GOCHENOUR: J. Bact., 1956, *72*, 79.
WIERINGA: Ant. v. Leeuw., 1936, *1*, 263; 1939, *6*, 251.
WOLLIN: Bact. Proc., 1960.
WOLLIN et al: J. Bact., 1961, *81*, 911.

ZEETTI: Giorn. Batt. Imm., 1937, *19*, 834.
ZEISSLER and RASFELD: Z. f. Bakt., 1949, *153*, 304; *154*, 200.

ALPHABETICAL LIST OF THE ANAEROBIC SPECIES CLASSED IN THIS MANUAL

(The generic name follows the specific name)